MEMORIES OF W

MEMORIES
OF
WELSH ISLANDS

by

MARY E. GILLHAM

CYHOEDDWYR
DINEFWR
PUBLISHERS

Published in 2004 by
Dinefwr Press
Rawlings Road, Llandybie, Carmarthenshire, SA18 3YD.

A CIP catalogue record for this book is
available from the British Library.

ISBN 1-904323-08-1

Printed and bound in Wales by
Dinefwr Press Ltd.
Rawlings Road, Llandybie
Carmarthenshire, SA18 3YD.

Cover Photographs:
Front cover: Islets off the south of Ramsey Island.
Spine: Puffins.
Back cover, lower part: Thrift or Sea Pink.

ACKNOWLEDGEMENTS

I am indebted to all those who contributed so much to corporate island life through the years, their lively companionship, erudite discussions on weighty ecological matters and a good measure of day to day fun.

Hugh Chater, father of botanist Arthur Chater, set my feet on the island road as my botanical advisor on the then rather unusual project that I chose for my student thesis in the 1940s.

Islands beg allegiance as complete entities and broaden the mind. As Peter Conder, warden on Skokholm during my first seven years and essentially a birder, put it:

> "If it is on the island we are interested – be it rocks, weeds or insects."

Accordingly we dabbled in fields other than our own, gaining the wider perspective that is essential to the complexities of a modern understanding of the environment.

We were all beginners in our various fields in those early days, spreading through the community during the next half century and enthusing others to come and experience the magic for themselves.

BY THE SAME AUTHOR

SEA BIRD ISLANDS
Sea Birds. Brompton Library, Museum Press, London, 1963.

A Naturalist in New Zealand. Museum Press, London and Reeds, New Zealand, 1966.

Sub-Antarctic Sanctuary; Summertime on Macquarie Island. Museum Press and Reeds, 1967.

Islands of the Trade Winds, An Indian Ocean Odyssey. Minerva Press, London, 1999.

Island Hopping in Tasmania's Roaring Forties. Stockwell, Devon, 2000.

WELSH COUNTRYSIDE
The Natural History of Gower, Edn I and II. Brown, Cowbridge, Glamorgan, 1977, 1979.

Swansea Bay's Green Mantle. Brown, Cowbridge, Glamorgan, 1982.

Glamorgan Heritage Coast. I. Sand Dunes. Glam. Heritage Coast, 1987.

Glamorgan Heritage Coast. II. Rivers. Glam. Heritage Coast, 1989.

Glamorgan Heritage Coast. III. Limestone Downs. Glamorgan Wildlife Trust, 1991.

Glamorgan Heritage Coast. IV. Coastal Downs. Glamorgan Wildlife Trust, 1993.

Glamorgan Heritage Coast. V. Cliffs and Beaches. Glamorgan Wildlife Trust, 1994.

The Garth Countryside: Part of Cardiff's Green Mantle. Lazy Cat, Cardiff, 2001.

A Natural History of Cardiff: Exploring along the River Taff. Lazy Cat, Cardiff, 2002.

CONTENTS

COLOUR PLATES

SKOMER I
Warden's house on isthmus between North and South Havens, 1976.
Rabbit-trimmed Heather, 1976.
Part of the magnificence of Bluebells, May, 1978.
Massed Red Campion, July 1961.

SKOMER II
Sea Campion lacking red pigment (anthocyanin).
Puffins.
Amy the goat and a three-week-old Shearwater, 1963.
Scallops, Crawfish, Coral, Urchins and diving kit, 1964.
Skomer Vole.

RAMSEY I
Part of a splendid Thrift community, 1969.
View to St. David's Head from the north end.
Spring Squill among low Heather.
Blue sward of Spring Squill extends right to cliff edge.

Facing page 192:

RAMSEY II
Escape to Utopia, Sea Campion.
Lenorthis alata, Ordovician fossils, 1969.
Massed Gorse among Bluebells.
Gorse topiarised by Rabbits and thickly sprinkled with their pellets.

BARDSEY I
Lighthouse beyond old lime kiln at hay time, 1984.
Nibbled Gorse by Old School House and Cristin.
Sheep maintained the closely rabbit-grazed turf after the 1983
Myxomatosis.
Connemara Ponies.

BARDSEY II
Honeysuckle on the 'Mountain'.
Little Big Foot, the egg-shaped Bunny.
English Stonecrop invades among burned Gorse.

Foxgloves, a later stage after Gorse burning.
Sheep explore the new barricade on the Narrows.

PUFFIN ISLAND I
Puffin Island from Penmon Point.
Puffin on Puffin Island limestone.
Garden Tiger Moths from elders by ruined Norman church.
Three newly fledged Kittiwakes.

Facing page 256:

PUFFIN ISLAND II
Razorbills.
Fulmar Petrels.
Cormorants.
Young Shag.

CALDEY I
Golden Samphire among limestone boulders.
Brother James on West Cliff, 1980.
Brother James outside his excavation cave.
Sieve for extracting artefacts.
Erratic Bluestone showing newly exposed and weathered surfaces.

CALDEY II
Cistercian Monastery.
Priory and Medieval Church.
Quay from the dunes.
Lady's Finger or Kidney Vetch.

BRISTOL CHANNEL ISLANDS
Three Dinosaur footprints, Bendrick Rocks.
Triassic Ripple Marks, Bendrick.
Unconformity on seaward facing cliff of Sully Island.
Yellow Horned Poppies on Sully Island pebble beach.
Yellow Horned Poppy.

Facing page 352:

FLATHOLM I
Two boats leave around Arch Rock, 1971.
Tiled Water Catchment below 'Driftwood', 1986.
Small Wrinkle Folds on limestone of West Beach, 1971.
West Beach Mini Anticline showing eroding clay shales
   below limestone rock, 1983.

FLATHOLM II
Peony flowers, June.
Peony fruits, supporting three snails, October.
Small Tortoiseshells on Ragwort, October 2001.
Wild Leeks in June drought, 1989.
Wild Leek flower head, August 1986.
Henbane seeds plundered by Goldfinches and Linnets, October 1979.

FLATHOLM III
Castle Battery in October 2001.
Massed Scurvy Grass on East cliffs, April 1980.
Crow's Nest in moribund Hawthorn, east side, 1963.
First Mohair Kids born on Flatholm, March 1992.
Wallflowers and Great Mullein plants on East cliffs, April 1980.

FLATHOLM IV
Lime Kiln above West Beach, 1983.
Marconi Memorial, erected 1974, photo 1983.
Hounds-tongue from fruit burs preened off at Nissen Hut door, 1983.
David Worrell, project manager, burning a heap of botulised
   Gulls, 1983.

PREFACE

This is a collection of reminiscences of the Welsh Islands garnered over a period of fifty years. It explores the character of these natural gems strung around our sea coast in the spirit of Leslie Thomas's *Some Lovely Islands* but the narrative is imposed on a more down to earth portrayal of the natural landscapes.

As a field ecologist, as well as a lover of islands for their own sake, I have not neglected the basic features of land form and land use that spread the canvas for the fun of island life – the people, their livestock, the droves of rabbits that dominate the scene on most and, particularly, the birds and mammals of cliffs and ocean that few people are privileged to see.

Many of the islands have had a great deal of ecological research carried out on them. This is no attempt to summarise the results from the learned journals. That would need a weightier tome. Work going on when I was present is touched upon as it affected our daily activities, but apologies go to those who seek only hard facts.

This is a book of memories stretching across the years since I was demobbed from the Women's Land Army at the end of World War II. As a post-war ecology student in the University of Wales, I had to select a subject for my honours thesis. Having been enchanted by Ronald Lockley's writings of his island years in Pembrokeshire, where else should I choose to head but to those same delectable spots?

The result was not only unbounded satisfaction and pleasure in the short term, but the start of a lifetime of island hopping world wide, from the Tropics to Antarctica, visiting islands as magic as they come but which never quite replaced my affection for those off the shore of my adopted homeland.

INTRODUCTION

The first eleven chapters are devoted to those favourites of so many island-lovers, the ones off Pembrokeshire in South-west Wales. From there we move north along the west coast and east along the south coast, seeking features in which each locality differs from the next.

The two islands that I know best have been afforded more than their fair share of space. First is Skokholm, the one that will always be my favourite. The other, Flatholm, is a workaday island of very different calibre, but doing good work in catering for large parties of school children as well as more discerning visitors.

Less oceanic, Flatholm lacks the pelagic birds and mammals and sweeps of flowery maritime heath of the others. Historically, before the advent of the local authority's 'Flatholm Project' during the past quarter of a century, it was regarded as an island of lost causes – non economic subsistence farming, an isolation hospital serving but a handful of patients and fortifications against Napoleonic forces and a World War II invasion which never happened, with no shot fired in anger from either set of gun batteries.

From north to south we visit Puffin Island off Anglesey, which resembled Flatholm in being dominated by hordes of gulls stimulating a wilderness of coarse weeds and elders which is being fought back by dedicated conservationists.

Next comes Bardsey, the Island of Saints, off the Lleyn Peninsula, mostly devoted to sheep ranching but grading to a wind-whipped shear-water colony on 'The Mountain'. Choughs are a speciality here, as on our next.

Ramsey off St. David's Head in North Pembrokeshire, approaches closer to my idea of a really maritime island, with magnificent spreads of sea pink and sea squill in spring advancing through foxgloves to heather as the seasons progress, but most of the sea-birds are hidden on the western cliffs. The beaches host Wales's largest colonies of grey Atlantic seals at pupping time, closely followed by Skomer.

Skomer off South-west Pembrokeshire is like a larger version of Skokholm and might well rank as my favourite had I spent more time there, although anyone who has lived for the stipulated week or more in the delightful community of naturalists centred round the Skokholm Wheelhouse must acknowledge the greater sense of comradeship pervading there than in the more scattered community of Skomer, with its hundreds of day and short term visitors.

Grassholm, the Island of Gannets and the subject of my first paper in a major scientific journal in 1953, is an island apart. There were three thousand pairs of gannets nesting there when I made my vegetation surveys in the late 1940s. Now there are thirty three thousand pairs, a magnificent spectacle which must be viewed only from the sea, because of lack of space ashore to keep a respectful distance.

Caldey Island off the south coast is another 'island apart' in a quite different way. Dominated by the fine Cistercian Monastery and with vast numbers of day visitors flocking across from the Tenby holiday beaches, it is a more gentle landscape, pastoral and wooded. Part Old Red Sandstone like Skokholm and part Carboniferous Limestone like Flatholm, it is the only island with an appreciable amount of sand, including a small dune system, but most of the sea-birds nest on the satellite island of St. Margaret's.

Following the limestone east along the Bristol Channel, from the Elegug Stacks with their clamorous guillemots, we touch briefly on the five tidal islands around the Gower Peninsula in West Glamorgan, queen of which is Worm's Head, with its residual auk population.

Tusker Rock, the Bendricks with their Dinosaur footprints, Barry Island, now joined to the mainland by the docks complex, and the Scarweather and Nash Sandbanks have deserved comment, then on through Sully Island at the end of its dangerous tidal causeway, and so to Flatholm.

These were my student stamping grounds, giving me the basis for work on others in the Southern Hemisphere, where penguins stand in for the auks of the North but shearwaters, petrels, gulls and waders are not very different.

MARY E. GILLHAM
Cardiff

1.

SKOKHOLM: A DAY TO REMEMBER

Perched on a slaty block of old red sandstone, a brisk wind blowing through my hair, I gazed down upon a scene of pure magic. Blue-green waves rolled relentlessly shoreward from the far horizon, crashing onto the rocks below to rise in an avalanche of droplets, white with their new intake of salty air.

An oyster-catcher scuttled up the beach to safety, spooking a half grown gull chick, while a grey Atlantic seal floated just beyond the maelstrom that fringed its home element. Tissue-thin flowers of sea campion leaned away from the gamin breeze, supple stems as resilient as any, waxy blue-green leaves holding on to the essential water that was so easily sucked from the less well prepared.

A clownish black and white head popped out from behind a tump of thrift – a puffin, seeing if the coast was clear for take-off. Its fellows were scattered across the slope, pattering back and forth, a few steps at a time, gazing to right and left to see what everyone else was doing.

Seemingly inadequately short wings were unfurled by the newcomer from underground and the portly little bird launched itself onto the wind, planing effortlessly down towards the sea and only just clearing the worn grass sward. The exit was not quite perfectly judged, but the less than streamlined bird bounced off the fescue tussock, no harm done, and slid down an air lane to a patch of slack water, diving almost immediately to avoid the threatening approach of a great black-backed gull.

The lilting song of a lark trickled down from blue heights, interrupted by the throaty bleat of one of the dark brown Soay sheep grazing along the distant rim of the land. I lay back and abandoned myself to the caressing warmth of the sun and the medley of sound rising from the busy shoreline below. This was heaven indeed. I was perched on the edge of Skokholm Island, South Pembrokeshire in South-west Wales – a place that I had longed to visit ever since reading Ronald Lockley's *Dream Island Days* as a teenager.

It had started for me just twenty-four hours before, trundling out from Haverfordwest Railway Station in the back of the Dale Fort Field Centre truck. I was wedged firmly between netting bags of cabbages and cardboard cartons of groceries, with poorly wrapped kettles and enamel mugs skating across the floorboards.

With four other expectant islanders, I had bedded down in a corridor at the fort – all bedrooms being full – rising to a light breakfast at 7.00 a.m. with the promise of more to come on arrival at the island. While waiting for the contingent travelling on the overnight train from London, we strolled along the shore, viewing the last trees and the last warblers of the week.

We were to sail less than ten miles, but it could have been a hundred, to an environment where house sparrows were never seen and where blackbirds were rare, but where we should be handling birds that most of us had not yet set eyes upon.

Shearwater, formerly the Dale Fort boat, had been lost at sea the year before, in one of 1946's major storms, and a Scotsman by the name of Craig took us across on this brisk June morning. Grey waves slapped at the hull, building up to a vigorous heave-ho in the tide race off St. Ann's Head as we sailed out of Milford Haven. Our attention was diverted, however, by the splendid anticline, where bent layers of old red sandstone swooped skywards and back again to sea level, with green seas battering themselves to foam against the base of the great infilled arch.

Gulls took up station over the stern, escorting us into the open sea, but razorbills and gannets sped past without giving us a second glance. And then came the puffins, surging out in what it pleased us to regard as a welcoming cloud of plump little bodies from the eastern cliffs of the island, where the figurehead of the *Alice Williams* did duty as a sea mark from her patch of whitewashed rock. With their comical deportment and over-large red feet, puffins are everybody's favourites. We credited them with all sorts of anthropomorphic motives as they hesitated alongside, undecided whether to escape by diving or making a running take-off.

It was half tide, with vaguely menacing waves sweeping over the steps at the South Haven landing, so we were taken a few at a time by dinghy into a narrow gully and disposed ourselves as a human chain to pass bags and baggage, calor gas cylinders and grub boxes up mudstone slopes as bright as those at St. Ann's.

Caroline, the Welsh black cow, was part of the deputation that came to meet the boat. She gave each of us a desultory sniff or lick as we attained her level, but she had other matters on her mind. Just what they were I discovered when I lifted the bread box to carry up to the house and found a sizable chunk missing from each loaf on the top layer. Caroline never missed Saturday mornings at the landing!

Not long before she had inadvertently been shut in the wheelhouse, which served as kitchen-cum-diner. Her bread was supplemented on that occasion by ground rice, custard powder and the dried milk which we used instead of what she might have provided had she been allowed a male consort.

She lacked company of her own kind but was still a herd animal. Having fallen out long ago with Sugarback, the lighthouse keepers' pony, she became one of us and got the blame for many mishaps, although it was the pony that was finally caught stealing the soap from the warden's window sill and working up a salivary lather like an urchin blowing bubbles.

Peter Conder OBE, late chief of the RSPB (Royal Society for the Protection of Birds) which now boasts over a million members, was then in the first of his seven years as Skokholm warden, and one of his least favourite jobs was de-Carolining the wheelhouse yard. This was 1947. John Fursdon, warden on the island through its post-war re-opening as a bird observatory the previous year, was now in charge at Dale Fort and had been there to see us off.

Over our belated second breakfast Peter put us in the picture regarding island life. Among many other matters we learned the ritual of collecting gulls' eggs for the pot – half the island for the observatory and the other half for the lighthouse, with one colony of birds immune.

Full clutches of three were to be avoided. The island cook learned quite enough embryology from the supposedly more newly laid ones and twos. Gulls will lay at least two replacement egg clutches if they lose the first, so there were plenty for the taking until later in the season, when they were left alone to maintain the population.

The eggs were delicious, with rich orange yolks and pearly, semi-translucent whites like duck eggs. Only the odd, extra large great black back's egg was likely to have a fishy taint, adding just a little extra piquancy! Mild excitement pervaded on the days when boiled eggs were served for breakfast, with everyone wondering what they would find within the shell. This pleasure was reserved for the cook when eggs were served in other guises.

At this time, fifty-five years back, gulls had not embarked on the dramatic rise in numbers that made them such a menace to other, less pugnacious sea-birds. In later years different techniques were employed to keep their numbers down. Until more sophisticated means were evolved, the final clutch was pricked to let the air in and render them infertile. The eggs were left in the nest to hoodwink the proud mother into thinking that she was still doing a good job of work and that there was no need to lay more in order to raise a family.

We left on our introductory conducted tour that first morning like a pack of ferrets sniffing along the dry stone walls in search of storm petrel nests. These little Mother Carey's chickens or St. Peter's birds – because of their apparent ability to walk on water – crept into holes between the zig-zag courses of flat stones that characterised the herring bone dry stone field walls in this part of Pembrokeshire.

Storm Petrels at nest hole.

The odour was strongly reminiscent of sardines and was much the best way to locate the petrels' cryptic hide-outs. The great thing was not to disturb the bird, both for its own sake and to prevent ones clothes from smelling for evermore of sardines when the bird's last meal was ejected in an unerring stream to a point just below the olfactory organ.

The exercise was academic rather than practical as stormies were not ringed at the nest like other birds, even if they could be extricated, because they were prone to desert if bodily disturbed, unlike their larger relatives, the shearwaters.

We did ring some before the week was out, and many more in future years with the aid of a mist net erected along a wall top after darkness had fallen. As the swallow-sized birds encountered the net they got caught up in pockets of fine mesh which their impact

Storm Petrel, mist net and herring bone wall.

pushed through the larger meshes of the supporting net. This prevented too much flapping which might have caused bodily harm. We all helped to gently extricate them, but only registered ringers with adequate training attached the rings while a visitor acted as secretary, recording the ring number and any vital statistics by torchlight.

Everything at this end of the island was bathed in a gentle crimson glow from the lighthouse, which identified potential trouble for mariners by its warning colouration, as surely as a ladybird does to a sparrow. This warm colour was bird-friendly and Skokholm did not suffer major casualties among night migrants such as occurred at other islands, including Bardsey, where the lighthouse keepers might need a wheelbarrow to cart away the feathered corpses after a night's kill. Before the Skokholm light was automated, like all the rest, its beam was changed to ordinary white light.

After the morning's 'wall patrol' we all scrambled down a broken cliff face to witness the ringing of a young herring gull, which was found to have been dealt with the previous day. No time and motion studies were carried out on the efficacy of sea-bird ringing, so no-one worried that a dozen able-bodied individuals had spent considerable time and effort on an abortive task. This was all part of the fun of island life, with plenty of anti-stress fringe benefits – something that nobody had thought to invent back in the leisurely forties.

Many island birds were wearing rings. Those not so easy to catch, like wheatears and meadow pipits, which were the subject of individual studies, were furnished with special combinations of coloured rings so that they could be recognised in the field and related to their home territory and domestic menage.

A total of 6,096 birds were ringed on Skokholm in 1947 and almost 8,500 the following year. These figures are sufficiently impressive to be worthy of this first ever British bird-ringing observatory, established by Ronald Lockley when he was farming here in the 1930s. The island was evacuated by government order during the war but, along with two others in Scotland, the Isle of May and Fair Isle, was quick off the mark to re-open as a ringing station in 1946.

Regaining the clifftop, we moved on and lay down to peer over and count guillemots on a ledge below. These birds were more streamlined than the razorbills seen at sea, less chunky, with tapered bill and a rich 99% cocoa-rich chocolate-brown instead of the all-black of the others. Their eggs were a delicate greeny-blue instead of speckled brown, these, too, tapered at one end. With wading birds the narrow end allows the clutch to sit cosily in the nest, points to middle. With guillemots, it enables them to roll round on their own axis when jolted by the jostling crowd, instead of falling off the ledge to the rocks or sea below.

The chicks were still small, just a week or so old. At three weeks they would take matters into their own hands and spread inadequate wings to free-fall to the sea. Being almost weightless an unscheduled bounce off a ledge on the way down did little or no damage. One of the adults here was bridled, a thin white line encircling the eyes like a pair of steel-rimmed spectacles. This character increases northward and became quite familiar on Scottish islands visited later.

Stepping carefully around the edge of Mad Bay, none of us would forget the magnificence of the great sward of thrift or sea pink in various shades from deep rose to the palest coral, with a few aberrant white blooms. This carpet spread further inland here than anywhere, nourished by blown sea spray, although the red cliffs were a hundred feet high.

Sea Milkwort, Chaffweed and Bog Pimpernel.

Still on the north coast there was a marked contrast as we dipped into the shelter of Windmill Gully, with its fine scattering of late-flowering primroses and the round, farthing-sized disc leaves of marsh pennywort clustered round spikes of brookweed flowers. Oddities here were salt marsh plants growing on high cliffs – sea plantain in the open and sea milkwort nestled among lush fiorin grass in cliff flushes.

Proceeding west a disgruntled puffin was removed from its burrow to have its finer points demonstrated, and then a more quiescent Manx

Manx Shearwaters, Thrift and Sea Campion.

shearwater. Both birds were ringed and the latter, at least, seemed to have grasped the fact that handling did not pose a serious threat.

The south-western headland by the lighthouse proved the most boisterous yet. There the sea is never still and acorn barnacles are plastered well up into the extensive splash zone, in no danger of drying out. Above was the honeycombed, burrow-pocked peat of the island's largest shearwater colony, where we were to stumble round in the dark ringing birds that very night. Intense burrowing and the collapse of islanded tumps prevented the magic effect of a pink herbfield like that of Mad Bay here.

A trek along the steep south coast, where the tilted sandstone beds fall almost vertically to the sea in a series of giant steps, and we were in Crab Bay. The grassy slope reaching half way to the beach was riddled with neater burrows in a flowery sward, less threatening than the half dead, undermined mounds of thrift in the other. This was Puffin Town, where I stretched myself in the evening trying to take it all in.

Peter pointed out the generous supply of driftwood on the beach below and intimated that there would be no fires on wet days if we didn't busy ourselves getting some of it up to the house.

There was a wonderland of marine life here, as in many of the sheltered eastern coves, some of it very different from the exposure-tolerant species of the west end. I didn't know it then, but this 'other world' was to keep me busy for many happy hours when I launched out on my ten-year research period here in the near future.

Ostensibly my work would be on the reactions of the land vegetation to all the extremes ranged against it – drying gales, falling salt spray, grazing herbivores, burrowing birds, accumulating guano and a weekly intake of visitors throughout an ever lengthening summer season, but very little had been done as yet on the seaweeds. My professor during my post-war studenthood at the University of Wales in Aberystwyth was Lily Newton, Britain's seaweed queen and author of the definitive identification tome, so I could scarcely not embark on a study of these too.

We reassembled for lunch in the wheelhouse, with healthy physical appetites and mental indigestion as we tried to absorb this strange environment that was so much more natural than the one in which we spent most of our time and which we regarded as the norm. After the warden's daily ritual of roasting the ground coffee beans in an aluminium saucepan prior to steeping the brew and handing round the mugs, he set about elucidating the week's tasks.

Most visitors were set to mapping bird distribution – wheatears, skylarks, rock and meadow pipits. I was allocated the vegetation, as anticipated. Not a lot had been done on the plants since Lockley compiled his original list of 185 species between 1927 and 1940, although a lot of data was building up on the birds. Many short term inputs had resulted in a skeleton card index. There were card indices for everything in the ringing room – an essential research tool in those far off days, but one which would need explaining to today's generation growing up with computers and the internet.

In the afternoon we were left to our own devices, setting off with binoculars, cameras, pencils and notebooks and that now little heard of item of botanical equipment, a capacious metal vasculum to hold the collection. That was before both the takeover of polythene bags and the very necessary banning of picking specimens in nature reserves. Now one takes the identification book to the plant instead of the plant to the book.

This particular afternoon I needed no book because I joined up with Dr. Nils Dahlbeck, head of the Swedish Nature Protection Society, who was squeezing a few days on the island before attending a conference in Switzerland and further business in London. He worked principally on maritime plants and had a special love for 'tinies', which achieved their complete life cycle against horrendous odds by remaining little more than an inch high. Skokholm's rabbits had a similar dwarfing effect to the arctic climate on the tundra closer to his home and he was in his element.

We spent four hours on rabbit-razed turf, principally on our hands and knees, exclaiming over minuteae. He would rise for awhile, then throw himself down on his stomach to tweak a few blades of herbage and explain their whys and wherefores in his quaint lilting English. We crawled along walls, up rocky bluffs and through bogs, overhauling North Pond so thoroughly that I felt I was already well on with my survey.

Some of our finds were new and rare, among them the much branched allseed (*Radiola linoides*) of the flax family and chaffweed (*Centunculus minimus*), which later became coupled with the charming little pink bog pimpernel as *Anagallis minimus*. Here were tiny plants of water blinks and creeping St. John's wort, while the capitate-headed version of pink centaury was not much bigger. It took us a long time to find the fourth species of pearlwort, but we did eventually. Without the mowing down of other plants by those much maligned bunnies none of these trifles would have stood a chance in a normal sward.

Nils did have eyes for the wider scene too, and he was as mightily impressed by the acres of flowering thrift as any of us. His eyes roved appreciatively over the scene.

"A remarkable flora. Truly remarkable!"

Then he launched out on the best (Danish) method of finding the 'minimal area' to get a representative selection of all the plant species present by examining larger and larger circles until no new species appeared. Soon he was down on the ground again, sorting out the three tiny scorpion grasses – mini hairy versions of the more rumbustious water forget-me-not of the ponds and streams.

There was a break after high tea, when we wandered off to soliloquise, then we were at it again. The heat of the pace and the day paled, however, and it was quite chilly when we adjourned to the common room at the appointed hour of nine for hot cocoa and doorsteps of bread and marmite. This was the time for collation of the day's weather and bird records (we had a Stevensons screen for meteorological data) in the island log, a less formal version of which was then passed to one of the visitors to record their personal impressions of the day's happenings.

Featuring among today's birds were six turnstones, along with the more usual buzzard, lapwings, starlings and a few other non-residents, which loomed much larger during the spring and autumn migrations. A big triumph for the man who had cut the grass in the garden Heligoland bird trap was that, after weeks of inactivity, three wheatears were caught there for ringing soon after the job was done. Peter was doing a long term study on these birds and had established that they were always associated with closely rabbit-grazed turf. Throughout most of South Wales this service is provided by mountain sheep.

A grasshopper warbler had been captured in the wheelhouse, so we had not seen our last of this group at Dale after all. Remarkably another of its kind had been ringed this year and that, too, had managed to trap itself in the wheelhouse.

All day we had been expecting a naval landing craft to touch in at South Haven and take us to the Grassholm Island gannetry, so we were grieved to learn on the morrow that a boatload of people had gone directly there from the mainland. The weather was perfect (a rare happening) and there had been too many takers from Dale, leaving no room for another large gang of eager beavers.

At 11 p.m. I climbed the ship's ladder to the angel loft, the usual female sleeping quarters, this leaving the larger bunkhouse for the always more numerous men. I lay fully clothed for a few hour's nap before engaging on the next activity of this busy day. The hours of daylight were long in June and shearwaters did not dare to flock in from the sea until after dark, when the predatory gulls had ceased their lethal patrols. We thought of them as nocturnal, but they were as diurnal as any when out at sea. They could scarcely be otherwise as there was nowhere else to go. The first to wake to the eerie cacophony of wailing that they set up on arrival had instructions to wake the rest.

No amount of warning quite prepared me for the mephistophelian hubbub that poured from hundreds of avian throats as each incomer called to their mate below ground. In subsequent years during sojourns on sea-bird islands in Australia and New Zealand this sound was to become all too familiar, but I was greatly impressed by its initial impact.

Groping my way down the ladder I woke the warden, who bedded down in a corner of the bird ringing room in the absence of a room of his own. He emerged tousled and sleepy-eyed, complaining about people who never had the sense not to when he asked them to wake him. I crept back up, woke my room mate, a missionary from India, put on two extra layers of garments and joined the shivering group outside.

"Not a good night. Too light. Too short. Birds will soon be off again to sea."

Peter only took a hundred rings but could have used many more, although even at that relatively early stage in the ringing programme, we picked up many birds which had been marked previously.

We trudged along the 'railway lines' that guided the horse-drawn trolley between landing stage and lighthouse, to the other end of the island, Caroline plodding stoically in our wake, the party having started from her customary snoozing ground outside the house. As part of the herd, when we became nocturnal, so did she.

Strictly this was the pony's highway, but when he used it he was at work and he disliked work. With the whole of the island at his disposal, he would have been impossible to catch on 'boat days' to haul stores without the chain attached to a hind fetlock, which slowed him down suffi-

Thrift, moribund and flowering shoots.

ciently for one of the three lively characters who manned the lighthouse to make contact. His favourite ploy when the boat was sighted was to stand in the middle of North Pond, the largest body of water on the island.

Bad night or not, the air was full of hurtling black and white missiles which didn't always miss our trudging forms as they plopped earthward to scuttle into a nearby burrow. The size of pigeons, but longer and more slender, the occasional impact could come as a surprise, but was more often just a flick of a long, tapered wing.

Legs were set close to the tail – the ideal place for underwater swimmers – but this made progress on land difficult. They often sat around for a while, or shuffled along in short bursts, sometimes half rowing with their wings, so were relatively easy to catch. We soon got the hang of picking them up to take to the two with the rings, fingers encircling the body so that they lay quiescent in the hand when turned tummy up to have the ring attached.

There was many a tumble as we lunged for new birds in the wilderness of hummocks and hollows that years of burrowing had produced in the partially bare terrain, but we fell softly on resilient thrift cushions or crumbly peat. The gentle glow from the lighthouse augmented the fitful gleam from wildly swaying flashlights hung round cavorting necks – essential aids when we were careering round near the cliff edge.

By the end of the session I was able to bring a bird in each hand, holding them far enough apart to prevent them from sparring, no doubt blaming each other for their predicament. Reluctantly I let my last two birds go when the shearwater rings ran out. Only marked birds were required then, to check their ring numbers. Among the several hundred birds handled tonight only one had been a storm petrel, this duly ringed.

The exodus was less spectacular than the arrival. As a pale yellow glow appeared in the eastern sky, birds released from nest duty by their incoming partner slipped away into the dawn, the 'goodbyes' a lot more muted than the 'hallo dear, where are you exactly?' of incomers seeking their more softly crooning mate below ground. They would be away for five days or so, feeding in the Bay of Biscay or thereabouts, longer if the nights were too moonlit for them to return safely for their next five day spell on the nest. The air had seemed full of birds, but no more than a fifth of the population were abroad on any night, apart from a contingent of non-breeding individuals.

Some scrambled up trackside rock faces on all fives, using the hooked bill as an extra appendage, parrot fashion. Even so, take-off from high points was difficult without a fair wind to bear them aloft

When the single youngsters are finally abandoned by their parents, they have to undergo a perilous passage to the cliff edge on foot before they can hurl themselves off to comparative safety. Fortunately for the true sea-birds, gulls, which are mere shore-birds, cannot dive, so the sea can be a refuge from their unwelcome attentions. Many fall victim if they have to go far overland and find no friendly unoccupied burrow to hide in when daylight comes. Their corpses – wings and legs on a stripped skeleton – are common by the ponds and streams which serve as dining areas for the predators, which like drinks to be laid on at mealtimes.

The most successful marauders were great black-backed gulls. After stabbing the shearwater to death, they would take its slender hooked bill in their own more massive one, shaking and tossing the body around until it came away from the skin, which was left turned inside out, the

Manx Shearwaters in flight.

stubs of the quills outermost and the feathery parts inside. Rabbit skins likewise were left inside out, detached as neatly as any poacher could have done with pocket knife and practised fingers.

One wonders how the shearwaters keep up their numbers until realising how long they live if they survive early hazards. Only ringed birds can tell us their age, even if the easily corroded aluminium rings of the early years had had to be replaced by the more durable monel metal ones in later use. A pair of birds living to around thirty-five years old may have had 28-29 chicks during that time, only two of which need to survive to replace them and keep the population static.

The discovery in 2002 of a ringed shearwater on Bardsey Island that could have been no less than forty-nine years old must have been a record! (Geoff Gibbs, 'Welsh Islands round-up', *Natur Cymru*, 5, 2002).

At 3.30 a.m. we were disposed about the common room, sipping endless sweet tea and tucking into marmalade butties, listening to our Swedish doctor discoursing on continental game laws. The plaintive whistling of awakening oyster-catchers was already filtering in through the open door.

It had been quite a day. Or was it a day and a half? Almost unbelievably, everyone was up again bright and early at 7.30 a.m., even those who had been on the train through the night before the shearwatering. It is good to be young!

2.

SKOKHOLM:
THE REALISATION OF A DREAM

There are special days for everyone that can change the whole course of their life. One such for me was when I joined the Women's Land Army at the beginning of World War II, heading my destiny away from the streets of London and into the wide open spaces, with fresh green grass (or mud) underfoot and fresh clean air (spiced with the heady aroma of cow dung) in my nostrils.

Another was the 21st June, 1947, when I fell for Skokholm Island in a big way. As a post-war student in the University of Wales at Aberystwyth, I would soon have to choose a project for my honours thesis. What better place than this? But first I had to persuade the powers that be. Prof. looked doubtful.

"Oh dear! We don't know anything about the place – whether it's suitable. Aber botany students always do their research on Tregaron Bog – a wonderful place. There are all sorts of exciting things going on in bogs!" (She spoke as an ecologist.)

I persisted and she relented, sending me off to the island the following year with Hugh Chater, the delightfully cooperative staff ecologist who would be my research advisor. I was saved a lot of squelching around in sodden peat and headed in the direction of becoming an island ecologist.

But, back to that first fateful, life-changing week in June 1947. After breakfast on the second day everybody was busy with 'chores', the everyday jobs that kept the wheels turning. The vegetable fatigue was usually preferred to washing-up, but tasks were evenly shared. Taken as a matter of course by the few females present, the number of eyes to be removed from a potato to render it acceptable to the cook introduced a new dimension to the work ethic of most of the males.

Spud bashing was accomplished by a team seated companionably along a bench in the wheelhouse yard or squatting beside a couple of buckets of water carried up from the spring or baled from the rain tank

Author with storm petrel, 1948.

for the befores and afters. This proved quite a popular job, involving much ribaldry and flying water, particularly in subsequent years when we kept goats.

Certain of these when young, and especially Francesa, daughter of Ivanhoe and Rowena, always regarded a bent back as a convenient perch from which to oversee human activities. Usually the back was mine, as I knelt to milk her mother, and those sharp little hooves fitted uncomfortably on sunburned shoulders.

Each year's cook set the standard for kitchen hygiene, usually high. One in later years, frustrated by the tightly-balled washing up mops that never dried out, brandished one at every bunch of newcomers with: "Chrysanthemums, not tulips!"

A subsequent, more innovative cook left a bowl of hot soapy water at the ready for everyone to rise and wash his own plate after each course. This proved a great success. The worst chore of all, emptying the Elsans, was nobly undertaken by the warden, who sometimes roped in assistance for digging a new pit at a suitable distance.

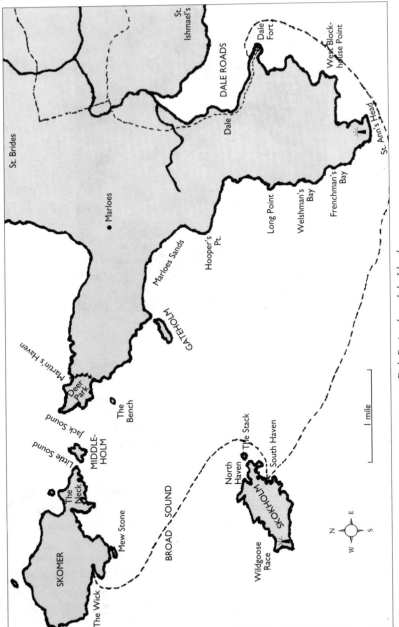

Dale Peninsula and the Islands.

SKOKHOLM I

Lighthouse on south-west corner.

Goats, Winter Pond and Sorrel across island centre in 1979.

View along the north coast to the Stack.

Sorrel and Sea Campion on the Neck in 1979, Middleholm beyond.

SKOKHOLM II

Shearwater chick.

Sheepsbit.

Guillemots on northern ledge, 1965.

Adult Manx Shearwater.

Razorbill chick.

SKOKHOLM III

North Pond, 1979.

Carol and Steve Warman, wardens in 1979.

Lighthouse Relief Boat off the Neck, 1979.

Big expanse of 'Ramalina siliquosa' lichen.

SKOKHOLM IV

Tang, 'Alaria esculenta'.

Furbelows, 'Saccorhiza bulbosa'.

Bluebells.

Sea Pansies.

Waste disposal was always something of a problem. Tins were usually flattened with a mallet and buried. During the period when we had a point two two rifle on the island (I can't remember why) we cast unflattened tins into the sea off Hog Bay's 'Alice' and lay on the cliff shooting at them until they sank, bringing a taste of baked beans or bully beef to crabs and lobsters in the depths below.

Chores completed on the second morning of that eventful week, visitors went about their allocated tasks until lunchtime. I started on a cliff survey in the south-east but was constantly deflected to gather potable-looking gulls' eggs, watch a crow scrapping with a gull or a pair of ravens tumbling through the air with gay abandon.

At lunch the warden asked if any brave spirits would like to accompany him to the Stack – a sea girt islet of red sandstone off the tip of the Neck.

"One creeps across a swaying sixteen foot plank between sheer rock walls with the tide racing through below . . . Rather fun in fact!"

This was accompanied by one of his infectious schoolboy grins and a toss of the thatch of sun-bleached hair. Few were put off by the colourful enlargement of the possible hazards and the three girls were certainly not to be outdone by the men.

Soon afterwards a full quota of brave spirits assembled at the end of the Neck and set about the enjoyable task of watching the tide go down. What better occupation at siesta time on a scorching June afternoon?

Lockley's description of the vivid colours here seemed too good to be true when read in a sombre mainland setting, but they were no exaggeration. The sea was as blue as the great swathes of bluebells sweeping back from North Haven, where bracken would soon mask their wilting remains. The rich dark red of the cliffs matched that of the flowering sorrel on the plateau behind, the two separated by the inimitable pink of the thrift. Flipping across the canvas of this pseudo-tropical seascape came gulls, glinting in the sun, a kaleidoscope of snow-white, dove-grey and coal black or tweedy-brown.

Just below us lazed five grey Atlantic seals, three spotted cows and two darker bulls with high ridged noses and powerful necks. They seemed as interested in us as we in them, particularly when someone started crooning, a lilting song not so different from their own, and one which evoked a few responses.

Everywhere between us and the Devil's Teeth were the flashing black and white forms of auks, raising little turrets of spume as they disappeared beneath the surface in pursuit of sand eels. A flight of curlew winged past and a raven came cronking across the strait from Skomer. Two great black-backs screamed at us from their point of vantage across the narrow gullies separating us from our goal.

Caroline blew hot air down our necks at intervals, unable to indulge in her favourite pastime of nudging us towards a brink while we were lying prostrate. In this she was less of a menace than Larry, the Soay ram, hand-reared as an orphan, who I had as yet to meet. His favourite pastime was to approach quietly from behind and dive between a pair of legs, to skip nimbly down the broken slope beyond, sometimes ahead of his victim.

When Peter deemed the tide to be reaching the optimum state, he manoeuvred the sixteen foot plank down to sea level with the help of a couple of stalworts. This was not needed for the first obstacle, which was a gully full or oarweeds and thongweeds swaying rhythmically back and forth over boulders carpeted with a sea meadow of gelatinous red weeds.

This first crossing achieved, it was up and over and down into the next gully, where the plank was being manoeuvred diagonally across a twelve foot rift at a seemingly perilous angle to utilise the only available ledges. Footholds on the face leading up from the further end were scarcely apparent from our side, but the crossing had been achieved many times before and would be many times again, so we had to give it a go.

Peter Conder returning from the Skokholm Stack.

There are ways and ways of crossing bridges and we all made it, striking various attitudes – half sitting with one foot dangling, astride with both dangling, on all fours (backward, to accommodate the downhill gradient) or less untidily on hands and knees. Only the warden and vice warden remained erect – much the safest way, as I soon discovered in subsequent years, when I seldom missed the weekly adventure, if only to show off to the novices.

Familiarity breeds contempt, but things got a deal more difficult in later years when a ladder was substituted for the plank. Ladders lend themselves admirably to near vertical passage but not to almost horizontal progress as the rungs are more than a foot's length apart. Hands and knees seem more appropriate then, as accomplishing a wider span. The seemingly unscalable wall beyond proved no problem in plimsolls once we found the appropriate crack that brought us safely to the summit.

And all this for the purpose of ringing two great black-backed chicks, as the shags and cormorants which frequented the Stack were not breeding there. In fact for me, as a plant person, this was the most exciting part of the island. Here were no grazing rabbits, sheep or goats and few trampling humans. The vegetation on top was unbelievably lush, benefiting from summer increments of guano, diluted by rain to beneficial proportions.

Tree mallow grew tall and flowered as profusely as on the Stack Rocks in South Pembrokeshire, where limestone pinnacles and the Green Bridge of Wales reared from the sea to supply nesting sites for massed guillemots and razorbills.

Shining leaves of bottle-green sea beet sprouted all ways – a sharp colour contrast to the mealy grey ones of sea purslane, which should by rights have been on a salt marsh rather than high and dry on a rock waving merrily in the wind. Almost equally grey halberd-leaved orache was the usual island representative of this group from the salt bush family. That was on the Stack too, along with common orache and Babington's orache (*Atriplex glabriuscula*). It hybridised with the last, the cross confirmed subsequently when I sent a specimen off to Mr. Wilmott at the British Museum. He came up with another gem from our collection: *Atriplex hastata var. genuina forma salina*. The whole lot, along with white goosefoot, were more or less confined to the seabird cliffs on Skokholm.

How Caroline and Sugarback would have enjoyed getting their teeth into the tall dark green swathes of red fescue grass and the scurvy grass, rock spurrey, wall pennywort and other juicy vegetable matter on the Stack.

Most remarkable of all was a special hairless, oversized, succulent and erect variety of buck's-horn plantain, reaching to all of 35cm. A few similar but smaller plants cropped up later on inaccessible bird cliffs unaffected by grazing animals. This was a veritable speciality, contrasting

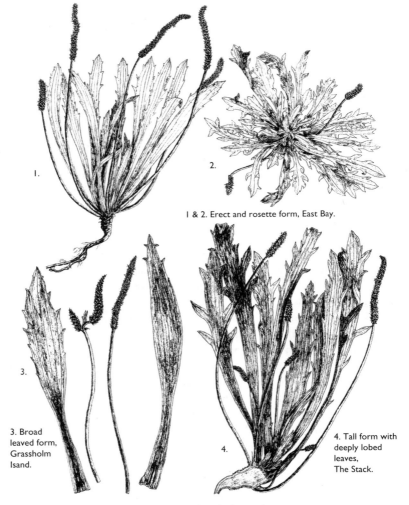

1 & 2. Erect and rosette form, East Bay.

3. Broad leaved form, Grassholm Isand.

4. Tall form with deeply lobed leaves, The Stack.

Succulent variety of Buck's-horn Plantain.

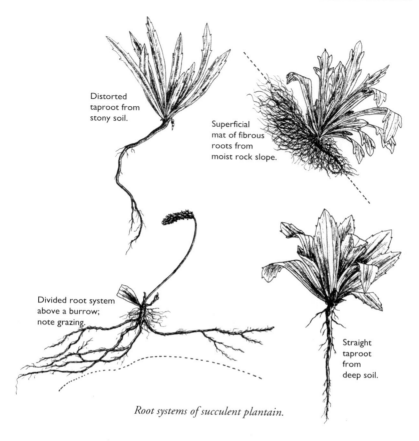

Distorted taproot from stony soil.

Superficial mat of fibrous roots from moist rock slope.

Divided root system above a burrow; note grazing.

Straight taproot from deep soil.

Root systems of succulent plantain.

widely with the normal small-leaved, hairy form that usually grew as ground-hugging rosettes on these cliffs. Only where other plants gave sufficient protection did wispy leaves of the common species grow erect in search of light, and the pygmy form, *Plantago coronopus forma pygmaea*, was frequent.

Specimens and photographs perplexed the experts, who came up with a number of different epithets, from *Plantago sabrinae to Plantago ceratophyllum*. For want of a better name, we referred to it as *Plantago coronopus var. maritima*, or PCVM for short.

To prove that it was a genotype, dependent on its own genetic make-up rather than a phenotype, dependent entirely on environmental factors, I germinated seeds in pots, side by side on the mainland. They came

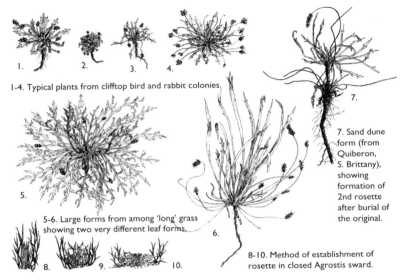

1-4. Typical plants from clifftop bird and rabbit colonies.

7. Sand dune form (from Quiberon, S. Brittany), showing formation of 2nd rosette after burial of the original.

5-6. Large forms from among 'long' grass showing two very different leaf forms.

8-10. Method of establishment of rosette in closed Agrostis sward.

Normal and pygmy forms of Buck's-horn Plantain.

true to type, although obviously missing the combination of sea salt and sea-bird guano that had led to such super succulence. I grew them alongside the ordinary buck's-horn plantain, which grew much larger than on the island, but did not approach the robustness of the other. The two remained distinct and refused to hybridise over several generations.

Field sketches made to measure illustrate their uniqueness. I have come across half-hearted versions on other sea cliffs around Wales but none so outstanding as on my first and favourite island. Pundits ascertained that it was not a polyploid with an increased set of chromosomes. These last matched those of the normal buck's-horn plantain, scuppering the suggestion that they might have arisen from a cross with the always succulent sea plantain.

All three appeared in dwarf form on drying pond beds in summer, when the blown salt spray left behind by evaporation proved a rather too powerful mix for the usual pond plants, but the special form was grazed off as soon as sheep and rabbits moved in.

But, back to our second day on the island. I am allowing this strange little plant to run away with my imagination, as it did back in 1947, 57 years ago.

As we had anticipated, the warden's lurid description of the plank and its terrors had been grossly exaggerated. We eased ourselves down the rock face and made the uphill return more gracefully. It emerged later that it was only the previous week that he himself had first made the crossing in the vertical.

Next morning dawned wet and I sprawled on my bed, which was right against the window of the angel loft, listing plants and making out index cards. Even here there was much to divert my attention. A pair of gulls down towards Wreck Cove was driving a carrion crow from the vicinity of their nest. One grabbed a wing tip and a few primary wing feathers floated down, while a rather lopsided crow flapped away, wishing he had steered a wider berth. Two wheatears were mating on the wires of the garden trap above the currant and elder bushes which eked out a living in the lee of the house under stunted sycamores, which were the only real trees on the island.

Something like an earwig dropped onto the sill under my nose, landing on its back. When I tried to right matters it leapt a full thirty centimetres into the air with a sharp snapping sound, but with no apparent movement of legs or wings. It proved to be a click beetle or skipjack, emerged from a pestiferous wire worm such as I had become familiar with in the land army. My wartime world had not been so different from this little scrap of earthy paradise, unlike that of less fortunate women working in the munitions factories.

The less likeable wireworm phase of this little beast lasts for four or five years before this ginger-brown, bullet-shaped beetle emerges. The adult's self-righting mechanism if it falls on its back involves a small peg under the thorax, which springs into a cavity when the back is arched, throwing the animal into the air. Mine failed to right itself on the first few leaps but made it in the end – like Bruce's spider.

The sun emerged after lunch and I sallied forth with pencil and notebook. I had scarcely settled on a tussock in North Pond, with water half way up my gumboots, when I spotted the warden haring towards me. I went to meet him, to discover that there was a boat in South Haven waiting to take us to Skomer. This was before the days of habitual use of walkie talkie radios, let alone mobile phones, and islanders had to be ready to 'jump to it', whatever it was, at short notice. A flag was run up on the flagpole in future years when the boat was sighted but islanders were not always looking that way.

Dumping my gear, I made all speed down to the landing. We were not far out from the haven when the fun began. Craig, the boatman, was anchoring the dinghy against our return, as we were not going ashore on the larger island but sea-bird watching from sea to land instead of the more usual land to sea.

John Fursdon was in charge of the bigger boat, chugging gently back and forth awaiting the skipper. As we proceeded slowly astern there was a yell of warning from Craig and a horrendous scrunching as we 'tailed up' on a partly submerged rock. The boat tilted alarmingly, all the gear sliding forwards into the bow while we passengers grasped the gunwhale to prevent doing likewise.

Craig seemed to be nearly falling out of the dinghy, waving his arms in suitable directions. Just as some of us were proposing to lessen the weight in the stern, a friendly wave came and lifted us off. John grinned sheepishly. This was not the first time. He put about to pick up the irate Scotsman and once out in the open sea there were no more obstacles.

The sun did us proud as we sped across Broad Sound, able to view our island home from a new angle, but it was certainly not a 'Grassholm Day' like the one before. We rode a big swell as we came abreast of Skomer's Mewstone. Even John, seasoned sailor that he was, leapt to his feet, pointing through the spray to the mountainous wave that had just passed so smoothly beneath our little craft, grinning hugely, in a mixture of wonder and relief. It grew larger as it rolled into the shallows but had been exciting enough before. Craig relaxed visibly as we chugged into the sheltered waters below the Wick.

Skomer is not old red sandstone like Skokholm and St. Ann's Head, but a grey igneous basalt, like Grassholm. The great cliff of the Wick rose vertically or slightly overhanging to our right, walling one side of a rift in the southern coast. We glided in beneath, where little sploshes of white excreta rained down into the shadowed waters at intervals.

The thronging birds were a never-to-be-forgotten sight and sound. We wondered how they all found room to sit, let along raise families. It was a dense mix of silvery kittiwakes and richly dark guillemots, all shouting the odds at our intrusion. Nests of the first were plastered with a guano/saliva mix onto sheer faces, guillemots crowded narrow ledges, making no attempt to build.

The clamour increased as a herring gull swooped in on a smash and grab raid. The grab came first, of a clean and thus newly laid guillemot's egg. The smash was later, across the narrow gut where puffins thronged on the less precipitous slope opposite and where the robber landed to consume his prize.

We counted three bridled guillemots without the aid of binoculars and learned that the northward increase of this character was so marked that more than half Iceland's guillemots were spectacled.

When we had gazed our fill Craig's sturdy little craft breasted the waves in fine style and brought us safely back to the comparative calm of Skokholm's South Haven. The tide was too low for us to land at the steps, so we were put ashore in the dinghy. The skipper pronounced it full, then decided that the last four could squeeze in to save another journey. There was a mere three inches of freeboard, with green gobbets of water sloshing in over the gunwhale. As the human cargo stepped lightly from the bow, the little craft lifted her nose gratefully and water belched from beneath the floor boards to swirl round the ankles of those of us in the stern.

We were already late for supper and, as Craig launched into a long and talkative tea, sampling as many jams as he could locate on the long table, we were nigh famished when our steaming plates were finally set before us.

Dr. Dahlbeck left with the skipper and was replaced by another Swede who should have arrived with him but had missed the Saturday boat. This mishap had been to his advantage as he had been able to join the Grassholm gannetry trip. There was still the best part of three weeks for him to savour the delights of this delectable corner of Pembroke-shire.

He was a lad of sixteen, unburdened as yet with conferences and business meetings. His name proved unpronounceable and he became known as Thomas. Understandably, he looked puzzled when asked to collect the swedes from the Baron's workshop for peeling. This language really is a snorter. He had no objection to being laughed at, which was just as well, because he said some remarkably funny things.

By the end of the week he was more fluent and I, who sat opposite at meals, had learned a little soon-to-be-forgotten Swedish from the label on his jamjar. My moment came when I was able to distinguish the blackberry jam from the blackcurrant for him, by using the latin Rubus and Ribes. They may sometimes be a mouthful, but thank goodness for internationally understood scientific names.

Thomas appeared in an interesting collection of garments. There was a grey knickerbocker suit for cold weather, green corduroy shorts and jerkin for warm and a bright blue woollen creation with white shoulder tabs and elastic round the ankles for night work. We dubbed this his sleeping suit, but were told it was worn by athletes when exercising in the cold Scandinavian air. British joggers caught up with this cosy garment a couple of decades later.

A group of us spent the evening stalking puffins, which were quite easy to approach in these early days, although becoming warier in later years. Stout wire puffin hooks mounted on poles were fashioned to hook round the bird's legs and draw it gently in until it could be taken by the free hand. We wriggled up on our tummies – collecting our severed buttons later.

The quarry watched fascinated as we got closer, turning the head from side to side to assess the situation under the false eyebrows donned for the breeding season along with the garish beak. When all seemed to be going well, a large foot was lifted and placed deliberately on the hook. Sometimes we could slide the bird towards us in this position but the hold was too tenuous to last. The quarry was off, with one derisive glance backwards which clearly said, "Gotcher".

No matter. The fact that they allowed us so close was what gave us the real buzz – a feeling of intimacy with these wild creatures of the ocean which venture into our territory for as short a period as they must. Later we started reaching down their burrows for unringed adults or young. The chicks unearthed were delightful, clownish little objects even without their parents' multi-coloured bill. They were swathed in sooty down, putting me in mind of miniature dodos.

Many of the burrows showed curved scrapes along the side walls where the gaudy parental beak had been put to work enlarging the passage, and most contained a small amount of bedding material – bracken, thrift or campion – and sometimes what looked like a mock egg. This was a rough oval of red clay rolled around with grass and screwed together into what looked like a pot egg or comforter. Nobody at the evening's recording session had any idea what it could be.

Shearwater burrows might be shared with rabbits in the complications of the communal labyrinth, where almost everything had to live underground, for want of trees or other cover. An excavating rabbit could bury a sitting bird, which had no trouble in digging itself out, none the worse, but the egg would not be retrieved and would addle. A displaced egg rolled into a neighbour's nesting chamber could not be accommodated as a shearwater has only one brood patch (the featherless area where the heat of the body can come into direct contact with egg or chick). One of the eggs would go cold.

A 'doormat' of newly excavated soil outside a burrow mouth denoted a rabbit, with or without feathered co-diggers. Both puffins and shearwaters could make their own burrows, although there was little need, with so many present already, but birds spread the ejected earth more finely, so that it sifted down among the short vegetation, as just another rising mound among many, with no furry youngsters emerging to nibble the front garden and kill the struggling plants.

On the way up the cliff we came upon a rock pipit's nest. Tucked back in a crevice, the neatly circular cup was lined with fine grasses. Inside were three newly hatched youngsters, whose beaks opened into three incredibly large yellow gapes when we spoke nicely to them. Having no flies or caterpillars to pop in, and thinking we had made a find, we took a bee line to the top of the cliff to mark the nest for future reference, only to find a numbered stake already in place. Not much on Skokholm missed the keen eyes of the ornithologists in those days.

Our only useful contribution to the log when we got in was yellow shell moths, which we later discovered were commonplace, and a dung beetle rolling a rabbit pellet off and stuffing it down a burrow as sustenance for the larva which would hatch from the egg laid alongside.

Everything that could be certainly identified was recorded apart from those species always present, but we were not what came to be called twitchers, interested only in lists. Shearwaters were the main topic of conversation tonight. Was the birds' specialisation for life at sea an evolutionary advance or a retrogression, carrying as it did so many disadvantages? As with so many others, including seals, the disadvantages obtained only when they were ashore, and that was a relatively small part of their lives. Each bird tolerated this alien medium for only half the time that the egg took to hatch and the chick to fledge. Ringing had already shown that birds migrated to the South Atlantic to winter in the southern summer off the coast of South America and travelled as far as the Bay of Biscay to feed during the northern summer. The verdict: Mother Nature knew what she was at.

Because they were often found in association with baleen whales, it was earlier thought that they might feed on plankton, but a glance at the slender hooked bill spoils this theory. Nothing looks less handy for shovelling up tiny organisms over a broad front. It is, however, ideal for catching and gripping fish during long underwater swims with half furled wings used as oars. In fact many take shrimps and prawns and these small organisms are often lumped together as krill.

3.

SKOKHOLM: ORNITHOLOGISTS
AND LIGHTHOUSE KEEPERS

During my peregrinations through a razorbill colony the next morning I was surprised to find a lot of the eggs marked with indelible pencil. I expected at any moment to find one inscribed 'Denmark' or '3/6 a dozen'. So says my journal, so that is what we must have been paying for 'new-laids' in 1947. That is 17.5 new pence per round dozen.

Razorbill territories were more accessible than guillemots' as they laid in crevices on broken faces or among boulders rather than on narrow ledges. One bird usually stood sentinel above the nest, but they were absurdly easy to approach if I moved circumspectly. The watcher would gaze at me first through one eye and then the other, turning the head through an angle of 180 degrees in order to do so. How fortunate we are to have binocular vision!

Populations had opted for island life, away from cats, stoats and foxes on the mainland for so long that they seemed to be losing their fear reaction – like the antarctic penguins that had never known predators on land until man appeared on their unsullied scene – and had no objections to shaking flippers with me when I encountered them in later years.

In fact the owners of the inscribed eggs were well used to visitations by Joan Keighley, Peter Conder's assistant warden, during six years of that first decade. She hailed from the very different flatlands of Cambridge, but had taken to life among the rugged western rocks like a duck to water. We had already learned something of her oyster-catcher survey.

There were fifty-eight pairs of these dapper, noisy birds on the island that year and Joan was monitoring them daily, recording data on incubation periods. The birds were not only coastal, as often, but nested all over the plateau – widely spaced, as each needed a territory on land to supplement its shoreline foraging. The scanty nests were almost invisible against their background of tousled vegetation or scuffled peat, but each was marked by a numbered stake set at a little distance.

Peter Conder, Tom Jenkins, the author and Nell at the lighthouse.

The trios of chicks which hatched were as cryptically mottled in shades of brown, in marked contrast to their attendant parent. It could take them as much as three days to push their way out of the encompassing eggshell after their first warning cheep as the egg tooth on the bill tip got to work on the prison wall, but they made up for lost time afterwards. Their long legs were in working order quicker than a new born foal's and they soon scuttled off to melt into the undergrowth.

Joan did the rounds every morning before most of us were up, in order to catch them before they disappeared. Sadly, too many of the rings were found later in gull's nests when the near perfect camouflage had proved not quite perfect enough. I came upon one nest where a new hatchling was drying off beside his unhatched brethren – right in the middle of a lesser black-backed gull colony, their survival thus far a miracle of devoted wardenship by their parents. It behoved them to leave as close to each other as the staggered hatching allowed if they were to make a clean getaway but their chances seemed slender. Were their parents young and inexperienced to choose such a site?

Joan's special study area for razorbills was on the stepped cliffs below the south-western lighthouse – not where I had found the inscribed eggs. The rest of us were exhorted not to enter that site lest we disturb the courting couples and complicate the results. It transpired long afterwards that there was courting of another sort going on along those broadly accommodating cliff ledges.

Some years later Joan announced her engagement to the senior light-house keeper, Tom Jenkins. Those uninterrupted hours had borne fruit. Tom was older than Joan but less than his hair colour might indicate. He had 'gone white overnight' after being washed off the Smalls light-house some years before, but was rescued to live a long and happy life.

The couple left the island and set up in a small farm on the Cardigan-shire cliffs at Tyrffynon near Newquay. It was hard going – a seven day week of chores with the livestock and the raising of a son and daughter. Visitors were likely to find her in pinnafore and gumboots trudging round the yard with heavy buckets or hay bales.

When Tom died she carried on alone, with help from son David, who finally took over when she became crippled with arthritis and unable to cope. She wrote faithfully every Christmas, in neatly clipped handwriting as orderly as the tables of bird counts and measurements in her other life.

Her daughter Mary joined the women's army corps, the ATS. She was posted to Germany and became an expert in cross country orien-teering, a vocation arising from the union of the two open air spirits who were her parents. Because of my long standing correspondence with Joan, Mary wrote to me, as a married woman living in the north of England, to tell me of her mother's death.

In my reply I enlarged on Joan's professional life among the island scientists, orienteering around the nests bright and early every morning and of the high esteem in which she was held for her painstaking efforts with records and research data. This, apparently, came as a revelation to the second generation, who had known only life on the little farm, satisfying but restricted, particularly for the hardworking farmer's wife.

Skokholm addicts splayed out into many walks of life, all deeply influenced by those evocative island years in the great out-of-doors. Peter Conder, warden for seven years from 1947, eventually married Pat Higginson, long term bursar at Dale Fort, who was responsible for organising our weekly rations on the island.

He rose to become secretary and then director of the RSPB, Britain's most prestigious ornithological society. His pre-island life embraced two very different phases, first as public schoolboy and chorister, then in the armed forces with a long spell as a prisoner-of-war, in association with John Barrett, John Buxton and Kenneth Williamson, ornithologists all, who made notes on birds seen outside the confining fences in miniscule notebooks that were all they could muster. All became prominent in

British ornithological circles on their eventual release, and all started as wardens of observatories where they became well known to the many visitors, Barrett at Dale Fort, Buxton on Skomer and Williamson on Fair Isle.

After lunch on my first Tuesday some of us were detailed off for a bird count, excluding the too numerous sea-birds around the cliffs. The more experienced took the difficult terrain of the island centre: I had the south coast and Julian the north, starting from the lighthouse and working back towards the Neck.

We needed to distinguish rock and meadow pipits, skylarks and wheatears, the flight of whimbrel from that of curlew and not to do a double count of the oyster-catchers that circled round from behind to settle in front. We were relieved when we got back to the record book to find that our result tallied approximately with that of the previous count.

Julian was a great character. Dressed like a tramp and discoursing like a gentleman, he had been brought up among the Lake District fells and hoped to climb Everest when he left Oxford. Always ready with a helping hand, he did more than his share of the chores and had the kind of appetite that left the rest of the assembled company speechless. We felt obliged to decline when he came round the table offering second helpings, knowing that he would clear the lot himself and still have room for more.

He was on night patrol this week, having undertaken the mapping and estimation of shearwater numbers, which could only be done by being out among them. Nevertheless, he seemed to be about most of the day too. All that energy expenditure had to be fueled somehow, the extra calories standing in for lost sleep.

People in the grey world of the mainland often remarked during my subsequent summers in residence: "How can you possibly bury yourself on a tiny island for months at a time, away from everybody and everything?"

Needless to say, I met far more interesting characters by 'burying myself' on this particular island than ever I would have done in the humdrum world of nine to five. Apart from the nucleus of stalworts, there was a changing population week by week, all slightly eccentric and the more entertaining as a result.

There was, for instance, Piglet, whose double-barrelled surname eludes me. He used to turn up for a week or so every summer during the years when the nucleus of 'long-termers' were 'into' "Winnie the Pooh".

Piglet, Peter Driver and Goodie Goodman at the bunkhouse door.

Piglet was a great moocher, quartering the open acres in a dream world of his own. Somehow the title stuck.

Thirty years later a strange middle-aged man wearing a dog collar joined a large gathering of nature lovers that I was leading around the Glamorgan hills. He was not one of the regulars, but there were always newcomers. Approaching me at one point, he came out with the simple statement: "I'm Piglet" – bringing back floods of memories.

No longer the callow youth of the old days, no-one would have guessed. His contemplative musings had led him into holy orders and his wanderlust into becoming a ship's chaplain in the Merchant Navy. This had taken him all over the world, in stranger company, no doubt, than his old acquaintances on Skokholm. When his ship had docked in Cardiff he had seen the excursion advertised and recognised the name. I have not seen him since. A ship that passed in the night, like so many others that crop up from time to time.

More recently, at the close of the year 2001, when my eightieth birthday celebration got a mention in a conservation journal, a man from the Midlands wrote to me, opening with: "I met you on Skokholm in the early 1960s."

Seeing so many visitors week by week I failed to recognise the name of Godfrey Nall, but this contact launched an exchange of letters and poems inspired by island life. There is something intangible about Skokholm that seems to get under the skin of all who visit. And the weekly boats are still taking visitors across to produce new converts!

On that first Wednesday afternoon there was great activity around the buildings, with everyone putting their hand to some maintenance or constructional job in readiness for Ronald Lockley's arrival on the Saturday. The bustle resembled that in a Welsh Valley town before the arrival of the Prince of Wales.

Peter Conder (Warden) mended a window. Peter Perry (ex-Eton and navy and a Cambridge classics undergraduate, also secretary of the Cambridge Bird Club) joined Julian to spend the day with pails of cement and halyards erecting a flagpole on the wheelhouse roof – at great personal risk, so they said. My fellow bird-watcher in the angel loft sewed vigorously at a dark shearwater on a white flag that was to summon future generations of islanders to meals, and the rest of the population set to redecorating the outside of the house or gardening.

Skokholm Farmhouse. View to Skomer and Middleholm.

While waiting for my whitewash brush to materialise I helped the gardeners to sort out the finely divided leaves of lesser swines cress from the baby carrots with which they cohabited. Those weeds had developed camouflage to a fine art, but how did they know we were going to plant carrots and not lettuces?

A quick glance around and I realised that there would be no future for lettuces. The garden was alive with snails, which congregated in horny clusters on tops of the posts holding the rabbit-proof netting. Snails need lime for their shells and this was not a limey habitat – except for all that whitewash.

When it arrived we climbed, dripping and slipping, up and down ladders, plastering all parts of the wall within reach. The tallest ladder was not quite tall enough, so I crept along the edge of the roof and sat astride the ridge, leaning over to apply my brush with good effect. Fresh ammunition was passed through the window of the angel loft by the erstwhile seamstress.

Joyce at the other end of the ridge fared less well. Legs waving wildly over the eaves, she yelled for help, causing six foot five inch Peter Parry to dump his bucket of water in mid meadow and race to assist. There was much laughter but, as Lilian, our light-hearted cook, remarked: "This is a funny world."

Tired of being watched by the island's most efficient work dodger and tall storyteller, who strolled or slept around the island wondering why the birds did not come up and pose for his camera, we gave him a whitewash bucket to hand up as necessary and save us coming down. As the watching lighthouse keeper remarked: "A triumph of good organisation."

In the midst of all this activity there was a cry of "Boat ahoy!" from another lighthouse keeper standing above North Haven. Everyone downed tools in the expectation of Grassholm at last. Complete with whitewash (we thought the gannets wouldn't mind, they were used to that sort of thing), we gathered gumboots, thick gloves gannet hooks and a basket of food and made all haste to the north landing where the keepers indicated, the tide being wrong for South Haven.

Disappointed again! It was too rough for Grassholm and the boat had brought a party of WRNS from the nearby naval station, who were being landed, half on the rocks and half on the only little sandy beach that the island boasted at low tide.

Crestfallen, we returned to our whitewashing and continued until the eighty pounds of lime at a shilling a pound had become exhausted, as also had we. Lighthouses and bird observatories must be the most frequently painted buildings anywhere. High tea was badly overdue as the Wrens invaded the wheelhouse. There was talk of ringing this flock before it escaped, but the bare legs that eventually waded out to the dinghy were unadorned.

Fates decreed that whenever there was a boat at one of the landings there was a bird in one of the traps and this was true today. On the way from North Haven Lilian and I had spotted a wheatear caught in a triangle of wire netting in the big Home Meadow trap, trying in vain to get out. We dug down to free the netting, so that a hand could be reached in to transfer the bird to the catching box at the head of the funnel. From here it was easily removed from the outside through a sleeve door.

The Heligoland trap, a widely splayed funnel, was 'baited' with undergrowth containing food items and was built around a stream with yellow irises and tall marsh plants for cover. Ninety feet wide at the entrance to the assembly area with strategically placed baffles to prevent return along walls and roof, it tapered in sections to a small glass window, promising

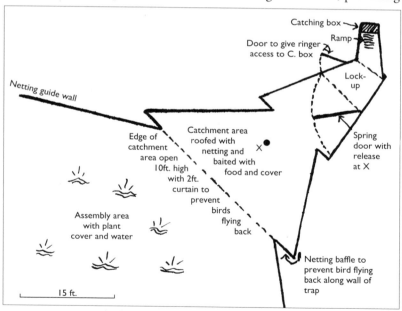

Heligoland bird trap in the Home Meadow, 1947.

escape but causing the bird to drop into the catching box below. A series of trap-doors were operated from a distance to imprison the catch as it moved in, or was driven on by a line of slowly advancing catchers.

I accompanied the captive wheatear to the ringing room to observe procedure. Measurements were made of the tarsus, from 'heel' to 'hock' and the primary wing feathers and the colour of eyes and bill were noted before ringing. Any male wheatear with a ring measurement over 100mm or female over 96mm was regarded as belonging to the larger Greenland race. Coloured celluloid rings topped the metal one for field identification.

There was cooperation between bird ringing stations, Skokholm exchanging sea-bird eggs for others from the Isle of May in South-east Scotland, to see which island the hatchlings returned to after their winters at sea.

Following our belated high tea, I joined a party exploring the cliffs under the lighthouse. We came across several dead Soay sheep and one goat, victims of the bitter winter when students from Aberystwyth had been ferried up into the Welsh hills to help farmers dig their sheep out of snowdrifts. The horns of the goat came away easily from the bony core, but those of the Soays stayed firmly attached to the weatherbeaten skulls.

Lingering over these, I got left behind so, when I succeeded in catching an unmarked razorbill the man with the rings had disappeared. With the bird tucked comfortably under one arm, a puffin pole, pair of goat horns and sundry oddments under the other, I had to accomplish the handless climb up the face on knees and elbows but made it to the rings. The bird behaved like the lady she was, venting her spleen only on the ungloved hands that applied the ring.

Everyone was late for 'log' and it was my turn to be keeper of the book, with instructions to be as funny as I liked about the afternoon's activities. From the time I had completed the record until about 11.30, 'Doc' led an interesting discussion on genes and hereditary. Then someone realised that lanky Peter II and little Thomas had not returned. They were thought to have gone after guillemots and the latter was exceedingly nimble and slightly hare-brained on cliffs so a search party was organised.

We divided into pairs and took a quarter of the island each. My pair was a trio, with the lethargic gent and the sixty-year-old lady with no head for heights. I appropriated the powerful flashlamp and went ahead. About half way to the sea I spotted something wet and shiny in a crevice,

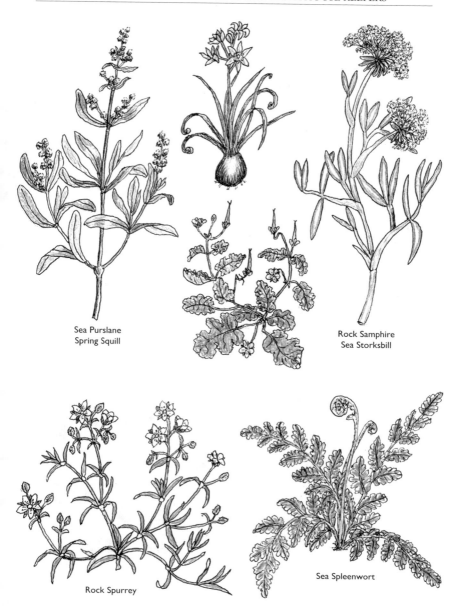

Sea Purslane
Spring Squill

Rock Samphire
Sea Storksbill

Rock Spurrey

Sea Spleenwort

Characteristic cliff plants.

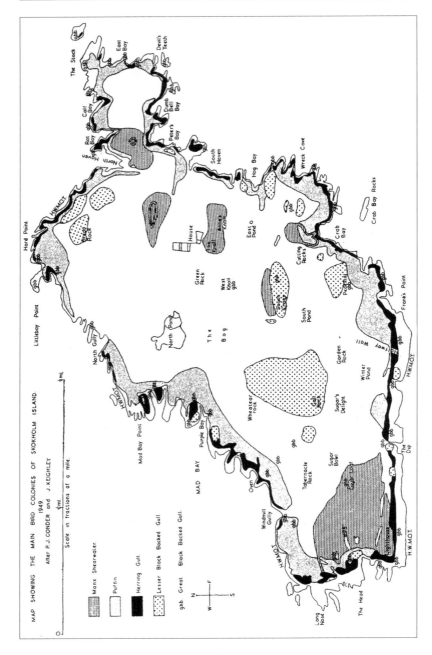

MAP SHOWING THE MAIN BIRD COLONIES OF SKOKHOLM ISLAND.
1949
After P.J. CONDER and J. KEIGHLEY

Scale in fractions of a mile.

Manx Shearwater
Puffin
Herring Gull
Lesser Black Backed Gull.
gbb Great Black Backed Gull.

like a bloated slug. Closer investigation revealed it to be not a corpse but a bull seal which had come ashore under cover of darkness – as they will to sun themselves by day on seaweed covered rocks when the tide withdraws, leaving them stranded.

I responded to a frantically flashing light on the other side of the bay, wanting to send a morse message in best girl guide style, but wondering if it would be understood. The two lights converged. The other was held by the warden, who had been missing when the search parties left and wondered where everyone had disappeared to. A shout from the darkness intimated that the wanderers had returned, to the inevitable: "And where the hell do you think you've been?" followed by an apologetic Peter: "Frightfully sorry, but we were after guillemots and had no idea that you all . . ."

Shearwatering and gulling had been on the programme for tonight but, as it was already one o'clock and many of the shearwaters were already safely in their burrows, most of us decided that we were too tired, but three of the boys went.

Gulling was a sport that nobody tried that week and we gathered that nobody but the warden, who usually succeeded in grabbing two or three, ever managed to take an adult gull by surprise. Speed was of the essence. The party approached the sleeping gulls to within about thirty yards, then dashed in at full speed, tucking sleepy gulls inside their jackets or anywhere else, to leave their hands free. Lockley held the record of six birds in one swoop.

This would take place just before dawn, when the birds were not properly awake. According to Julian, who was abroad at night, the razorbills and guillemots did not wake until later and could be approached quite easily during the few minutes after first light.

On Thursday morning most of us were involved in a more detailed bird count, with time spent later trying to observe where the elusive rock pipits took those beakful's of food, but their patience was usually greater than ours. They were not revealing the whereabouts of their nest when there was a pair of binoculars pointing in their direction.

I asked for an update on the current numbers of birds on the island and was amazed at the magnitude of the populations. Manx shearwaters 40,000, with over 24,000 breeding birds. Storm petrels 1,200. Puffins 40,000, razorbills over 2,000 and guillemots 250. Lesser black-backs 1,600, herring gulls 600, great black-backs 100 and oyster-catchers 120. Rock pipits 80, meadow pipits 80 and wheatears 30.

After high tea I set off with Lucy and Joyce for an evening with the lighthouse keepers. Although Skokholm was classified as 'a rock', earning extra pay for the men than a mainland station, these keepers were never short of company and it was a popular posting.

Oyster-catcher.

The three keepers and Nell, the terrier, we had already met, but we were introduced to Larry and the goats. On arrival, although fresh from our meal, we were plied with food and drink. Our hosts insisted that we occupy the three keepers' chairs, while the curly headed young 'chief' made himself as comfortable as might be in the coal bucket and the other two on the stairs winding up to the lantern.

The two ends of the island were on excellent terms. The *Trinity House* steamer put into South Haven with stores and coal once a month and gave assistance also to the bird-watchers if it was too rough for a small boat to get across. Sometimes an interesting package fell off the horse-drawn trolley by accident on purpose as it passed the whitewashed homestead.

The keepers went along with our eccentricities and were bird-watchers themselves, recording a few birds on their windswept end of the island that we missed on our more sheltered end. Fortunately, few of

Guillemots on ledge.

Wheatears with Thrift and Plantain.

these were casualties of the benign red beam. There was no need of screens and perching rails around this light as on some of the others.

This happy state continued for forty to forty-five years, when Trinity House changed the beam from red to white for better visibility at sea. On one occasion, in 1996, forty to fifty bird casualties were picked up below the white light, almost half of them dead. In 1999 a red filter was fitted, leaving only the seaward sector white, and this helped greatly. The worst kills occurred when rain or fog brought habitually high-flying migrants down low. It was the flashing which blinded them and St. Ann's, which glowed with a steady white light, was less of a hazard.

We were taken on a conducted tour of the business quarters. The oil pressure, 75 pounds to the square inch, put me in mind of the recently visited Anvil Point lighthouse. It seemed inconceivable that the deflated mesh of silk netting of new mantles (for ease of travel) should become so full blown and brittle when subjected to heat.

The great foghorn with its three funnels facing in different directions to broadcast their message, performed for four seconds at a time with six second intervals between blasts. Unfortunately a broken reed introduced a jarring note, but keepers were paid extra – I think it was a ha'penny or a penny an hour – when it was on, compensating for lack of sleep.

It turned foggy with darkness tonight and its unmusical boom mingled with the shearwater din, so that we wondered how the keepers could sleep at all when they said that a slight whistle down the speaking tube from the man on duty would waken them to immediate action. A clock recorded when the foghorn was functioning, to settle any argument which might arise if a ship got into difficulties.

Modern automation is a lot less effective at detecting a fog bank rolling in from a distance and it cannot help mariners cast ashore and in need of the succour that lighthouse keepers were so good at administering. This impersonalisation of maritime services is a worldwide problem, more keenly felt on the remote shores that I worked on later in the Antipodes.

Back in the living room, the receiving and transmitting set was demonstrated and we listened to the fruity talk of the trawler captains in English, Welsh and Breton. This was our first contact with the outside world for a week and we learned that the temperature in London had reached 85°F. Here it had been 60°F! We learned about the Smalls and other lights where these men had worked and, at 9 o'clock, when we should have been assembling for log, we went outside to milk the goats.

As an ex-land girl and dairy maid I had to have a go. Storm, a quite charming kid, was tethered to keep the two nannies from wandering and to give his dam some peace from his persistent bunting. He was enticed down from a rocky eminence, untied and tucked under the chief's arm, from where he proceeded to lick his face. His mother and grandmother and Larry the Soay lamb followed the pair into a lean-to shed erected against a vertical-sided bluff.

When I moved in with bucket and stool to milk Blitz, she was up in the roof somewhere, the rough rock proving no obstacle to her nimble feet. She was located by the light of the tilley lamp and hauled down by a ladylike ankle, secured by a horn, and then gazed over her shoulder in wonderment at me, a stranger in her ordered life. No attempt was made to withhold her milk and, with only two teats, I found myself finished when half way through by bovine standards. Storm's mama breathed warmly in my face throughout, before junior was released to help himself at her milk bar.

The lighthouse was built in 1916 and remained operational until 1983. Long before this the movement of personnel and stores were by helicopter rather than ship, bringing new keepers and stores direct to the door. This was many years after Sugarback had been pensioned off and eventually departed this life, to be buried in the middle of North

Pond, his favourite retreat when work threatened. His horse power had been replaced by a motorised dumper which needed no railway lines – these now a rusting reminder of the old days.

The helicopter cured one of the problems suffered by the keepers in the early days – that of surprise meals. Wet transfers of stores at the landing were apt to result in a collection of tinned food lacking labels. I shall always remember the disgruntled keeper: "Absolutely famished I was, looking forward to bully beef and baked beans. And what did I get? Raspberry pudden!"

The facial expression accompanying those last two words struck everyone but himself as funny. It is odd how such inconsequential trifles stick in the mind over the years. They were happy days. Lighthouse keepers are an extinct breed now, since automation of all the lights, and the world is a poorer place without them.

Friday morning dawned wet and stayed wet, my greatest achievement being the rediscovery of creeping willow at East Pond, alongside the one noble and soon to be extinct tuft of royal fern. The willow, a tree, albeit an almost prostrate one, had been seen by Lockley, but not for the past eight years, having apparently gone underground for the war.

The proposed gull count was abandoned because of the rain, the technique being to drive down on the colony and put the birds up so that they came down to rest on the sea where there were no obstructions and they were easily counted.

Puffin hooking was substituted. There comes a time when one is so wet and muddy that it doesn't matter any longer and we had no qualms about wriggling through wet bracken and sliding through red-tinged puddles. Like heifers, puffins are intensely curious and little groups would come trotting towards the mountain of muddiness that was trying to look as though it wasn't there, to stop about 2 feet from the extended hook and goggle owlishly.

Tickle the white breast feathers and they would peer in alternating directions, as though suspecting danger but not regarding it as imminent. They were not as stupid as they looked, however, and most got away. As the warden insisted, puffin catching was a sport and not to be made too easy.

When the last of the targeted group went happily on its way, I continued to lie face down where I was, watching the breakers dashing themselves on the rocks below. Shearwaters were gathering in great rafts on the waters of Broad Sound between Skokholm and Skomer. There were said to be usually about ten thousand birds in these gatherings, waiting to come ashore on one or other of the islands under cover of darkness and I could well believe it. Storm petrels never gathered like this. They just slipped in out of the darkness, one by one, and disappeared into their nest holes.

On the Saturday we were in high hopes that it would be too rough for the boat to come and take us off. Knowing that Lockley was hoping to come out, however, it was inevitable that he would try and make it if at all possible. Peter was no help. He prophesied that we would probably get very wet and uncomfortable, but that it wouldn't be quite bad enough to prevent us going. And then, through the howling wind and rain, came a lighthouse keeper with the news that a gale warning had been issued. Nobody crossed in the teeth of a gale warning. Nobody, that is, except Lockley.

Breakfast was a cheery meal. We took young froghoppers from the vases of wild flowers and raced them along the table, seeing whose specimen could carry the largest number of hogweed petals for longest. Doc (Tony Matthews) treated the company to a long story about one of our ground burrowing beetles, the minotaur.

Minotaur Beetle, Allseed and Pearlwort.

"Thus, his life work done, he comes above ground and lays him down to die. And so ends the sad story of *Typhaeus typhoeus.*"

Much to our disappointment, the fog cleared and we saw the boat bounding towards South Haven, where the warden had gone with the hand bell to help guide her in. Aboard were Ronald Lockley and his wife Jill, John Buxton (poet, naturalist and ex-Skomer warden) and his wife, Schifferley (head of the only large bird ringing station in Switzerland), Penny (the returning island cook) and the legendary Baron of the Baron's workshop – a key room between wheelhouse and bunkhouse.

Passengers and cargoes were exchanged among a welter of wet mackintoshes. Men hauled on ropes, Lockley yelled instructions from the shore, Craig yelled more from the boat, Peter Conder and John Fursdon leapt to obey both, like a couple of scalded cats and the human cargo shifted from side to side to even the load, as instructed. Every time we won free an extra large wave lifted us back onto the rocks, with that ominous scrunching sound.

A seal hung in the water a few yards away, watching operations with interest and wondering what all the fuss was about. Then Joan was rushing down with a bit of forgotten luggage. Craig backed in as far as he dared while Peter climbed out by the gantry and hurled it across the watery gulf. At last we were away.

This was life as it should be lived, stimulating, challenging and satisfying. Waves swept in over the bow and were pumped out over the stern by the boatman's mate. Three fulmars glided above, wings held straight and motionless, at one with the elements. I was not the only one who knew I would be back!

4.

SKOKHOLM:
SEMI-DOMESTICATED LIVESTOCK

Although I had so narrowly missed Ronald Lockley during my first week on Skokholm, he came to the island quite frequently in the ensuing years. At first he was farming at Dinas Island, actually a promontory near Cwm yr Eglwys along the coast, and of which he wrote the book *Island Farm*. Subsequently he moved to Orielton House Farm, later a Field Centre, where he pursued his research on rabbits and seals and busied himself with the West Wales Field Society, of which he was one of the leading lights.

We were culling some of the Soay rams on one occasion, to prevent sex imbalance and the possibility of starvation in hot dry summers or cold wet winters. I had become a dab hand at skinning rabbits during the years of meat rationing in the Women's Land Army and thought it would be nice to have a Soay fleece, but this was an altogether different kettle of fish. Lockley offered to help.

The carcase was suspended upside down in the Baron's workshop and he guided me through the stages of opening up, emptying out and

Soay Sheep.

unthreading the limbs, finishing up with a fine pelt, dark brown and curly. Piglet materialised to help us scrape off the sub-cutaneous fat, stretch it out and apply alum and/or salt petre, the details of which elude me.

Sadly, when I sent it away to be professionally cured, the message came back that it was moulting and useless. The skin was not returned. The firm had gained itself a fine bit of leather, with or without a woolly coat, and without having to pay carriage.

It seemed I would have to make do with the skull and its fine sweeping pair of horns as my trophy. Most of the soft material was removed by boiling, when the cook wasn't about, but it was impossible to clean it thoroughly. Instead we placed it on a busy anthill in the Wheelhouse yard and the ants did a fine job of work on it. I bore it away in triumph when they finished and have often wondered where it got left during the course of my ensuing travels. A grisly prize for some unsuspecting landlady somewhere, perhaps.

Soays are wild sheep. They are never shorn, neither are they rooed (the wool plucked), as with Shetland sheep. It is just discarded in the course of their everyday life, itchy bits rubbed off on rocks or heather and littering the island as a useful resource for nest-building birds.

Not needing to be sheared, Soays make admirable conservation tools in remote nature reserves, requiring minimal management when a neater sward is required in rough country. The breed falls between the wild moufflon of Europe and modern domesticated sheep and is thought to have arrived in Britain with Neolithic farmers in the third millennium BC.

Remnants of the breed survived on the tiny island of Soay in the St. Kilda Group, a hundred miles off North-west Scotland. When the islanders evacuated in 1930 a hundred and seven Soays were transferred to the main island of Hirta, where the population grew to between a thousand and fifteen hundred animals by the 1980s. There were transfers of sub-flocks to other parts of Great Britain and the first of these to reach Wales was established here on Skokholm in 1934.

Flocks followed on Cardigan Island in 1944, on Middleholm off Skomer in 1945 and St. Margaret's Island off Caldey in 1952. Three of these flocks, including Skokholm's, died out during the early 1960s, leaving only the one on Cardigan Island.

Interest in the breed has been growing and there are now many other flocks, including a small one on Flatholm Island, but most are 'ornamentals' in farm parks or 'conservation aids' in nature reserves. Although of little use as a source of meat on a commercial scale, specialist craft weavers have created a demand for their short-stapled, coarsely-kempy, richly coloured wool. Our more familiar white-fleeced sheep are said to have been introduced much later, by the Romans.

During the decade in which I remained closely familiar with Skokholm the flock size fluctuated between sixty and a hundred and twenty, twins being common and triplets not unknown. Some of the surplus rams were pushed over the cliffs in fights with their fellows, but in later years their numbers were controlled by shooting, the meat making a welcome addition to the larder when appropriately hung, venison style.

It added more than lamb to our menu as, along with rabbits, which were never in short supply, it could be swapped for crabs and lobsters with the Breton fishermen. No doubt each rendezvous at South Haven would have been arranged on the shipping radio wavelength by our friends in the lighthouse, this being half a century before mobile phones flooded the market. The lamb went well with the big parasol mushrooms (*Lepiota procera*) that sprouted plentifully from the grassed areas at certain seasons. On crab days the table was laid with bowls, hammers and pliers as well as the usual implements.

In the early days, when humans returned to the island after the empty war years, the Soays were very wild, fleeing as deer will flee, but they got progressively more used to people. They had a great deal more individuality than today's domestic sheep but rather less than the goats' – which have the reputation for leading the mixed flocks of the Middle East into trouble, hence the recommended separation.

If adopted young, they formed a close attachment to their human fosterers, but did not entirely desert the flock, as most hand-reared lambs do, spending time with both. The pet lambs in 1956 were Kelly the ram and Chop Soay the ewe. They came and went as they chose, but left the flock to come trotting back when called.

They were undecided as to whether they were sheep or goats. Accepting the leadership of the nanny goat, Persephone, without question, they shared yard and goatshed with her tribe for much of the time. That is, they shared the goatshed when there was room but, when all wanted to crowd in out of the rain, they were the ones that got squeezed out, particularly when the shed also contained the front half of the horse. Both ram and ewe thought it a fine sport to exercise their sharp little horns in charging every passing pair of legs, a pastime which made them increasingly unpopular as they grew larger.

A young lamb which has lost its mother will adopt anything on legs which seems likely to function in lieu, and I enjoyed the amusing spectacle of a new-born Soay lamb trying to foist itself as foster child onto an unwilling sheepdog bitch.

The chosen unfortunate was Rickie, the black and white collie from Dale Fort, who was always banished to the island when on heat. To say she was bemused at this supposed orphan reaching for her milk bar was to put it mildly. Never brave, she was plainly mortified. She scuttled away but the tiny lamb outpaced her, so she tried to escape by stealth.

Half crouched to the ground, tail between legs to partially conceal the unyielding mammary glands that peeped so temptingly from her fur, she crept in and out among the boulders, one eye cocked back over her shoulder to see if she had shaken off the young offender. The situation was eventually saved by the reappearance of the ewe, bleating hysterically at the temerity of her offspring in approaching so large a potential predator and calling him away.

It would not have occurred to the gentle Rickie to damage the wee creature. On more than one occasion I have seen her dashing at full pelt across the island with the Soay flock in hot pursuit. The only dog they knew, the tiny ageing Nell, seemed a much less formidable threat and she only ventured out with her masters in later years and not even that towards the end.

During her younger days Nell could easily outpace Rickie in pursuit of rabbits, but neither were a patch on the whippet which spent a season with us rabbiting, when her prey had been cleared from the mainland by Myxomatosis in 1955. Instead of blundering through the bracken like the other two, she leapt lightly over the top, like a pronking gazelle, putting me in mind of the Sika deer on Lundy Island.

Cats were never tolerated by the bird observatory, for obvious reasons, but there was one at the lighthouse for a time. The keepers assured us that this black paragon of virtue would never dream of hunting birds and we did not enquire too deeply. Certainly, whenever I saw him he was perched innocently on the tall mantlepiece above the kitchen range and I never visited the lighthouse when he was missing. He met his end on the cliffs when still quite young and from 1949 on there were no cats.

In 1947 the three island goats were lighthouse property, but soon after that the skipper presented them to the observatory – as a constant source of entertainment for visitors, as well as providing us with fresh

Goats on cliff.

milk – which tasted better in custards than in tea! They certainly added atmosphere in more ways than one. Herd size seldom exceeded five and sometimes dwindled to two, each member with its own individuality.

It must have been in 1949, when I was working on Spider Cave promontory that I looked seaward to see two peculiar figures sharing the stern seat of an approaching boat. One was wearing a battered straw hat which we came to know well in future years, the other head was surmounted by a splendid pair of horns.

The first proved to be Dr. Freddie Parker-Rhodes, eminent genetiscist, statistician and mycologist from the staff of Cambridge University. This was the first of his many visits to the island, where he made comprehensive lists of the fungi and entertained all and sundry as only eccentrics of his calibre can. He was particularly entranced by the toadstools growing on the pony dung and one of his learned papers was entitled

'The Intestinal Basidiomycetes of *Equus caballus* L.nom Sugarback, on Skokholm Island'. His first paper listed ninety-five other higher fungi.

On this occasion his travelling companion was the new billy goat, whose head adornment we came to know only too well. As first seen, he looked decidedly dejected, seasick perhaps. Freddie, a restraining arm about his companion's neck, was puffing vigorously at the pipe from which he was seldom parted, whether to ward off the pangs of sickness or the aroma of billy goat it was difficult to say.

Both appeared relieved when on terra firma and the resident nannies, reduced to grass widowhood long since, were delighted and gave them a vociferous welcome. These two, recently acquired from the lighthouse, were Big Ma and Little Ma, or more correctly Mrs. Minniver, that great wartime film heroine, and Mrs. Dombey. Mrs. M. had a vigorous, domineering personality, Mrs. D was the opposite, allowing herself to be pushed around. While she waited timorously in the Wheelhouse yard to be milked, her tormentor pushed open the door and helped herself to stale bread until shooed out. It was only to be expected that she produced twice as much milk and a finer kid.

Big Ma came to a sticky end, in spite of frequent warnings of her declining powers as the years advanced. On one occasion a muffled bleating led me to the lime kiln into which she had toppled when reaching too far in to nibble the overarching brambles. I had a cherished area of 'no grazing' inside as a 'control', but that was the end of that. Ropes and manpower were sought, the first fastened round her belly, the second struggling manfully to haul her back up. Big Ma was no lightweight. Her dignity was severely injured and she stalked off when released, head in air, without so much as a bleat of thanks.

The next mishap was on Rat Island, not a true island but reached with difficulty across a crumbling isthmus. Rabbits seldom ventured there, so the plants were lush and green, a prize for the venturesome and a trap for the unwary, but also another of my ungrazed control areas. Alas for my hopes.

Big Ma was still undisputed leader of the free range herd (the billy arriving with Freddie having to be tethered because of his belligerence when not suffering mal-de-mer). Little Ma's son had grown into a lusty male and would soon be relieving her of this role.

On this occasion the elderly one had led her little troupe across. They had eaten their fill and scrambled back up the cliff, all except herself. The ascent had proved too much for her aging limbs and portly bulk.

Dr. Geoffrey Matthews gets the better of Ivanhoe.

Disconsolately she watched the others amble off and tucked into more of the appetising plant life.

When rescuers appeared she set up an indignant bleating, asking why we had taken so long. Ropes were once more made fast about her by an intrepid climber and up she came. Rat Island became a favourite foraging ground for the little band but, be it said in Big Ma's favour, she did not venture to make the crossing again to our knowledge, much as it went against the grain. It was rather pathetic to watch that once proud matron picking forlornly at the sparse greenery left by the rabbits on the worn cliff edge while her despised contemporaries hogged all the goodies.

We all come to it in time! This was the beginning of the end. The young billy took command and the former leader failed to survive the winter, suffering the usual ultimate fate of her kind in falling off a cliff.

The offspring of Big Ma and Little Ma by the imported billy were Rowena and Ivanhoe. Each was very different from its mother. Rowena remained timid to the end of her days, although the finer, fatter kid of the two. Ivanhoe resembled his mother only in his lean and shaggy appearance, possessing none of her meekness. From the start he made his presence felt, bullying her until she appeared leaner and more harried than usual. Long after he should have been weaned he continued to bunt furiously at her ill-used udder. Very likely he had been getting insufficient all along. He tried hard for some of Rowena's share, but Big Ma would have none of him.

The kids were firm friends and spent a carefree youth gambolling on the assemblage of boxes, planks and ladders erected for their pleasure. Row remained nervous, Hoe investigated all and sundry. Later in life, with a great spread of horns and terrific power in his shaggy neck, he became a menace as he pursued his childish games with his human friends.

A favourite pastime was to hook one of those formidable horns round the back of ones knee and then step back, felling his companion to the ground in one neat movement. To drag him by the horns to a gate and then slip through was of no avail. He would leap nimbly over the wall ready to resume contact.

Shooing was only part of the game, but there was one chink in his armour. He hated water in any form. Arm oneself with a mug of this and shake it under his nose and he would flee to safety, just as he fled to the goathouse from wherever he was on the island at the first few drops of rain. As each shower started there was a thundering of hooves as he made full tilt for the Half-Way-House, which served as goatshed and

Goats, family party.

69

woodshed and was later converted to something more palatial as the cook's bedroom. Nannies and kids were in less of a hurry and, if there was insufficient room for all, it was not the lord and master who waited outside.

The habit became ingrained in the family. In 1955, after Ivanhoe had passed on to a rumbustious billy goat heaven, the herd still huddled about the cook's door when it rained. They sneaked inside if the door was ajar and were not sufficiently well mannered to stay at floor level. Old habits die hard. Hard on the cook, too, to find her bed occupied. Needless to say, another shed had been erected for the goats nearby.

Rowena, mated with her half brother, bore a number of kids, but outlived them all. Her first, Francesca, had all the cheek and charm of her father as a kid. She was born on Frank's Point, hence the name, on a practically inaccessible ledge such as her mother always chose for these events. Sometimes she would leave her kids and return with the herd at milking time, only giving away their position after much careful stalking. At others both she and the kids appeared to be stuck and had to be located and rescued.

A lot of rope work was necessary on one occasion – this the easy part as it was a long way back to the yard. There were two of us, Peter with one kid, me with the other and Rowena blaring along behind. Only when the kids were on the ground did she respond to their cries. When they were up in our arms they could bleat their little heads off but she cast about wildly looking for an expected pattern and unable to locate the sound without. As a result, we had to proceed in short laps, one holding a kid on the ground for her to fuss over while the other was carried on a few hundred yards and put down for her to see.

Francesca's twin was a billy and had to be put down, much as Peter hated this sort of job. One billy goat on the island was quite enough! The lack of a playmate of her own age increased Francesca's affinity with humans and her inability to resist leaping onto a bent back wherever she spied one. It was never possible for me to milk her mother and grandmother without four pointy hooves sticking into my shoulders and a soft little nose probing inside my collar.

Pandora, one of her successors, improved this game by jumping along a series of backs at different levels, but seeming a little bewildered on reaching the highest. Pomegranite, out of Persephone, had yet another version: she used the pony as a back. That she was allowed to do so says much for her charm, for Sugarback generally tolerated the goats at no price and had to be excluded from the yard at milking time. Tiddly Pom, as she was known in her youth, was permitted the privilege only so long as she refrained from chewing his ears.

She joined me one day in the Wheelhouse, where I was melting paraffin wax on the calor gas stove to seal my specimen tubes. The long rope to which she was habitually attached got thoroughly wound up among the legs of tables and benches, but she showed remarkable intelligence in unwinding herself with no help.

Francesca's two forebears were fiercely protective, always chasing the Soays from their offspring. She learned the habit and, as she grew bigger, was often seen putting the entire flock to rout on her own. The sight of her tiny form bouncing along behind fifty or more sheep in full retreat, was quite as entertaining as the flock in hot pursuit of the apparently more formidable sheepdog. The kid's more cumbersome elders were quite unable to keep up with her on these occasions.

Sadly, this little one died bearing her first kid and her mother and father remained the sole survivors during 1952. It was accordingly decided to accept the offer of two nannies who had been living in splendid isolation on Middleholm Island for the past five years.

The older of the two had been banished there with her kid after enjoying a meal of nightgown hung temptingly on a clothesline within her reach. The younger one had had practically no dealings with the human race and it was expected that they would be very wild, but it was resolved that an attempt should be made.

Middleholm is difficult of access and I was anxious to botanise there, so I was put ashore there early one morning with instructions to locate the goats while the rest of the party went on to Skomer.

I expected to have to search around the craggy slopes for hours, recording plants the while, but I had reckoned without the all-pervading odour of billy goat that clung about my corduroy slacks. So accustomed were we to the proddings of Ivanhoe's shaggy head that we had become immune to the smell. Not so those two sex-starved nannies, widow and spinster for five long years!

As I topped the crest of the north-western cliffs the goats lifted their heads, flung their noses into the air, sniffed ecstatically and bounded down to make my acquaintance. With quivering nostrils and excited little bleats, they sniffed and rubbed those slacks, from waistbelt to turnups, and for the rest of the morning we were a threesome.

As a goodly portion of my notebook disappeared between grimy yellow teeth, my sympathies went out to the owner of the nightgown and I tried to deflect them by feeding them toffee papers. After finishing the lunch bags they began to tire of me, disillusioned that I had brought no more than the smell, and they wandered off. When the boat was nearly due they were nowhere to be found.

They failed to materialise until I had made three circuits of the island at different levels, and then only the older one, who we christened Guinivere, allowed herself to be caught. With my raincoat belt fastened securely about her neck, she trotted amiably enough beside me, up the slope and down to the landing rock. Her daughter, Persephone, was rather dubious, but trailed along behind at a safe distance.

We were too soon, so the two of us lay side by side on the rocks waiting, while the youngster hovered nervously, advancing cautiously, then jumping back in alarm at the slightest untoward movement. Never having met a billy in the flesh, she had probably decided that my tantalising odour was but a myth and not worth risking her neck for. Not so her worldy-wise Mama, who had no desire to budge now that her chin was resting snugly on those delightfully smelly slacks.

Eventually the little boat hove in sight round the Neck of Skomer. Peter and his assistant jumped ashore between waves while Persephone dived for cover between two boulders. They entered her stronghold, one from either end, thinking they had her cornered, but the goat took a mighty leap over the warden's head and was gone.

We chased her up and down and round and round, me leading the uncomplaining Guinivere as a decoy, but to no avail. Persephone was last seen in the middle of a flock of Soay sheep, wild as they, with a gleam of terror in her eye.

She had to be left, as Reuben Codd in the boat below was having to work continuously at the oars to prevent being swept away through Little Sound since the outboard motor had been shut off. We signalled him in, bundled the old nanny unceremoniously aboard and jumped in after her.

Possibly realising that she had lost her daughter and lifelong companion, or confused by the proximity of so many people, the unfortunate goat tucked her head forlornly between my knees and drooped miserably all the way back to Skokholm.

Once there her feelings changed. She was first out of the boat and set off at once, plodding purposefully up the track. It was now my turn to be hustled along unceremoniously at the end of the gaberdine belt. As she approached the buildings and the billy smell waxed stronger, her pace quickened and she ran the last few score yards.

Careering into the Wheelhouse yard, she located without any hesitation the spot where Ivanhoe was prone to lie and settled down to luxuriate in the goaty odour until its producer should materialise. She had not long to wait. Hoe and Row, astonished beyond measure, appeared at the gate and stared.

The billy was beside himself with excitement. Stiff and quivering with emotion from nose to tail tip, he circled the newcomer. His eventual greeting was somewhat exuberant for one so unused to amorous advances, and she ran to me for protection. Better the devil you know . . . even a little. I was bowled out of the way by the ardent suitor, who had eyes for no-one but this long-haired newcomer, as shaggy as himself and quite unlike the smooth-coated Rowena.

His ardour diminished little during the first week, while Rowena was left out in the cold. Patently jealous, she emulated her rival in every way, following her round, eating the same plants, even if this meant a radical change in her diet, and even defecating at the same time, but to no avail. The faithful companion of a lifetime offered none of the excitement of this newfound acquisition. She would still be there when he tired of the new love!

A landing party was sent to Middleholm later in the year to bring Persephone to heel and a goodly dance she led them. Both she and her pursuers were exhausted, but she submitted to capture in the end and was rewarded with a reunion with her old Mum and a fulfilment of the joys of motherhood for herself.

For Guinivere the opportunity had come too late. She was out of practice and she died bearing Ivanhoe's kid, but for Persephone life was just beginning. She soon learned to come twice daily to the Wheelhouse for her ration of stale bread – more if she could steal it while the cook's back was turned – to suckle kids and submit to being milked. As a grandmother, she became respected leader of the herd which, by 1956, included two Soay lambs, to which she had been well used on Middleholm.

In July 1953 some of Persephone's frothy milk was intercepted at milking time for Peter and Pat Conders' seven week old son, who was having an early introduction to island life. No heir presumptive to this little kingdom could have wished for it fresher.

By this time the warden had tired of rescuing terrified female visitors from the billy, at great risk to his person, and Ivanhoe had been sentenced to solitary confinement on Middleholm. This order had been rescinded, however, due to transport difficulties, and the great old warrior had fallen to a rifle bullet, to be succeeded by the lame Cadwallader.

Other tales could be told of the goats, of the charm of the young nanny who insisted on flirting with the Soay rams and then hopping coyly over a boulder and watching while they fought over her. Then there was the nanny who, having lost a kid in February, became pregnant again almost at once and yielded a considerable quantity of milk before kidding in the Autumn.

Only two attempts were made to keep pigs, these flatulent naked animals not fitting into the island ecology like the better endowed sheep and goats. They seemed unsuited to free range. Percy was the first and he yielded the observatory no profit, having failed to reach the required dimensions by the end of the season. He was passed into the keeping of the lighthouse folk when the island staff went ashore. They promised to take good care of him. Come the following spring they pronounced him delicious!

No further attempts were made until 1956, when two weaners were imported. The larger became known as Sampson, the runt as Simpson, the change of vowel stemming either from macro and micro or major and minor. People were heard singing the relevant verse from the popular camp fire song, 'The Darky Sunday School':

> Sampson was a strong man with lots of lovely curls,
> He fought against the Philistines and flirted with the girls
> But he flirted once too often and Delilah laid him low
> So he pulled down the temple on the whole damn show.

It wasn't Delilah who laid our Sampson low. He grew away from his brother so fast that he was exported in mid season and re-imported as pork. With him came a successor who inherited the name but not the stature and he never caught up with the runt.

The pigs were bedded down with dry bracken and wispy purple moor grass in a corrugated iron hut a field's distance from the house. This and the similarly bedded outdoor run were bordered on one side by a natural rock face and on another by one of the old field walls. Before their capabilities in this direction were realised, they were liable to hop over the wall and come trotting through bracken and heather to the house if breakfast was late.

When these high jinks were prevented, they used other talents, burrowing through the base of the wall (a rock-faced earth bank), filling their premises with the proceeds and arriving at breakfast in a distinctly dishevelled condition. The last time I saw them they were safely penned behind wire netting, with Sugarback leaning companionably over the wall, paying his daily call.

Rabbits were not so matey, this wall being clad with a delicious array of lush plants which they never attempted to sample, however little there was beyond. The deterrent cannot have been pig dung at this height. It must have been the unknown potential of piggy snorts and smells.

Sugarback, the lighthouse pony, was the island's oldest inhabitant and owed allegiance to no-one. Lighthouse keepers, wardens, cooks and research workers came and went: Sugarback remained. He was quite an island institution already by 1947 and was still going strong when last seen in 1956.

It was not only coal, oil and stores that had to be dragged the length of the island from the landing place, but freshwater from the well, all of us sharing the same spring. He was harnessed to the railway trolley by long traces, which gave him ample opportunity to get mixed up with ropes and chains or, once, to tip the whole caboosh over the edge into South Haven, without going that way himself – as had one of his predecessors.

Sugarback, the lighthouse pony, by North Pond.

Ron Williams and author with Sugarback, the lighthouse pony.

In 1954, when he was pensioned off and succeeded by a rubber-tyred, motorised dumper, a low wall was built alongside this section of the path, the lesson learned. Sugar knew just how much he was prepared to pull up that first steep incline and no-one could change his mind. Often his efforts had to be supplemented with a loan of the stretchers on which the observatory stores were carried up, these sometimes serving as rickshaws on the way down.

Where the gradient began to descend gently nearer the lighthouse, there was no holding him and this is the stretch appearing on the maps as Sugar's Delight. As already indicated, he learned to read the semaphore and morse of flags and bells heralding the boat and melted into the undergrowth. Between boats he could be approached anywhere and was often the prime mover in making contact.

He was never broken to the saddle. I saw a number try and fail. A favourite ploy was to wander into the Wheelhouse yard when the coast was clear, his target the bin into which waste food was tipped. He never managed to get the lid off without making such a clatter that his cover was blown and his intentions thwarted.

This often happened as soon as the boat was out of sight, the stores carried a short way from the quay and stacked, awaiting his pleasure. A cook emerging from the Wheelhouse, bread in hand, was of obvious interest and he usually failed to notice the belt going round his neck before it was too late. He had it coming to him sometime. These were only delaying tactics to stress his superiority. In no way could all that paraphernalia be got to the other end of the island without his assistance. I occasionally had the pleasure of leading him down to the haven after the keepers had spent a fruitless hour chasing him around. It was nice to see those scowling faces change to smiles.

Sugar could be sweetness itself when it suited him and everyone got quite fond of him, but he could be a menace where scientific undertakings were concerned.

In 1948 a party of geographers from the University of Wales at Aberystwyth erected a system of grid posts dividing the entire island into two hundred yard squares preparatory to mapping. To ensure visibility from afar these were five feet high, just right for back scratchers in the complete absence of trees. Within two years not one was left standing.

Because they provided such good, supposedly permanent, markers, a quadrat had been pegged out at the base of many for repeated mini-mapping and recording of vegetation changes over the years. The first two years' changes were nullified by the churning of hooves, recovery usually unrecorded because of the loss of the marker.

Other casualties were the big wire mesh cages set over strategic nests to trap lesser black-backed gulls being used in homing experiments. Being only two to three feet high, the pony found these more effective if he rolled on them!

I suffered similar problems with the rabbit-proof enclosures erected in different plant communities to track the vegetation changes on the elimination of grazing. One sunny May morning, he watched with great interest as I transplanted succulent water plants onto drying mud at the

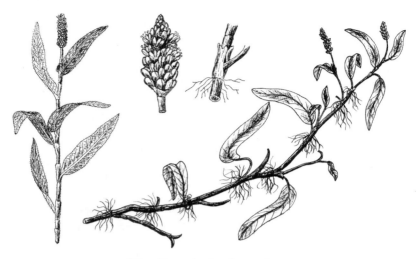

Water Bistort, land and water forms.

edge of North Pond to observe the adaptations of growth to the new medium.

Foolishly, I intended to return with the posts, mallet and wire netting to ensure their safety, but I should have given these priority. The temptation was too great, although he was quite capable of wading into the pond (his final resting place) and helping himself. His favourite was water bistort. Chasing him away was of no avail, he always got back quicker than I did. Experience is a great teacher.

Caroline, the Welsh black cow, ceased to be an asset to the community quite early on. The difficulty of communicating with an AI Centre for semen during the brief period when the time was ripe proved insurmountable. No-one relished the thought of getting the cow into a boat or swimming her behind one to meet a spouse, so she eventually left as more easily transported butcher's meat in 1948.

5.

SKOKHOLM: ANIMAL PROJECTS DURING THE EARLY YEARS

It was good to be able to share our island with the livestock and respond to the many diversions which they instigated, but there was plenty of serious work going on as well.

The early years seemed to be the most productive. This was virgin territory for staff and visitors alike, a newly opened book, bristling with possibilities for novel investigations and the trying out of new ideas. It was probably inevitable that the hive of activity of the forties, fifties and sixties should slacken off, as the more easily studied wildlife situations were elucidated.

A headmaster, David Stanbury, who had brought over three hundred boys to stay in the observatory during the previous twenty-one years, wrote to this effect. I quote him from the March 1980 bulletin of the West Wales Naturalists' Trust:

> The trapping and ringing of birds have gone. I regret that the boys do not see careful research being done by experts and learn to respect and handle the tiny migrants who visit the island . . . Catching shearwaters was great fun and a recovery from Australia of a bird caught by one of the boys, or realising from the rings that the shearwater was older than the boy who was holding it were useful lessons.

Stanbury welcomed the new bird hides for use by day and the chance to sit quietly at night in an undisturbed shearwater colony and just listen to one of Britain's natural history 'spectaculars'. These more sedentary aspects appeal to the old rather than the young, who need the urgency of active participation, but this is sadly the modern trend in this age of spectatoritus and virtual reality.

By the end of 1977 the four Heligoland bird traps had been dismantled and the wardens were hoping to erect a goat and rabbit proof fence around the older ones to preserve the thicker vegetation, but there was to be no more ringing, even of small birds. Many of the more exciting passage migrants would thus be missed.

The modern Skokholm holds organised courses, like those at Dale Fort and other centres of the Field Studies Council. Art courses were offered from 1979. By 1982 there were others in photography, natural history, bird-watching and a special week for young persons at half price.

At around the time when Stephen Warman and Carol Hellawell were wardening, I was leading my own parties there, with students from the Cardiff University's Adult Education Department and the Merthyr Tydfil Naturalists' Society, the last one in 1979, when the goat herd had built up to nine animals.

Stephen and Carol went on to warden St. Abb's Head in Berwickshire and later Aride Island in the Seychelles, among the very different tropic birds, noddies, boobies and frigate birds that I too enjoyed in those parts, both with a party of Cardiffians on the main group of islands and in a four month research spell on Aldabra, the island of giant tortoises, and Cosmoledo. Others from Skokholm took that path to the Indian Ocean or the even more exciting one to the Galapagos Islands Research Station off the Pacific coast of South America.

Peter Davies, formerly of Lundy Island and later of red kite fame, succeeded Peter Conder as warden in 1954 and moved on to warden Fair Isle between Orkney and Shetland, another favourite of mine. He 'retired' to do valuable work on Tregaron Bog National Nature Reserve – that plot of wetland that might have deprived me of my island experiences. Other names come to mind; Chris Perrins, now a professor and Director of the Edward Grey Institute of Ornithology, now Field Studies, at Oxford: Peter Driver, an insect man and Barbara Whittaker, a future warden of Lundy and working wife of Dr. David Snow of Oxford on the Galapagos Islands.

That modest little plot of land that is Skokholm, in its early, more active years, was a great training ground for field scientists of the future. Many were ornithologists. Ask around the world-famous Edward Grey Institute and there will be few who have not passed time on that scrap of paradise off South-west Wales – the stamping ground of so many youngsters who went on to live lives of interest and discovery.

One who loomed large in the forties and fifties was Dr. G. V. T. Matthews (Geoffrey) of Cambridge University and bird migration fame. He became expert at handling birds and could mesmerise them by laying them on their backs. I have a photograph of him making hypnotic passes over a great black-backed gull lying obediently, feet uppermost, on the grass, awaiting his ring.

Another shows him in the Wheelhouse yard labelling a consignment of cardboard boxes marked URGENT: LIVE BIRDS. These were being air-lifted to various parts of the world to see how long they would take to find their way home from places not on their usual migration route. They invariably made it, guided by no previously known landmarks, only the night sky and such built in magnetic responses that they might possess.

The individual that hit the media headlines with the greatest impact, was a shearwater transported to Boston, Massachusetts. There he was released and twelve and a half days later he was back on his nest on Skokholm, seemingly none the worse. The minimum number of miles he could have flown, using the great circle route, which would involve surviving unfamiliarly low temperatures, was three thousand and fifty, or about two hundred and fifty miles a day.

Without map or compass, radar or radio, rocket take-off or TV communication, liquid oxygen or artificial fuel, with no companion, no previous knowledge of the seascape travelled, where landmarks are non-existent anyway, and no desire to be where he was, he made it home, to relieve his patiently waiting mate on the nest.

This was as expected, Ronald Lockley having had a bird fly back over the unfamiliar territory of the European Alps in a previous year. Nevertheless, his performance was one of the great natural history miracles of our time and one which we are still a long way from understanding fully.

Who knows how far these birds travel when they leave Skokholm? The shearwater ringed here and recovered in South Australia was thought to have been caught up in the westerlies blowing around the sub-antarctic convergence when it was about its lawful business overwintering in the southern summer off South America. That one did not find its way back.

Geoffrey worked with a large number of birds, their burrows 'lidded' for ease of daily supervision. The roof of the burrow functioned as a trap-door above the nesting chamber, the turf replaced after each examination of the inmate, supported by a flat stone if necessary and chinks of light excluded. This technique was also used for studying incubation time and monitoring weight increases of the growing chick, both shearwater or puffin.

Geoffrey's homing experiments in 1951 involved 103 shearwaters. Birds released in Cambridge were back in their burrows in as little as 6.75, 8, 8 and 8.5 hours, this including any time spent on the sea or rafting before coming ashore at the appropriate time. More set off in the correct compass direction when released on clear nights, departure being random when it was overcast – pointing to navigation by visible heavenly bodies. Eggs hatched successfully after temporary desertion of up to sixty-five hours.

A major puffin project was inaugurated in 1954 with large numbers of ringed adults and juveniles. Their nests were marked with coloured metal pegs and numbered so that it would be known if they returned to the same burrows in subsequent years. This study could also reveal the age at which they started to breed and how long they lived. Tracing the course of the burrows for the construction of trap-doors, could sometimes be achieved by observing which plants grew above.

Ringing of chicks had to be deferred until they had grown sufficiently for the ring not to slip off over the foot. Oyster-catcher chicks, being nidifugous, or fugitive from the nest from day one, with large, capable feet, could be ringed soon after hatching. The size of fish being carried into the burrows by adult puffins was a good guide to the size of the offspring for which they were intended.

Other workers with seabirds collected fluid from blisters on the feet of stiff-winged shearwaters suffering from shearwater disease. This was Puffinosis, named, as often, after the specific epithet of the host. It is odd that the derivation of the popular 'puffin' was applied to *Fratercula arctica* and not to *Procellaria puffinus*, the Manx shearwater or other shearwaters, for which Puffinus is the generic or surname.

Some years later gentoo penguins in the sub-antarctic were found to be suffering from the same virus disease. Had the two species come together off the Falkland Islands or South Georgia and passed it on?

The study of flat flies, sliverlike insects lurking between the close-set feathers of birds, provided another distraction for the ornithologists.

My particular involvement with birds as a botanist was two-fold. Firstly, how were the native plants reacting to the sometimes generous helpings of guano to which they were subjected and, secondly, what non-indigenous species were being brought in by birds feeding on the mainland.

Guano, like beer, is full of nutrients, but a little goes a long way. Rich in phosphates and nitrates, it can boost growth of the more demanding plants, particularly when decently diluted by trickling water. In quantity, or during dry spells, it becomes too concentrated and can have the opposite effect, 'scorching' the foliage and causing the sparse soil moisture to draw much needed watery cell sap from the roots.

Lush, guano stimulated growths are best seen on the cliff faces. Those appearing on top are either trampled to near extinction by the donors of

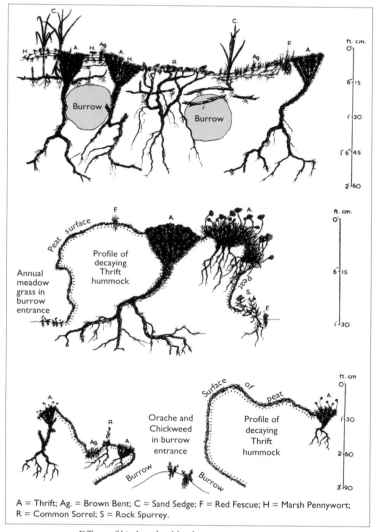

A = Thrift; Ag. = Brown Bent; C = Sand Sedge; F = Red Fescue; H = Marsh Pennywort; R = Common Sorrel; S = Rock Spurrey.

Effects of bird and rabbit burrowing on vegetation.

Great Black-backed Gull with chicks and crab.

the nutrients, gobbled up by rabbits, sheep or goats or felled by salty gales. Nothing is simple in island ecology.

Pacing the clifftops, as I did, it became very apparent that the little clumps of arable weeds or cereal grains springing up in the gull colonies were newly arrived, their seeds cashing in on the sort of soil they liked, scarified bare of other plants and well manured.

Gulls feeding on the mainland, often around refuse tips, coughed up crop pellets on returning to their favourite standing out plots on the island. Some seeds might pass right through their alimentary systems, to be deposited with the guano, but to grow just as surely. Like pollen grains, seeds are readily distinguishable one from the other and an interesting selection has been identified from these crop pellets.

Some of the more outlandish which arrived in this way were fluellen (*Kickxia elatine*) with little mauve, snapdragon-like flowers, and corn marigold. Others were corn spurrey, black nighshade and oats, wheat and barley.

Weed seeds are likely to be introduced by gulls feeding indiscriminately on grubs and insects, the hard seed coats protecting the germ of life within from their digestive juices. Cereal grains are selected as food but some escape digestion and germinate, to the delight of island grazers and seed-eaters.

Gulls have individual feeding preferences. In some of their standing areas I found only crab remains or mollusc shells collected locally. In others there were fish bones and the smoothly polished otoliths from the inner ear of their prey fish, possibly brought from the Milford Haven fish docks. True sea-birds feed only at sea and few of the resident seed-eating passerines leave the island to forage, so gulls are of primary importance in introducing new species in this way.

With warden, cook and comfortable living accommodation laid on, student birders on Skokholm could concentrate on their particular interests – Mike Harris on oyster-catchers, Euan Dunn on gulls and, much later, Clare Lloyd on razorbills. Others elsewhere, like Bryan Nelson, author of the authoritative work on gannets, had to wrestle with complicated logistics when setting up his research niche on Bass Rock in the Firth of Forth.

It was a relatively simple matter to learn to recognise the island's resident birds, but special expertise was necessary during seasons of

Rabbits on a corner of Spy Rock.

spring and autumn passage. Not only anything occurring in the British Isles might turn up, but also others from distant lands. Some might have been blown off course and grateful for a safe landing, however alien. Others might pass this way every year, following the coast but flying just offshore, so that mainland bird-watchers missed them.

The importance of islands to birders at those two seasons has resulted in the huge twice annual influx of bird-watchers – twitchers – to the Isles of Scilly in recent years, those more peripheral but easier of access. In the old days only the wardens might be present on Skokholm at these critical times, but the visitor season was lengthened, to monitor those birds that passed in the night but, hopefully, might stay to rest and feed during the day as well.

A selection taken at random from the old records (which are very extensive) includes the following:

> Red-footed falcon, hen harrier and hobby, Icterine, melodious, Bonelli's and yellow-browed warblers, rustic and ortolan buntings, tawny and Richard's pipits, wryneck, nightingale, red-breasted flycatcher, firecrest, long-eared owl and snow goose.

One which I took from the trap was a scarlet grosbeak, the first for the island and the fifth for Wales. There could be big falls of two hundred and fifty or so willow warblers and/or chiff-chaffs, siskins or chaffinches, with earlier passages of swifts.

My first September-October on the island was in 1949, when these newcomers more than made up for the absence of the sea-birds, most of which were away to their ocean fastnesses by now. There were scoters about and a little grebe spent several days on North Pond. The odd 'tame' dunlins were at their usual antics by the pond, characteristically hopping twelve inches into the air and flapping vertically raised wings on alighting. Other visitors there were wigeon, teal, common and Jack snipe, curlew, whimbrel, lapwing and turnstone.

Only eleven wheatears remained, and they would soon be flying off to winter quarters in the south. Two hundred and fifty meadow pipits came through one day, with several hundred swallows and lesser numbers of house martins, pied wagtails, robins, willow-chiffs and an individual wren, travelling solo. Some of these found their way into the traps for ringing.

Choughs were about for three days, visitors from the Old Deer Park opposite Skomer, perhaps, and the three resident buzzards were being given a bad time by gulls.

There were still a few young storm petrels about, their presence announced by high-pitched squeaks from their crevices at night. I rescued one which had got caught up in the hooked fruits of a burdock plant. Not many young shearwaters were left and most had shed the last of their down during the final starvation period and were out of the burrows at night exercising their wings in readiness for the marathon flight to South America that lay ahead, unguided by their elders. One unfortunate, which had made it to the sea, was being eaten by a victoriously flapping great black-backed gull on the water.

We were still out ringing them at night. It was more valuable to ring juveniles, because their age was known, as it never could be with birds ringed later. In 1976 a bird was picked up that had first been ringed on the island as an adult in 1946 – making this at least thirty-six years old, even if it had been caught in its first breeding year. Such finds show the value of long term operations such as this.

Razorbills cavorting on the sea were in their lighter grey winter plumage, looking very strange. There were no puffins to be seen and only a few, slightly oiled, guillemots, but hosts of gannets were diving quite close in. We watched a whale heading north between the island and the mainland.

This was pupping time for the seals, which were not breeding on the island in 1949, although a calf had been born in Calf Bay in 1948 and more were in later years, but there was plenty of activity about. Cows with gashes on their hides were being pursued by amorous bulls and much snorting and crooning emanated from East Bay and North Haven.

We crept into several seal

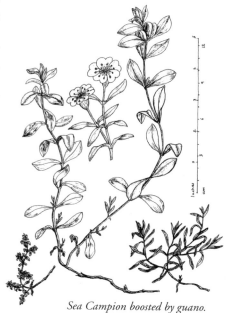

Sea Campion boosted by guano.

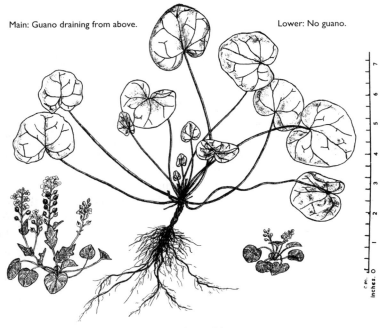

Main: Guano draining from above. Lower: No guano.

Scurvy Grass boosted by guano.

holes with torches at low tide, hoping no seals were at home, as there was scarcely room to pass, but we emerged unscathed. Sometimes, when swimming, we were more adventurous, exploring watery caves. There was an occasion when the somewhat portly Freddie Parker-Rhodes crept into a tunnel in North Haven and got stuck. We took turns at pulling him free by the ankles and he finally popped out, like a cork from a champagne bottle.

Seal Cave in the east was a long, permanently submerged tunnel with a series of blow holes and it was possible to lean into a chamber and listen to the animals blowing and wheezing or breathing sonorously in sleep. Seals sometimes floated under the openings and we would lie on the rocks above at low tide and watch them at close quarters. When the seal's nose broke surface, to breathe, we became visible and the animal was gone, in a flurry of spray.

This blow hole was known as Barbara's Cave after Barbara Whittaker, later of Lundy and the Galapagos Islands, got into it but was unable to get out. It was easy enough to relax and drop in, but, when she reached up to heave herself out, her shoulder muscles expanded and she no longer fitted the hole.

Being a resourceful young woman, she decided to leave by the underwater route used by the seals, who had, by this time, left in panic. She passed her clothes up and swam through the dark section to scramble out of the lower exit, faster than it took the rest of us to follow overland.

Not everybody, of course, worked on birds and some, like Hyde and Wade of the National Museum of Wales, left their 'props' on the island for the staff to monitor. These were sticky microscope slides that puzzled me during my initial visit, erected under minimal cover on the Knoll above the house.

Their purpose was to collect wind-blown pollen, which was later separated from dust cast adrift from the shearwater burrows or swept from the common room floor. Each tiny grain is distinct from those of other plant species – how else could archeologists determine what plants grew in deep peat cores extracted from prehistoric mountain bogs and ancient lake beds? They can be as ornamental as mini snowflakes, but vastly more durable.

Hyde and Wade, both long since deceased, were more interested in the mode of distribution of modern pollen. How far could these featherweight morsels travel to pollinate flowers in distant populations and maintain genetic uniformity? How far distant must an island lie to be out of range and to develop its own, inbred, population with its own individual quirks? Thus are new species made – island endemics – which occur nowhere but where they have evolved in isolation to suit conditions on their own natal island.

A similar study, but of air-borne insects, was carried out in 1951 by Alan Pearson. More ambitious, he flew 'Cody' type kites with insect nets attached at two hundred feet and more over Skokholm's windward cliffs, but caught nothing from as far afield as some of the drifted pollen.

A sticky trap, as for pollen, was set up five feet from the ground in the island centre, and caught a selection of residents to compare with the incomers and passers-by. These captured most insects on mild still days when the kites would not fly and the likelihood of new immigrants arriving was slight. Nor could the kites be flown on blustery days, when insects blown off course might have arrived on westerly gales from the New World, like the occasional migrant wading bird that made landfall on the island.

Medium northerly winds gave the best high level catches, with twice as many true flies as aphids. These last were of five species, only one of which was present as an island resident, showing just how far travelled these scraps of life can be, and how potentially damaging as carriers of virus diseases affecting crop plants – or of manipulated genetic material.

Plant broad beans, even several miles offshore, and, sure as eggs, the blackfly will find them. In fact there are relatively few broad beans on islands, so arrival is not enough. Many are unable to take up residence in the absence of their specific host plant – even assuming the wind dropped and allowed them to float to earth rather than meet a watery grave in the sea. Mother Nature is generous in allowing for mishaps and loss. Little is wasted. Those unsatisfied aphids could provide useful sustenance for meadow pipits or ground beetles.

Slugs, harvestmen, beetles and fleas, all came under scrutiny by visiting specialists. The warden's philosophy was, If it occurs on Skokholm it is of interest and we ought to learn more about it.

Not all 'studies' were carefully thought out. There was, for instance, the day when he and I lay on our backs on a sunny cliff facing the sea and counting the bumble bees migrating in singly over the water. A major influx, from the mainland, perhaps, or Skomer. When we sat up, we realised that it was a single bee going round and round on the same circuit and trying to fool us. Or were we lying on her nest?

There was an inbuilt urge to count everything that moved and 1947 offered just such an opportunity with butterflies. On 9th August large white butterflies were recorded moving out over the Atlantic from Grassholm Island, which is eleven miles offshore. From the 10th on, during a spell of warm, sunny weather, the same migration was occurring on Skokholm and on the 21st visitors were mobilised for a day-long butterfly count, spread along a transect at the intersection of two walls, which gave east-west and north-south base lines for assessing flight direction.

Red admirals, painted ladies and clouded yellows passed in some profusion, but it was the large white movement which was most spectacular, with a hundred and fifty passing over a twenty yard front in ten minutes when they were at peak.

Wind direction did not determine flight direction. With the wind blowing all day from the east, it was only in the morning that the butterflies were helped by it. In the afternoon the flocks flew to the east, directly into the wind (trying to make it back to the mainland perhaps before darkness set in?) At their peak passing, they flew to the north, across the wind. When air currents were helping they flew high, when those were hindering, the majority flew in the stiller air about two feet above the ground.

Other butterflies occurring with the ever present meadow browns in midsummer were dark green fritillaries, small heaths and small coppers. Humming bird hawk moths hovered over marsh thistle flowers, their long tongues extended to draw up the nectar, and there was always a good crop of cinnabar moths nourished on the ragwort.

The only small rodents finding a living on Skokholm are house mice, said to have been introduced in the 1890s. Selective evolution of the Skomer bank vole as a distinct island species had long been realised, but the Skokholm mice had been genetically isolated on the island for only seventy years when an intensive study was launched in 1960. They were diagnosed as an island race rather than a full species.

Unlike most of their kind, they live largely independent of man here and are markedly different from their nearest neighbours on the mainland in overall size, tail length, number of young produced and several skeletal characteristics.

Not for nothing are the wee beasties called house mice, living as they do largely in houses, barns and outhouses as commensals with man, since moving across Europe from the Middle East with early grain farmers. Individual family groups seldom stray from their home premises to mix with other housed populations, this life style very different from that of the far travelling Skokholm mice. Wild living populations are so unusual as to be referred to as feral, or gone-wild, from the norm of semi-domestication.

R. J. Berry (Sam to us) of the Royal Free Hospital School of Medicine and Animal Genetics, undertook a six year study of the Skokholm mice from 1960, publishing learned papers on his results in 1968, 1970 and 1974. He pronounced Skokholm as favourable climatically for these incomers from warmer climes for most of the year, but sufficiently cold in winter for over 95% of the population to die in a severe spell, usually February, although 60% may survive a mild winter.

This they do in hidey holes in the cliffs, spreading up to the plateau in spring and summer throughout the island except the wetlands, often sharing the herring bone walls with rabbits, wheatears and storm petrels. No mouse has been known to survive more than one winter, and Berry got to know many mice.

House Mouse and Kidney Vetch.

He released over three thousand, live-trapped, marked mice, his mark-ing system involving the clipping of different combinations of toenails. The animals had no qualms about entering his traps, which were baited with rolled oats and bedded with hay, complete with a few welcome seeds. These yielded impressive amounts of data for his several lines of enquiry.

Their life expectancy on the island was a hundred days, as opposed to five hundred days for pampered laboratory mice – although there are no mammalian predators on Skokholm and even the kestrel is a rare visitor.

When the breeding season finishes at the end of September, the popu-lation can be ten times greater than the overwintered population in the spring. Numbers build up slowly to start with, until members of the first litter begin to breed in midsummer, when there is a veritable popu-lation explosion.

Most larger mammals increase their insulation against heat loss in winter by layers of blubber or thick fur or both. Acclimatisation of small mammals is mainly metabolic, dependent on their brown fat content and an increased oxygen carrying capacity of the blood. Heart size can increase under cold stress to boost the latter.

It seemed that the mouse population as a whole rather than individuals had adapted to spending winter out of doors on Skokholm by increasing its reproductive rate during the favourable months of summer whilst dispensing with heavy energy requiring mechanisms for survival under winter conditions. This ensured survival of the race, despite the wastage of individuals, but on a less catastrophic scale than in some insects, like wasps and bumble bees where only the fertilised queen survives to carry on the line.

Given the opportunity to share human habitation, the Skokholm mice were more than ready to avail themselves of the facilities offered. Sadly for them, human warmth and comfort were not available when it was most needed, after the staff had gone ashore for the winter.

There were always mice in the Wheelhouse, some so bold as to skitter round while we were at table, and they did a splendid job hoovering up the crumbs and other fallen titbits at night. Peter tried all ways to exclude them. He filled all mouse holes with cement and later with cement impregnated with fragments of broken glass, but they always burrowed through, possibly starting before the cement was dry.

Berry set traps for them and we got used to the staccato clicks as they snapped shut during meals. These were lethal traps, not the out-of-doors live traps. Their catches contributed data to the anatomical studies of brown fat and blood tests.

They were adept at finding bedroom caches of chocolate and would gnaw their way through the most formidable wrappings. We got used to the pattering of little feet by night along the rafters of the angel loft. Who was it who coined that inaccurate phrase "as quiet as a mouse?"

6.

SKOKHOLM:
THE BELEAGUERED PLANT LIFE

By considering animal life first, we have rather put the cart before the horse. Animals are dependent in the first instance on plants, although they can have an important bearing on which plants survive and which fail. Plants are dependent on climate and soil, the local climate characterised by salty winds and the soil derived from the underlying geology.

My colleague from Aberystwyth in the late 1940s was Gordon Goodman, who was chemist as well as botanist. His detailed study on the island was of physical and climatic factors as they affected the vegetation and we worked together on the plant mapping. He went on to a long and distinguished career, partly in Sweden, working on pollution problems, in which he had received a good grounding with the aftermath of Swansea Bay's heavy metal industry.

Skokholm's 262 acres (106 hectares) is part of the sea-dissected peneplain of South Pembrokeshire and its rock structure is relatively simple, consisting of Devonian Old Red Sandstone throughout. Most is fine-grained purple mudstone, with little nodules of limey marl which weather out to form small pits. Some strata are sandier, with less slaty cleavage, but both erode down to produce a friable brown loam. The highest point, in the south-west, is 160 feet (49 metres) above sea level, with sundry humps rising from the plateau, the largest aptly named Spy Rock.

Springs bubble out along a fault line, the one supplying drinking water for observatory and lighthouse welling up under a protective flagstone. It has never been known to fail, although there is no obvious watershed on the plateau.

By putting the red dye, eosin, into various streams on the mainland and waiting for the colour to appear in the island water source, it was established early on that the water reached the island through rock fissures below sea level, and the parent spring was identified. Without it sustained human life would not have been possible on the island and the lighthouse would have needed its water to be delivered with the other stores.

The red frogspawn alga (*Batrachospermum moniliforme*) thrives in the spring, this rare, as are all freshwater red algae. I have only ever come across it in places such as this where pure unsullied water bubbles out of the ground. The only other water source is rain, collected from roofs and stored in tanks. This can be heavily laced with bird guano, mostly supplied by gulls which like to disport themselves on the local rubbish tips, so is more suitable for washing than drinking.

Pleistocene ice sheets scraped their way across the island long ago, dumping a broad band of boulder clay over the island centre from north to south. This is less permeable than the loam and holds water up in North, South and Winter Ponds and depression pans on the central bog. East Pond and Orchid Bog above North Haven are spring fed.

This last delightful damp corner nourishes the only orchids on the island, identified in 1948 as the hybrid between the common spotted and the early marsh orchids, their flowers the deep mauve colour of the latter. From a single plant recorded by Lockley in 1930, this has spread apace, migrating downstream to produce a colony of several hundred individuals by 1950, hence the name of the habitat. Plants are relished by the big black slugs, *Arion ater*, which swarm across the grasslands in wet weather and at night.

Orchid Bog was one of the places where we might find frogs and palmate newts, the only newt species on the island. It is also where I once witnessed a frenetic migration of elvers which had wriggled up the vertical cliff where the stream trickles over, weaving through the fiorin grass and clinging to fool's watercress and forget-me-not to assist them in their Herculean scramble to the heights. Had the flavour of this water seeping into the sea below deluded them into expecting a sizable river?

The short stream at the top would serve their needs for a little while, but there was no deep water beyond where they might develop into adult eels. To reach the nearest permanent water in North Pond would entail a long journey through grass, sedge and bracken on a wet night. Could they make it? Eels up to thirty centimetres long were found in South Haven and Crab Bay streams and in the well during the late 1940s. The island's only reptiles are slow worms and common lizards. Maybe St. Patrick was here, banishing the snakes.

Because of the reliable water supply the island has been habitable from earliest times. The name is Norse, given by the Vikings who harried

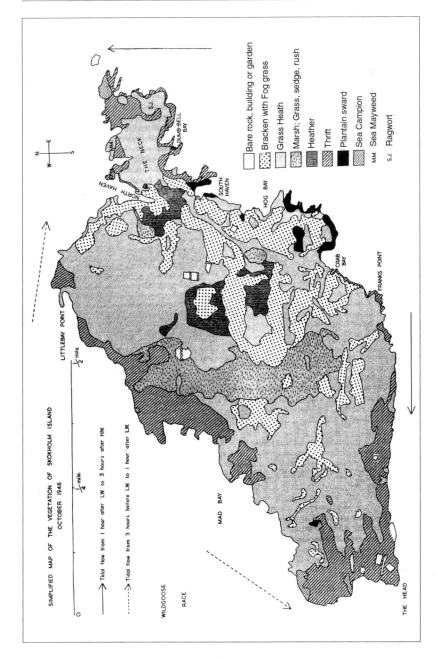

SIMPLIFIED MAP OF THE VEGETATION OF SKOKHOLM ISLAND
OCTOBER 1948

→ Tidal flow from 1 hour after LW to 3 hours after HW

·····> Tidal flow from 3 hours before LW to 1 hour after LW

WILDGOOSE

RACE

LITTLEBAY POINT

MAD BAY

THE HEAD

NORTH HAVEN

SOUTH HAVEN

THE NECK

DUMB-BELL BAY

HOG BAY

CRAB BAY

FRANKS POINT

Bare rock, building or garden
Bracken with Fog grass
Grass Heath
Marsh; Grass, sedge, rush
Heather
Thrift
Plantain sward
Sea Campion
Sea Mayweed
MM Sea Mayweed
S.J. Ragwort

this coastline between 844 and 1150. One interpretation is 'holm', the island, in the Sound. Others interpret the 'skok' as wood or timber, making this The Island of Stocks (on which boats were built) or of logs or Wooded Isle. There were no trees worthy of the name apart from the garden sycamore crouched behind the house in 1947, but there may once have been, particularly if we regard bluebells as a woodland relic.

The rabbits soon put paid to any potential woodland regeneration, however, these introduced from the Mediterranean by the Normans for their fur and meat. Sold to the Norman Earl of Pembroke in 1230, Skokholm passed to the Earl of Hereford and flourished as a rabbit farm from 1324 to 1474. The profit from this enterprise (on Skokholm, Skomer and Middleholm) in 1324 is recorded as fourteen pounds five shillings, a handsome profit to the earl after he had paid the rabbit catchers' wages of somewhat less than three pence per week – and presumably as many rabbits as they could eat.

Sheep, cattle, horses, pigs and deer infiltrated in subsequent years and Skokholm (Scowkom) was deemed to be worth three hundred pounds when it passed into the hands of the Phillips family of Dale Castle in the eighteenth century. A boat could be summoned when required by lighting a bonfire.

Farm livestock co-existed with gulls and rabbits and there are still substantial relics of the herring bone walled earth banks built to contain them – and a useful adjunct to the wildlife habitats. Fenton (1903) records pasture supporting eight cows and some enclosed arable land, which was periodically limed. The chief crops were oats and barley, furrow marks of the old ploughlands appearing in aerial photographs. One part of the island provided peat for fuel.

Farming enterprises were abandoned in both the first and second world wars, the lighthouse keepers the only residents – from the building of the lighthouse on the south-west corner in 1916. Between the wars came the well documented thirteen years from 1926 to 1939 when Ronald Lockley, author and scientist, farmed the island and set up Britain's first bird observatory here in 1933.

In 1939-40 'Cyanogas' treatment reduced the large rabbit population to an estimated four hundred and Lockley was able to take as much as three to four tons per acre of hay from the best land. Rabbits burrow in inaccessible cliffs, however, as well as just about everywhere else dry enough, so could never be exterminated.

From this estimated four hundred at the beginning of World War II, they had bred up to an estimated ten thousand by its end. These and the Soay sheep, which numbered ninety-six in 1951, were responsible for the state of most of the vegetation.

Its distribution, however, is controlled principally by the incidence of spray-bearing winds, which blow predominantly from the western sector, straight off the sea. The vegetation map shows four main communities.

Thrift dominates around much of the coast, particularly the west-facing sections, its place taken in more heavily trampled stretches of the east by plantain swards – these of miniature buck's-horn plantain where dry and ground-hugging mats of sea plantain where wet.

Bracken, its fronds dwarfed and scorched by salty gales, dominates in the south and east, sheltering broad swathes of richly coloured bluebells in May and June. It is odd how we think of bluebells as woodland plants when they flower so much more profusely on open Welsh mountainsides than in the shadier woods and grow so much larger than anywhere else on these coastal islands. They cannot stand direct sunlight during late summer when the fleshy fruits are ripening, but bracken fronds are just as adequate in excluding this as are trees.

Most of the rest of the island, apart from the central bog, is occupied by maritime grass heath, often 'waved heath' if the grass is allowed to grow long enough for every tuft to be swept to leeward, like waves of the sea, by the force of spray-charged winds. This is composed largely of bents and fescues, overtopped by Yorkshire fog grass, whose woolly-coated, acrid leaves are only cropped by rabbits when they can find nothing better.

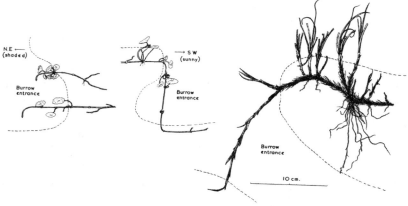

Sand Sedge and Marsh Pennywort.

They prefer the finer grasses and heather, a few depauperate patches of which survive on the eastern half of the plateau. Rabbits trim the clumps to low domes, sea winds kill the windward shoots, allowing the leeward ones to grow, so we have here another 'waved heath' migrating slowly to leeward. The mounds are readily overrun by bracken or fog, which latter is also common throughout the bog, along with rushes, sedges and Eleocharis club-rush.

It is interesting that much the commonest sedge here is the sand sedge, which is usually found on dunes. It has a wide range on the island, where it can be inundated by as much as 30cm of water, as well as on dry knolls with thrift and pasture grasses. Here its far-reaching, sharply pointed underground rhizomes can grow straight across quite large burrows, sustaining direction more rigidly when unsupported than the underground stems of others, such as the marsh pennywort.

The extensive lesser black-backed gull colonies of the island centre are mostly among bracken, whose fronds appear above ground in June, in time to afford cover for the well camouflaged chicks when they leave the nests. Herring gulls breed more often on broken cliffs and great black-backs like to establish themselves on knolls, where they have good views of potential prey and can lord it over all the rest. Here their excreta can nourish fleshy growths of wall pennywort and rock spurrey.

Shearwaters are thickest among mounds of thrift, where much is dead and digging in the peaty remains is easy. They are widespread, nesting also under bracken and grass well inland. Storm petrels prefer crevices in walls and the lime kiln or among boulders, like those of Quarry Bay under the lighthouse, which was a favourite ringing site for these little birds by night.

In the early days little owls were a problem, storm petrels figuring as their favourite food, although they are one of the few owls, along with the short-eared, that hunts by day. Little owls subsequently deserted the island as breeders and short-eared owls are only occasional visitors.

Puffins prefer short grass swards, but are equally happy among thrift. So heavy is the traffic of these birds, which stand about in big crowds on the cliff margins in the evenings, that they often reduce everything on their standing grounds to a dusty sward of plantain and sea storksbill. Only where pressure is less intense do we see the lush flowering swards of sea campion, and these only on the sheltered side of the island.

Nevertheless, those who visit the Farne Islands in Northumberland or

Skellig Michael in South-west Ireland will see puffin colonies occupying pure stands of sea campion. Rabbits seldom eat it but the big Soay flock relished its fleshy shoots. It is said to have increased greatly when they were removed in 1960, but the goat herd had increased to nine by the end of the 1970s and they could account for much. The plants come in two colour forms. Most have purple veining on the bloated calyces, others lack the anthocyanin pigment and appear a pale yellow under the spreading white petals.

While the mass of Ireland prevents the biggest Atlantic swells from reaching the north-west coast, the distance of 'fetch' to the south-west is 4,000 to 5,000 miles, so that big rollers are able to build up all the way from America, hurling sheets of spray over any plants bold enough to grow on these faces. Survivors are necessarily fewer, more specialised and keep well above sea level.

The occasional salty gale from the east can be more catastrophic, even if less fierce, because it batters a vegetation which is not geared to withstand its impact. Closely related plants differ in their ability to survive, common sorrel being better fitted than sheep's sorrel, fiorin grass than brown bent, red fescue than sheeps fescue and the dwarf four-petalled mouse-ear chickweed than the common species.

Sea plantain is more often a salt marsh plant and is inhibited by wind rather than salt water, descending over two metres below the little red seaweed (*Catenella opuntia* or *repens*) in places and overlapping with green seaweeds creeping up freshwater trickles from the splash zone. Perhaps the most characteristic cliff plant is rock samphire, but its fleshy leaves are palatable – even to humans – and it seldom ventures from the safety of inaccessible faces. Sea spleenwort, Britain's only maritime fern, takes refuge well back in crevices.

Lowest of all the land plants in the splash zone are three very abundant lichens, bright orange mats of *Caloplaca marina* and the grey, branched *Ramalina breviuscula* and *Ramalina cuspidata* which form broad, shaggy curtains or carpets a few centimetres high on vertical and horizontal faces. With these are thrift, rock spurrey (which is not either of the two saltmarsh species), the lichen *Xanthoria parietina* and little cushions of the olive-green moss, *Grimmia maritima*.

Salt spume wafted into the ponds is relatively harmless until the water evaporates, leaving the salt behind. As the waterline recedes tall plants of shoreweed (*Littorella uniflora*), their leaves bloated with air spaces to help them breathe under water, are vulnerable to grazing. Given a

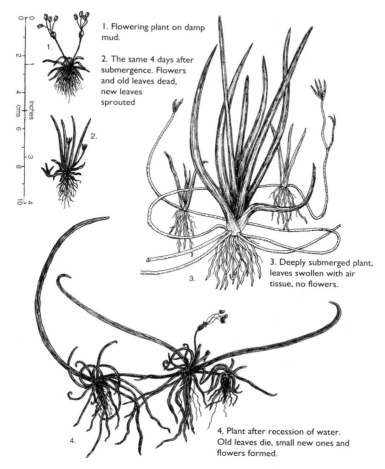

1. Flowering plant on damp mud.

2. The same 4 days after submergence. Flowers and old leaves dead, new leaves sprouted

3. Deeply submerged plant, leaves swollen with air tissue, no flowers.

4. Plant after recession of water. Old leaves die, small new ones and flowers formed.

Shoreweed, aquatic and terrestrial forms.

few days, they wilt and the replacement leaves are small, forming close rosettes, like the related plantains. In mainland situations this is a plant of pond margins where cattle come to drink and trample and this subterfuge is obviously effective. The long flowing fronds of alternate-flowered water milfoil are replaced by stubby little replicas of the pinnate, feathery leaves of winter.

An unusual incomer on the drying pond beds was and still is the red goosefoot (*Chenopodium rubrum var. pseudobotryoides*), replacing some of the diminished red-leaved water purslane. Bulbous rush is grazed by all and sundry, persisting as tiny rosettes where accessible, but growing tall in the protection of unpalatable marsh plants, where it is often viviparous, with little leafy plants sprouting from the flower clusters.

A rare beauty is the lesser water plantain (*Baldellia ranunculoides*), with linear leaves when submerged and tiny ones when high and dry, but broadly spoon-shaped ones associated with the white, buttercup style flowers in spring. The true white-flowered buttercups include one water species and two mud species, *Ranunculus aquatilis, R. hederaceus and R. lutarius.*

A fine fragrance of mint wafts from damp patches and rafts of pink water bistort flowers cover much of North, South and Winter Ponds and some of the smaller pools. Another aquatic delight is the delicate floating marshwort (*Apium inundatum*) which is so different from the

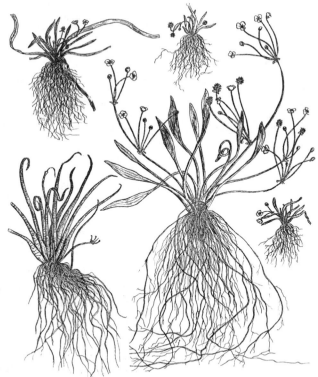

Lesser Water Plantain, seasonal phases.

Floating Marshwort.

coarser, commoner fool's watercress (*Apium nodiflorum*). A speciality in East Pond, formerly alongside the now extinct royal fern, is marsh St. John's wort, with its velvet-textured, unwettable leaves from which the water globules roll as off a duck's back.

There is a pleasant sequence of flowers in dry habitats too, from stately foxgloves spearing up in the shelter of walls to little blue globes of sheep's-bit tucked in crannies and wild thyme exploring over knolls. Lesser celandines and spring squills star the turf with yellow and blue or push up through the coppery trash of winter-buffeted bracken.

Exquisite wild pansies or heartsease, exhibiting various combinations of purple, mauve, yellow and cream, are a special treat in the Crab Bay area. Abbreviated versions of pink centaury and pale kidney vetch or lady's finger appear with the commonplace but gorgeously brilliant bird's-foot trefoil, whose flowers are often a luminous orange instead of the usual yellow.

Among the dwindling heather are wood sage and wild golden rod, but the fine-leaved heath was on its way out in the forties, the heather itself following it almost to extinction by the eighties. Flowers of the grass heath include tormentil, heath bedstraw, heath milkwort, creeping cinquefoil and silverweed where water lingers in depressions.

The seashore is steep, giving a narrow intertidal belt for the study of seaweed and marine animal zonation. Conditions are rougher than optimum for prolific weed growth, but two hundred and two species were identified, mostly the smaller red algae. This is almost four times as many as on the smaller, more exposed island of Grassholm but fewer than on Skomer.

The purple mudstone cliffs weather along bedding and cleavage planes to give gullies orientated mainly east to west. Harder bands of sandstone sometimes protect spurs parallel to the north coast, sheltering deep water gullies and increasing habitat diversity. The only sandy beach is in North Haven and is of shell sand, containing 75-78% of lime from fragmented shells. This and the few cobble strands are too mobile for plant attachment.

The ferocity of wave action is the main factor influencing seaweed growth. On the average mainland shore there are broad belts of Fuci or brown wracks. On the most exposed island shores wracks are virtually absent, their place taken by the stiffly branched little black marine lichen,

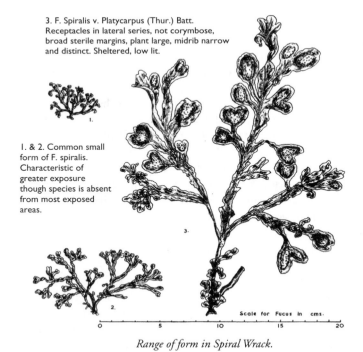

3. F. Spiralis v. Platycarpus (Thur.) Batt. Receptacles in lateral series, not corymbose, broad sterile margins, plant large, midrib narrow and distinct. Sheltered, low lit.

1. & 2. Common small form of F. spiralis. Characteristic of greater exposure though species is absent from most exposed areas.

Scale for Fucus in cms.

Range of form in Spiral Wrack.

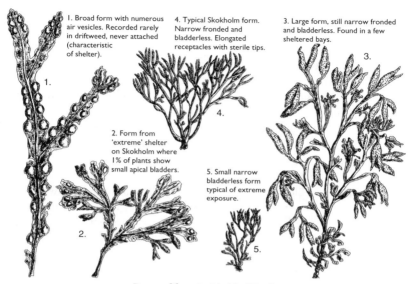

1. Broad form with numerous air vesicles. Recorded rarely in driftweed, never attached (characteristic of shelter).

4. Typical Skokholm form. Narrow fronded and bladderless. Elongated receptacles with sterile tips.

3. Large form, still narrow fronded and bladderless. Found in a few sheltered bays.

2. Form from 'extreme' shelter on Skokholm where 1% of plants show small apical bladders.

5. Small narrow bladderless form typical of extreme exposure.

Range of form in Bladder Wrack.

Lichina pygmaea, above a much broader band of even more closely adherent acorn barnacles.

The first wracks to appear where the waves pound less fiercely are stunted and without air bladders, the purpose of which is to float the fronds to the surface in still water, so that they can photosynthesise. Wave action does the lifting here. The usually conspicuous egg wrack is almost wholly missing, while saw wrack is able to withstand tidal swirl in gullies but not buffeting by broken waves.

Range of form seen in spiral or flat wrack and in bladder wrack are illustrated, practically all the last being the anomaly of a bladder wrack without bladders (*Fucus vesiculosus var. evesiculosus*). There is also a strange spiral form of the familiar little *Dictyota dichotoma* with marginal lobes or ramuli (see page 102).

The fingered oarweed, tangle or kelp (*Laminaria digitata*) is much the commonest of the big downshore weeds exposed by normal tides. Its long strap-like fronds get progressively narrower as wave pummelling increases until it finally gives way to the elegantly waving ones of the more widely distributed tang or dabberlocks (*Alaria esculenta*), its margins pleated into a pliant midrib with three inch long spore-bearing 'keys' clustered at the base.

Downshore in the comparative shelter of the east are the larger red kelp (*Laminaria cloustoni* or *hyperborea*) and the giant brown weed with pimply hollow holdfasts like half deflated footballs and conspicuous zigzag flanges above the knobbly base: *Sacchoriza bulbosa* or *polyschides*.

The two species of Irish moss or carragheen, *Chondrus crispus* and especially *Gigartina stellata*, and crusty pink corralline weeds are common red algae on all types of shore, but the broad purplish flanges of dulse (*Rhodymenia palmata*) prefer sheltered coves. Tang and dulse are eaten in Scotland, carragheen in Ireland.

Welsh laverbread is from Welsh laver (*Porphyra umbilicalis*), which occurs here in two forms. The edible type, so tasty fried with the breakfast bacon, resembles deflated red balloons and grows downshore. The smaller upshore form grows in crisply erect bunches or lines and sheds its spores early in the season, spending most of the summer as faded yellowish frills.

The Skokholm rabbit population must have been almost unique in Britain in being immune to the wave of Myxomatosis that swept across the country in 1955, exterminating many colonies and decimating others. Attempts had been made to introduce it artificially to Skokholm but had failed. The infected victims just holed up and died on their own.

It was soon proved that rabbit fleas were the vectors, passing the disease from one rabbit to another in the crowded conditions of communal burrows. Survivors were usually those which bedded down above ground under dense bramble or bracken.

Skokholm rabbits were not known to have fleas, so no amount of introducing infected ones was going to have any overall effect. The disease was rife in Australia when I arrived there in 1957, but the vectors there were mosquitoes, which had no influence on Skokholm.

Nevertheless, rabbit numbers did fluctuate from year to year, when the rabbits literally ate themselves out of house and home, usually after a hot dry summer when there was little or no plant growth to keep up with their gnawing. Under hunger stress lean animals could be seen standing on their hind legs reaching up to bite off nettle, thistle, hemlock or other unwholesome plants that were not normally touched. Their numbers could also be decimated by long cold winters such as early 1949 and the 1960s when spring growth started late.

Plants fall into three categories in relation to rabbit grazing. There are 'rabbit avoided' species which are seldom eaten and grow away at the expense of the rest. These are usually woody, coarse, prickly, stinging, hairy, acrid, poisonous or just plain unpalatable. Purple moor grass shoots are eaten only when young and often not then, as much is under water in early spring when growth starts.

Secondly, there are 'rabbit resistant' species,which are favoured as food but in which a resistant growth habit favours survival. These usually remain close to Mother Earth, either as tight-fitting rosettes or ground-hugging runners, some by remaining so small that even a close-nibbling rabbit can overlook them. Such plants have stooped to conquer.

Grasses have a great advantage in that their leaves grow from the base, lengthening the more when their tops are nipped off by teeth or lawn mowers. Most leaves are of fixed shape. When half is eaten they cannot regrow, and most stems have their growing point at the tip, the first part to be nipped off.

Thirdly, there are the 'non-resistant, palatable' species that are enjoyed by rabbits and have no means of growing away from them. Many are succulent, satisfying thirst as well as hunger, and all have their growing points vulnerably exposed.

When under duress rabbits will dig for underground roots and tubers like those of hogweed or the bulbs of bluebells. Other rabbits come to sniff at these little pits, so they may be scent marking sites.

In really hard years, plants which are normally avoided, like sand sedge and fog grass can be grazed back severely in the absence of any-thing better. Only in years of fewer rabbits can these graze more selec-tively, eating only what they enjoy. Over population leads to slum conditions, rabbits eating less than optimum, breeding only twice a year instead of four times, as often on the mainland, and remaining indi-vidually small.

The whole aspect of the island can change, depending on grazing intensity. In some years the entire plateau is covered with sorrel, both common and sheep's, the deep red swathe of their flowers plainly visible from the mainland two miles away. One such sorrel year was 1950, after ragwort had taken over much of the plateau during the intense 1949 drought and died back, leaving bare soil. In 1951 the downy grey fog grass extinguished both yellow and red. Another sorrel year was 1979.

No mammals eat bracken unless they must and this inevitably spreads year by year, cut back only locally by mechanical damage in rabbit warrens or on a wider scale by salty winds. Rabbits burrowing far beyond the current limits of the bracken stands sometime dig up old bracken rhizomes, showing where it has been able to grow in the past.

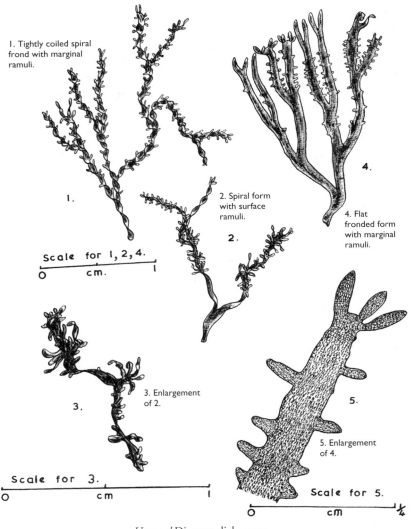

1. Tightly coiled spiral frond with marginal ramuli.

1.

2. Spiral form with surface ramuli.

2.

4.

4. Flat fronded form with marginal ramuli.

Scale for 1, 2, 4.

0   cm.   1

3.

3. Enlargement of 2.

5.

5. Enlargement of 4.

Scale for 3.

0   cm   1

Scale for 5.

0   cm   ¼

Unusual Dictyota dichotoma.

I erected small stock-proof enclosures in different communities all over the island to observe subsequent changes. They varied according to the materials available in this land of make-do-and-mend. The frame of one was an old wooden bedstead.

Results often gave an initial increase in species diversity on previously bare soil, followed by the over-running of all else by a few aggressive dominants. Thus a plot formerly dominated by thrift with a sprinkling of rock spurrey, English stonecrop, thyme and squill, would disappear under a mat of tall red fescue grass – formerly cut back to a few puny sprouts by grazing.

A plot of short bent-fescue turf with doves-foot cranesbill, common storksbill, dog violet and scorpion-grass would become a plot of long grass, the rest squeezed out. A plot in the bracken and fog grass of a disintegrating heather heath would allow the heather to return and fill the cage from side to side, to be grazed off flush across the top, where rabbits sat to enjoy the new shoots as they pushed through the netting. It was good to get the hard-pressed heather or ling back, but the other changes, while fine for pastoralists, worked very much against diversification of the flora.

While botanists watching the post-Myxomatosis changes on the mainland were rejoicing that there were many more species present and more were flowering when the rabbits had been wiped out, my message was the opposite. The first to agree with me in print was Max Nicholson, chief of the Nature Conservancy Council, writing of the East Anglian Breckland in 1957 and pointing out that most of the plants there are dependent on rabbit grazing to prevent them from being overrun by coarse grasses.

It is not only the plants which gain. Wheatears and choughs need short turf over which to feed and the pied wagtails which characterise domestic lawns and golfing greens are less often seen in the rough. Beetles, spiders and many more need the rabbits' assistance to produce their preferred and usually essential environment.

Nevertheless, champion of the little creatures that I am, there can be too much of a good thing – like guano. An 'average high' rabbit population is necessary to keep those fabulous pink swards of flowering thrift free of choking grass, but too many rabbits will be forced to eat flowers and leaves of the thrift itself and leave a barren, straw-coloured landscape – as in severe drought years.

Unlike mainland plants, most of those growing on Skokholm keep a low profile to escape the wind, so are automatically resistant to all but the closest of rabbit grazing and are of little use to sheep or pony, although I wouldn't put anything past the capabilities of goats when it comes to choice of food!

7

SKOKHOLM: THE WANDERER RETURNS
TO THE ISLAND OF RABBITS

Whichever way the wind is blowing, islands always have a sheltered side. As the summers rolled by, I got to know the best hidey holes into which I could snuggle to tidy up my field notes, convert long lines of figures into graphs and histograms and conjure some sort of order from the chaos. If the original survey had been done in unpropitious weather, as with readings of anemometer on Spy Rock, salometer in Quarry Bay or clinometer on northern cliffs, I had first to decipher the writing on the rain-sodden page.

When I felt like a little relaxation, I could indulge in some field sketching, the goats and rabbits offering obvious subjects. Sometimes the larks would sing me to sleep and I would wake to the raucous shouting of an oyster-catcher. Sleeping bodies pose no threat and my waking eyes might focus on a rabbit or a puffin at close quarters, or I could find myself the centre of a mob of quietly grazing Soay sheep.

As some of the Skokholm records found their way into print, headed by my thoughts on the vegetation of the Grassholm gannetry in 1953, I got the opportunity to go and look at other islands, a whole world away. Sheep on those were mostly hungrier Merinos, in direct competition with burrowing shearwaters – the staple of the Aboriginal and Maori mutton bird harvests in Australia and New Zealand. Gannets supplied an important part of the South African guano harvest.

I needed no second bidding, and came to feel very much at home in those English-speaking worlds so far away. The Southern Hemisphere oyster-catchers shouted just as hysterically as northern ones and gulls cast their urgent cries onto the westerlies over the Roaring Forties as those of Skokholm did onto the westerlies from the Atlantic Drift.

Gannets plummeted from the heights to cleave the waters just as neatly in pursuit of fish, while cormorants spread their wings to dry in the same languid fashion when the sun shone. The caterwauling of short-tailed shearwaters struck just such a Mephistophelian note as that of the Manx, only there were vastly more of them, while the Wilson's storm petrels of the South are regarded as the world's most numerous bird species.

Instead of just one of the albatross fraternity, the fulmar petrel, these were more and bigger in the South: royal, wandering, black-browed and light-mantled sooty albatrosses and giant petrels, with crowds of smaller, more elusive 'tube-noses'.

Streamlined birds which used their abbreviated wings to row themselves around under water were penguins, not auks, but they occupied the same ecological niches on land, some nesting in burrows like puffins, others in the open like razorbills and guillemots.

In higher latitudes there were Fiordland and yellow-eyed penguins of New Zealand with the little blue or fairy penguins, so much more widespread in Australia. In South Africa there were the jackass or black-footed penguins. In lower latitudes I shared crowded quarters with kings, rock-hoppers, gentoos and royals, the Australasian sector's version of the macaroni penguins.

A few species were common to both hemispheres. In the nesting territories of Antarctic terns I came across migrant Arctic terns, the same that breed in Britain, but these individuals more likely to be from the lands of the North Pacific. All fly that fantastic annual journey of eleven thousand miles from the Arctic to the Sub-antarctic and are harried during the southern summer by great skuas or bonxies, just as many are in the northern summer.

While rabbits are often banished to islands from the mainland in Britain, it is usually the other way round in Australia, where islands can be the only havens remaining sacrosanct from the introduced hordes which decimate the mainland grazings. To say that rabbits are not popular in that vast pastoral continent is to put it mildly. Anyone who introduced the little darlings where they are not already entrenched would be lynched by his fellows, sure as eggs.

In South Africa it was different. Rabbits are every creatures' lunch and there are so many predators on the African mainland willing to partake of this bounty that the only ones I came across were on small, predator-free islands in Saldanah Bay, off the Atlantic coast. Australian predators are too thin on the ground to deal with the problem, even where helped by introduced red foxes, so the bunnies add their persistent munching to that of the kangaroos and wallabies.

And now I was back, anxious to return to that little Welsh island

Rabbit and Sheep's Sorrel.

where it had all begun, to compare and contrast and, not least, to look at long term changes in any of my rabbit exclosures that had survived the years away.

Thus it was that, at 8.55 p.m. on Friday, 8th July, 1961, I left the bright lights of Paddington and rumbled west, like so many other transitory visitors to that scrap of land off the Welsh coast. There were no sleepers, but I was less prone to creaks and cramps then. From Cardiff, 7 hours and 10 minutes down the line (2 hours in 2002), there was at least room to stretch.

Six potential Skokholmites emerged into a grey morning at Haverfordwest and piled into two taxis for Dale Fort. With only one boat a week, leaving at 8.0 a.m., it paid to be on time. But there was always the weather to contend with. Rougher weather was expected on the midday high tide and 4.30 p.m. was suggested as a likely departure time today.

The skipper was playing safe after a near disaster the previous week. It was not turbulence he was up against then, but fog. Thinking he had rounded St. Ann's Head, he turned the boat accordingly into the blank wall of mist and nearly came to grief on the unfriendly old red sandstone of the last bay facing into Milford Haven.

Michael Crane, vice warden in charge on the island, did not hear the chug of the approaching engine above the pounding of the surf, so did not ring the guiding hand bell. Result: another near disaster on the rocks below 'Alice Williams'.

The boat in those days was still the 'Cubango', an old ship's lifeboat, and her skipper was still Reuben Codd, long term farmer and fisherman from Skomer Island. He had taken over as boatman and handyman when the former skipper, Harold Sturly, was accidentally shot at the helm off St. Ann's Head from the naval shooting range on the cliffs above. John and Ruth Barrett, long term wardens in charge of the Field Studies Council Centre at Dale Fort were aboard. Harold caught the bullet in the back of the neck and died almost instantly in Ruth's arms. With all that expanse of ocean to receive the shots, it was a cruel twist of fate that directed a lethal missile to that vulnerable spot. The victim had been out fishing only the night before, scorning the risk.

Today's Skokholm party wandered off, lured by the heady scent of hedgerow honeysuckle and meadowsweet, for which this delectable peninsula is so justly famous. We had not gone far when Reuben decided he'd give it a try, so long as we could get round St. Ann's before the tidal peak.

While rounding us up he enlarged graphically on what must have been the complete complement of drownings around this coast (just like the Bass Strait in the Roaring Forties of the South). He pointed out that it was those who hung onto the upturned boat who were rescued. Passengers who tried to swim for it, either didn't make the shore or got washed off it when they had. Then, in case anyone was feeling nervous: "'Cubango' won't sink. You just hang on!"

Several sumptuously equipped yachts had taken refuge in Milford Haven, but we made it safely, sliding up and down the glistening slopes as long waves rolled under those unsinkable timbers, and jarring as she thwacked into extra big troughs.

There were thirteen incomers, including Margaret Rusell, cheery cook from the Fort, who was to replace Penny, the island cook – coming ashore with John, her new fiancé, the island warden, for family introductions. Again there were Swedes, two fourteen-year-olds, Magnus and Anders, three Manchester Youths, two married couples and two men from the Ministry of Agriculture and Fisheries. These were a Welshman and a Scotsman, Gwyn Lloyd and Dan McGowan, the last a former colleague of Mike Ridpath who I had recently been sharing a two acre island with off Tasmania. A small world – or not? It had seemed a world with no boundaries to that young man and his petite French fiancée

Skylark and Dog Violet.

who were not just visiting but had emigrated – from the study of wood pigeons to that of marsupials.

What changes should I find after a five year gap? The new lab was almost completed when I left and a new washroom had now appeared between it and the warden's cott. Drinking water was now pumped up from the well instead of carried and the rainwater tank had been enlarged and connected to taps both inside and outside the Wheelhouse.

The calor gas cylinders, so heavy to lump around on the quay, but so buoyant when they dropped off it, sometimes with a man attached, were now powering two modern gas cookers. A capacious paraffin-fuelled refrigerator had been installed to thwart the mice. Rabbit stew, which often figured on the menu by mid week, was now more often used as a stopgap when the boat was overdue. This was just as well, now that the Conder-induced catching of bunnies on the hoof at night with torches was less popular – or just less successful.

Bedside cupboards had appeared in the sleeping quarters, but last man out of the common room still took the tilley lamp up the ladder to stand beside the jug and basin in the angel loft. Nautically flavoured wooden plaques on doors identified the various rooms: 'master' on the Wheelhouse, 'midshipmen' the bunkhouse, 'steward' the cook's quarters and 'carpenter' the married quarters behind the bird room.

Curtains, an unheard of extravagance, now graced both common room and bird room and the long extant hole in the wheelhouse yard wall had been plugged. A new flag floated proudly atop the mast to warn residents of an approaching boat or impending meal. This was pale blue, embroidered with the name of the island and two perky oyster-catchers. A carved plaque in Welsh slate had been let into the wall by the house door with the full title, 'Skokholm Bird Observatory', and images of two gulls, to tell shipwrecked mariners where they had finished up. The rest of us knew.

Tamarisk, Hydrangea and roses had been planted in the garden and no longer were there goats to be milked. Chores were as before, but not today, friday being a day of double spuds and much scrubbing up, or down, as the spirit moved, so that newcomers were not immediately faced with the nitty gritty of island life. Not that the policy of "Musn't make things too cosy, or we'll get the wrong sort of visitor" had changed.

But what of the wildlife? The island dreamed on, under its cloud of querulous gulls. Lesser black-backs seemed to have increased but their offspring were unseasonally late in hatching, due to culling of early clutches. All the great black-backed eggs had been confiscated and some of the adults shot, to curtail their predation on more vulnerable species, so they had no chicks to feed. Herring gulls had set up a new roost on the end of the Neck, causing degeneration from a grass sward, through thrift to sparse sea storksbill and plantain.

Puffins seemed fewer and warier than before. Had too many puffin stalkers tried the more worrying humped approach of looper caterpillars rather than the less frightening level-pegging sort? Shearwaters were as thick on the ground as ever. Wheatears, pipits and larks were fully fledged and cavorting joyously aloft in the brisk sea winds. Soon they would be joined by swifts, swallows and sand martins, willow warblers and whitethroats, moving ahead of the autumn gales.

Many of my rabbit exclosures had collapsed and the vegetation had reverted under the impact of busy incisors. Goats had broken through the roof of the bedstead, but it was still full of heather in a sea of bracken, though this was dying off and was pierced by two new fern fronds.

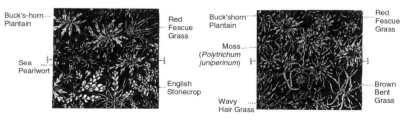

Enlargement of two one inch squares of turf.

In fact the voracious rabbit population had suffered a recent check. Many had starved to death during 1959 when a substantial proportion of the Soay flock was culled by shooting, to prevent their lingering death by starvation. Some had already died and currently there were only two ewes left, these running with the goats.

It was intended to bring in a breeding nucleus from Skomer to build the flock up, but not until Gwyn Lloyd's and Ian McGowan's rabbit studies had produced results uncomplicated by too much competition. These two were making regular visits every three weeks to monitor the recovery in numbers and growth rate, following the disastrous 1959 drought.

Rabbits surviving the drought had been slow to start building up their numbers because of a prolonged dry spring in 1960 and the population had also had to contend with the calamitous freeze-ups of the early sixties. It was August-September before there was any appreciable increase.

A short term but more continuous study was being carried out by the resident vice warden in the warden's stamping ground close to the buildings. Here a small colony of rabbits was contained within wire netting and their breeding burrows lidded with a thick turf which could be removed for a daily weighing of the youngsters within. Lifted out, popped in a cotton bag and suspended on a spring balance, these were found to put on an average weight of 5.5 ounces a day, in contrast to 9 ounces on the adjacent mainland.

Most of the animals trapped elsewhere topped the scales at between two and three pounds (thirty-two to fifty-four ounces), at which weight the semi-captives were released. Slow growth and small size is a common feature of the vast rabbit populations that often build up on islands where there are few or no checks. Flatholm in the Bristol Channel in 2001 illustrated this principal very aptly.

The Min. of Ag. men had undertaken a punishing live-trapping programme to gather vital statistics and had collected a hundred animals in the current season and nine hundred since May the previous year. Rabbit

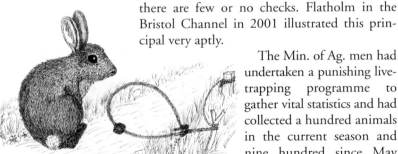

Rabbit and live snare.

recovery had had to wait for vegetation recovery, not getting away until the late summer in 1960. Gwyn had been visiting regularly since 1956 and thought the vegetation lusher in 1961 than in any of the previous five years. It certainly looked better than I remembered it.

The Home Meadow was covered with whiskery, mauve-topped Yorkshire fog stems, undulating in the balmy air currents, where before it had been nibbled to the consistency of a bowling green, where enthusiastic golfers had been known to practise their putting.

Instead of minuteae like allseed and pearlworts, there was abbreviated hogweed and a loose matrix of bird's-foot trefoil. Clover and self heal brightened a healthy sward in Orchid Bog and red fescue in the clifftop swards was actually flowering, although still dwarf.

Bracken was thicker, with fewer damaged fronds around the warrens, but this noxious fern encroached anyway, at all times, uninhibited by any factor except salty gales from an unaccustomed direction. Nothing grazed it, rabbits, sheep and goats working assiduously between the fronds scoffing all the natural competitors that might have helped to keep it in check. Thrift, which had long since given way to scrappy buck'shorn plantain on the end of the Neck, was looking very bonny in some of its other sites, with sea campion, mayweed and scurvy grass as floriferous as ever.

A Min. of Ag. live trap set in a rabbit run, consisted of a running noose attached to a peg and having a stop to prevent it from tightening and damaging the captive. Ordinary wire was too inflexible and springy stranded wire was used, this usually holding them round the neck, though a few approached more precipitately and got their front paws through.

Captives were removed, weighed, sexed and marked with a padlock shaped ear tag as used for ferrets and the wings of hens. This bore a number, which was backed up by a few black ink punctures before release, these showing distant watchers that it had been monitored, although not identifying the individual.

The day I went round the traps with the men they got ten, half already tagged. One youngster, trapped also the previous day, scuttled straight back into another trap when released. Some infants never learn. The rounds were usually done about 5 a.m. Left later the great black-backs might have helped themselves to the captives, attacking usually by pecking the head or the upper vertebral column.

These birds habitually turn their prey inside out, peeling the skin back as they work their way through. Preferring to drink with their meals, their remains, which were more often of shearwaters, were usually found by the ponds. Gwyn turned the rabbit pelts right way out when he came across them, to see if there was a numbered tag.

Rabbits encountered with a torch at night were usually lone bucks on the razzle, in pursuit of new sexual experiences (to prevent inbreeding) or of youngsters squeezed out of the parental colony to seek quarters of their own. Only these categories were likely to travel more than two hundred yards or so from the home warren. Mass migrations like that so delightfully described in *Watership Down* are the exception rather than the rule.

It explains the sharp demarcation so often seen between closely razed turf and long tousled grass, with only desultory inroads from the boundary of the habitual grazing area into the land of greater plenty. Thus it was that the few breeding nuclei in 1961 stopped increasing after the May brood, although there was plenty of food elsewhere – awaiting colonisation by the maturing youngsters, which should themselves be breeding in the autumn.

Despite the apparent dislike of travel, rabbits had good homing instincts. One from Wheatear Rock escaped indoors and spent a week in a cupboard. When rescued and released outside, near starving, it scarpered and was found a day or two later back at Wheatear Rock.

This was one of the many black rabbits, the melanistic form being much commoner in island populations than in the average mainland situation, where they stand out like sore thumbs and attract a greater range of predators. Blackness is recessive, but if a black buck gets busy in a sizable harem considerable pockets of blacks can build up.

The fugitive from the cupboard had to cross unfamiliar territory, which an incident this week suggested they did not relish. An amateur film maker, wanting a 'rabbit spectacular' of the wee beasties haring around on the cliffs, persuaded Gwyn to release a bunch of his trapped animals on the clifftop. Instead of doing their stuff, as intended, they just crouched with ears flattened, exuding fright and indetermination from every pore. My attention was attracted to the sorry performance by the capering and shouting of Ian. Instead of galvanising them into action, he seemed to have put the fear of God into them. They weren't used to cliffs and had no idea where to run in such bizarre territory.

The rabbiters experimented with netting, to save the labour of servicing the snares. A ten yard net supported on aluminium poles was

Melanistic buck rabbit and offspring.

set, often along one of the tumbledown walls, which offered some concealment. It was manned after the rabbits had worked their way towards the house in the quiet of the evening. A string brought the line of netting down to ground level to entangle the animals as they sprinted back into the bracken cover. It was not dropped over feeding rabbits as clap nets are sometimes dropped over feeding flocks of birds.

This method of waylaying them for weighing and marking proved too inefficient to be of real use. The first night only one was caught. The next night, when left rather late, it apprehended five shearwaters and a storm petrel, one of the bigger birds breaking the attachments. Always optimistic, they planned to bring stouter uprights from Guildford on their next visit.

Skokholm had the effect of promoting outrageously ambitious plans among researchers, be they amateur or professional. There was much talk this week of fencing off the whole of the Neck, thinning the rabbits out, marking the remaining population intensively and monitoring relative rates of increase of populations feeding on fertilised and untreated swards – the sort of thing farmers have been doing with more remunerative livestock from time immemorial.

The scheme remained but a dream. It was well known that rabbits did better on the central bog during the 1959 drought – this balanced against the threat of waterlogged burrows when the weather was more normal. The wise rabbits escaped this hazard by digging shallow burrows in the sides of anthills raised against old grass stools.

A less ambitious programme being currently implemented was concerned with the incidence of Coccidiosis, which was caused by a minute Protozoon (single-celled animal). This exhibits few external symptoms but causes white flecks on the liver, a symptom which Gwyn was finding in one of every eleven rabbits examined.

With all this rabbit-related activity going on, it was inevitable that the oft-told story of milking the local rabbits should surface again. The event related was from a time when two rather gullible gentlemen were on the island painting the lighthouse. Lifelong townees, they regarded the observatory folk as more than a little odd and expressed considerable puzzlement as to what really went on at "the other end of the island".

They gazed incredulously as it was explained that we placed coloured rings on birds' legs, weighed their chicks every day, collected the fleas and lice from their backs, measured their hind claws and bred maggots for baiting traps. After the account of how we planted plants in the ponds, erected complicated roofed structures, so that the weeds could grow undisturbed, crept out at dead of night to take water temperatures in the streams, collected pollen grains blown from America, studied the mating habits of the big black slugs and painted red dots on the cinnabar moths, they were prepared to believe almost anything. The narrator warmed to his task and, after a completely authentic but most unlikely account of some of our other doings, informed his mesmerised audience that we gained strength for these activities by drinking rabbits' milk.

This really intrigued them and it was arranged that they should visit the observatory the following morning to watch milking operations. Obviously the community could not let them down or they would begin to suspect our whole way of life. It was resolved that there should be a rabbit hunt that night and all hands turned to with a will.

Half a dozen lidded wooden boxes were produced to serve as stalls and placed in a neat row on the workshop floor, with a further box, carefully scrubbed, for a milking parlour. A nurse and a doctor were numbered among the week's visitors and they were able to produce other necessary equipment.

A party of volunteers sallied forth at dusk to collect the missing item, the rabbits. Rabbit hunts, as already indicated, were a pleasing pastime in which we sometimes indulged on the way back from nocturnal ringing expeditions, the only difference this time being that it was a "bring 'em back alive" sortie. Armed with torches, sacks and running shoes and a judicious combination of stealth and speed, the rabbits were soon safely 'in the bag' and fed and housed for the night.

The painters arrived at the appointed hour and proceedings went without a hitch. The milking parlour was swilled down and the appropriate parts of the rather startled rabbits wiped with a damp cloth and a ration of oatmeal doled out to each. Secreted within the cuff of the white-coated milkmaid was a large rubber bulb filled with diluted powdered milk and the contents were eased down the exit tube in a series of

Racing Rabbits!

gentle spurts into a waiting glass beaker as she massaged the rabbits' bellies.

The creatures were remarkably docile, but an assistant made sure that they did not suddenly change their minds about the indignity of their situation and make a bid for freedom. The painters' eyes opened wide as the level of the milky fluid built up in the beaker and they pronounced the result as "Very good. Almost like powdered milk!"

We were not quite sure how these proceedings had impressed them, but they went away muttering about "Them queer types of bird-watchers. You never can tell."

Seated on the cliffs towards the end of my stay, feet dangling from a comfortable rock, I watched a long line of gulls streaming out on their daily trek to the Milford fish docks, where catches were dismembered and deboned and the birds did a valuable job in clearing the offal.

A little green Breton fishing boat butted through a sea flecked with white horses, out of Douarnenez, perhaps, or Port Haliguen near Quiberon, where I had watched fish being landed during a cycling tour in those parts as a student. They put into Milford too, no doubt bringing the Breton onion men, who wheeled their bicycles around Haverfordwest and Pembroke with plaits of brown onions draped over the handlebars – a site I had been familiar with in London thirty years before.

My mind drifted back to October 1950 when the warden, Peter Conder, vice warden, Joan Keighley and cook, Shirley Townend of Southampton and Aberystwyth Universities, and I had been marooned on Skokholm after the last of the visitors had gone. Day after day we searched the horizon with binoculars for a boat, but even the Milford trawlers lay snug within the haven. The iron rations kept for such emergencies were running low and we were living on unleavened scones in the absence of bread until the better endowed lighthouse folk came to the rescue.

Peter was due in Holland in a few day's time, so it was with alacrity that we 'jumped to it' when John Barrett strode into the common room with the order to "Abandon ship". No British boat could be persuaded to come out, but the hardy Breton loups de mers, veritably wolves of the sea, had agreed and were lying now in the comparative shelter of North Haven waiting for us.

No luggage was allowed. That would have to follow. We jettisoned the half cooked rabbit pie intended for lunch, straightened things up as best we could and slid down the rope to North Haven where a dinghy awaited. Vice warden and cook scrambled aboard while Peter, waist deep in the water, steadied the bouncing craft. He spotted an extra large wave rolling into the mouth of the gully and took a header into the boat. The wave followed him in, the Frenchmen at the oars swore two mighty oaths and started pulling out to sea in the backwash.

Meanwhile I was still ashore with John Barrett and seaman Harold Sturly who had come to help. A voice from the retreating dinghy informed us in a foreign language but in no uncertain terms that they would not be coming back up the gully for us. After some deliberation another possible spot was indicated. We hauled ourselves back up the rope (which was a permanent fixture here) and down the hundred foot cliff, along a projecting promontory and once more to sea level.

As the dinghy rose to meet us I took off into the arms of a burly Frenchman and we grovelled together in the bilge water while the boat was sucked back into the trough. John and Harold came in on the next two waves and our crew of two stalworts got us clear while we were still in a tangle of bodies in the bottom of the boat. That was the safest part to be in. Even here, in the lee of the island, I felt as though I was afloat on a lentil in a cauldron of bubbling soup.

We still had to get aboard the mother ship. Peter leaned down and I reached up. On the first wave we touched fingertips before I descended six to eight feet into a trough. The second time we grasped hands momentarily; the third time our grip was firmer. I dangled for a moment and was then hauled unceremoniously over the gunwhale. The others followed, in equally undignified manner and the dinghy was hauled on board after them.

As we had so often observed from the island, the redoubtable little Breton fishing boats do not stop to climb over the waves but go through them. Water swished in over the bows, swirling knee deep along the deck before pouring off again aft. We hung on to whatever came to hand, dodging the loose lumps of iron than slid back and forth round our ankles.

There was nearly a cry of "Man overboard" as the pile of lobster pots on which John was perched skated across to the opposite rail, but he was caught up short there and crept back amidships. Peter was violently sick, the vice warden turned the colour of a newly opened primrose and the cook looked subdued while I, inexplicably, had never felt better.

After the excitement around St. Ann's Head, we could relax a little, peering into the hold and drawing up baskets of live crabs and lobsters. We talked of the anticipated grand biftek which we hoped we would soon be enjoying and found it much easier to understand Peter's french (acquired at a finishing school in Switzerland) than the fruity version emanating from the Bretons. There were still urgent cries of "vitement, vitement" as we were put ashore at Dale.

Our gallant rescuers would accept no cash payment – such is the chivalry of those who go down to the sea in ships – but were entertained to dinner at the Fort. They returned to France next day laden with rabbits and fresh fruit and vegetables. It was a fortnight before another boat got to Skokholm to rescue our equipment and personal effects, which I awaited in Aberystwyth before moving on to my two year spell in Bangor.

These little adventures had a way of happening at crucial times. Two years before, when due in Aberystwyth for graduation day, the lobster fisherman who was coming to collect me failed to materialise. When I spied Harold Sturly striding up from South Haven I greeted him with open arms, only to learn that he had come ashore to send an SOS from the lighthouse as his engine had broken down. (No mobile phones then!) This achieved, I left with him under sail and oars and we met our rescuers half way across to St. Ann's Head and were taken in tow. As we rounded Dale Point we were swamped with water from an exploding mine. The navy was clearing the harbour and had failed to see us coming!

Enchanted islands are not only places to relax in the sun and engage in scientific research, they are aids to self-sufficiency, team work and a great preparation for learning to deal with the unexpected.

8

GRASSHOLM: A GALAXY OF GANNETS

There is no doubt that the way to be sure of getting to Grassholm Island as often as possible is to be somewhere in the vicinity for long periods of time. 'Grassholm days', weatherwise, are few. The decision to visit is usually a last minute one and there is no time to round up those who are not on the spot.

Many a party from Cardiff or Merthyr Tydfil has travelled to Martin's Haven to board the Grassholm boat, to find waves butting aggravatingly at the shore and the trip off. Some parties get as far as Skokholm or Skomer, most find themselves walking the cliffs of Marloes, a by no means unpleasant experience, or scrambling up onto the tidal island of Gateholm, with its prehistoric remains and fine view of the other islands to seawards.

Being based for so long on Skokholm, I was lucky and paid many visits to the redoubtable little island that withstands the Atlantic gales eight miles west of 'our' lighthouse. Often we sat on our western cliffs with a telescope, watching long files of gannets streaming down to the eastern slopes and rising with tufts of long grass in their scimitar bills to add to their crowded nest mounds out of sight over the crest.

Then there were times when, after buffeting our way through the Wild Goose Race off Skokholm's Mad Bay, we found ourselves on a wild goose chase, the solan geese eluding us yet again. Having got that far, the choice was between turning back to visit Skomer or pressing on to circumnavigate Grassholm with no chance of going ashore. Queasiness ignored, the latter alternative always won. Although disappointing, particularly for a botanist, it afforded an unrivalled opportunity to view the great host of birds from the sea.

This is all anyone can hope for now, because landing has been prohibited since 1998 – the reason – the spectacle has become too great. Gannets have spread right across the island since those carefree days of the late forties and early fifties, when they were in process of spreading, and there is no longer room for humans as well. This means added

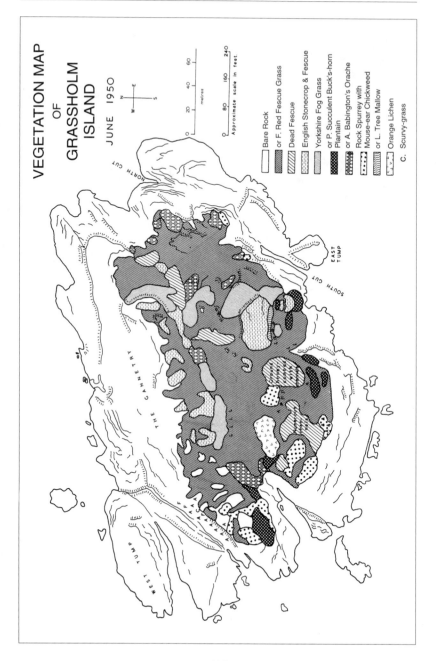

VEGETATION MAP
OF
GRASSHOLM
ISLAND

JUNE 1950

Approximate scale in feet

metres

Bare Rock
or F. Red Fescue Grass
Dead Fescue
English Stonecrop & Fescue
Yorkshire Fog Grass
or P. Succulent Buck's-horn Plantain
or A. Babington's Orache
Rock Spurrey with Mouse-ear Chickweed
or L. Tree Mallow
Orange Lichen
C. Scurvy-grass

NORTH CUT

EAST TUMP

SOUTH CUT

THE GANNETRY

WEST TUMP

Boat in South East Gut of Grassholm.

spectacle for viewers from the sea as they circle this, the second largest gannetry in the northern hemisphere, which now holds some thirty-three thousand three hundred nesting pairs of these magnificent birds, the numbers still expanding.

Vegetation as I knew it in the late 1940s is superposed on an outline map drawn by Peter Conder from an aerial photograph, and shows what a comparatively small amount of the island was then occupied by the close-knit bird colony.

Lobstermen came this way but not so often as to habituate the birds to seaborne visitors. As our boat rounded East Tump to nose her way into South Gut, clouds of birds would fly out to investigate. Flinging their 'hs' to the wind, they greeted us with shouts of "Urrah, urrah". With cold starey eyes amidships, close against the dagger bill, they pointed that instrument of punishment straight at us as they flew over the boat, heads bent to see what was going on. Being inedible, we escaped unscathed.

Moving along the leeward shore, the unmistakable and evocative odour comes wafting across. Some visitors have been heard to use the word stench. To the genuine bird-islander, this is part and parcel of the package, the titivator of a sense which humans alone, among those endowed with olfactory perception, have let go largely to waste.

Grassholm is the most westerly land in Wales apart from the Smalls, with its bleak lighthouse. From the sea its twenty-two acres appear as a rounded tump rising a hundred and fifty feet (forty-six metres) and shorn to an abrupt edge on the north-west side, which has been white with gannets since colonisation began. Where green with grass (in the old days) it is more gently curved. Now all is white apart from the grey wave-washed shoreline, where dark clinkery lumps lie among coarse particles indicative of its igneous origin. With Skomer to the east and the Smalls to the west, it is all that remains above sea level of an eroded reef of basalt.

North and South Guts on the east side are the watery corridors into which our various boatmen insinuated their little craft over the years. They are fault aligned. A mass of stratified sand and gravel floors the gully between the two – waterborne material from a period of higher sea level. Similar raised beach deposits, some fifteen metres above current sea level and overlain by angular head, occur above the south-westerly inlets. These are unsuitable for landing, being on the exposed side and broader, with waves funnelling through in gay abandon, particularly inside the West Tump.

The name Grassholm is no longer applicable, as it was in the forties and fifties – but what grass it was then, such as we never saw on Skokholm except on the ungrazed Stack. Now there is little left. It must have been equally striking in the ninth and tenth centuries when the Vikings named it Graesholmr. (Holm is Scandinavian for island, appearing in Skokholm, Flatholm, Steepholm and Gateholm.) William Worcester in a fifteenth century itinerary refers to the island by this name.

George Owen, Elizabethan historian, writes: "Far of in the sea standeth the iland Gresholme . . . a small iland viii miles from the maine and from the remoteness thereof and small proffetes yt yieldeth is seldom frequented."

There are said to have been periods subsequently when both sheep and rabbits fed from the spray-washed turf, but this was long ago, few traces of their activities remaining. Not until 1956 did Ronald Lockley discover signs of ancient human settlement on the guano-saturated strip of bare peat up to forty metres wide in front of the advancing gannetry.

These were investigated in 1972 by Douglas Hague. They proved impossible to date accurately, but were probably early medieval, although Iron Age remains have been found on Grassholm in the past. The settlement, of stone-walled house, garden and enclosures, is situated in a central hollow, a natural rain catchment where water collects on the rock surface half a metre down. This is now a sump for washings from the gannetry, but the water was probably potable when the intrepid inhabitants were in residence.

The only 'fresh' water currently observable is the seasonal, guano-fouled seepage below the gannetry in the north-west. This nurtures a phenomenally rich growth of the green alga, *Prasiola crispa*, like miniature sea lettuce, along with filmentous *Hormidium flaccidum and H. mucosum*, coated with green Chlorelloid cells and diatoms. The algae disappear as the seepage dries out.

Fish shoals, as well as drinking water, would have been more available to the early settlers than now, when they have to supply several hundred grey Atlantic seals which have haunted the island shores increasingly since 1890, as well as the many thousands of gannets.

Puffins, which occupied the island before the gannets, make inroads only into shoals of smaller fish, but are thought not to have been present in medieval times, to contribute their own plump bodies to the islanders' menu. Lockley, in *I Know an Island,* 1938, suggests that they probably moved into Grassholm in the early nineteenth century when they were being rigorously netted for lobster bait on Skokholm and Skomer – the usual story of exploitation by man.

They are said to have risen to half a million by 1890, but this must be a gross over-estimate on grounds of practical burrow density. Demise of the population was as rapid as its growth, with numbers down to about fifty in 1928, when a general collapse of the undermined topsoil had left a maze of roofless furrows where the nest burrows had been. The honeycomb of anastimosing channels persisted into the 1950s as a broad band of hummocky peat between the gannetry and the vegetated region.

It had undoubtedly been larger when the half million puffins were estimated, plants having colonised all but the part subjected to a rain of guano, moulted feathers and dripping salt water from overflying gannets. There must have been a period after the apparently sudden exodus of the puffins when the name of Grassholm was again inept. – a dark phase in contrast to today's white phase, when the guano-sodden soil is white even when the gannets are not in residence.

GRASSHOLM

Herring Gulls stealing marginal Gannets' eggs.

Great Black-backed Gulls on west Grassholm, 1965.

Massed Gannets from the population of three thousand in the 1950s.

Razorbills on West Tump, 1965.

SKOMER I

Rabbit-trimmed Heather, 1976.

Massed Red Campion, July 1961.

Warden's house on isthmus between North and South Havens, 1976.

Part of the magnificence of Bluebells, May, 1978.

SKOMER II

Puffins.

Amy the goat and a three-week-old Shearwater, 1963.

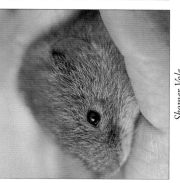

Skomer Vole.

Sea Campion lacking red pigment (anthocyanin).

Scallops, Crawfish, Coral, Urchins and diving kit, 1964.

RAMSEY I

View to St. David's Head from the north end.

Blue sward of Spring Squill extends right to cliff edge.

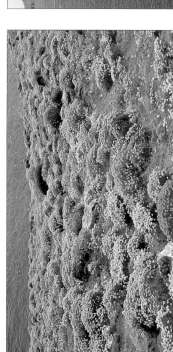

Part of a splendid Thrift community, 1969.

Spring Squill among low Heather.

When Huxley and Lockley made the film 'The Private Life of the Gannet' in 1934, the puffin population had dropped to a hundred and thirty pairs. Twenty-five pairs were recorded in 1940.

The few remaining puffins which we watched taking food to their young in 1948 were doing so in peripheral burrows. Usually it is the young and inexperienced birds which are relegated to marginal sites. Were these young and inexperienced, or the old and wise, who had clung to the last habitable outposts of their former fortress? Birds moving to the larger, more accessible islands – as most of them are thought to have done to Skokholm, which had few puffins before, would be in greater danger from bait-collecting fishermen. We saw other nesting pairs over the next few years and twenty birds were counted by a visitor in 1956.

Lockley, in *Letters from Skokholm*, 1947, quotes the following figures for gannets on Grassholm. 1820 no record, although there was hearsay evidence of some being present then. 1933 20 pairs, protected from 1890 onwards, but not very effectively according to a report by Drane. 1914 300 pairs, 1922 1,000 pairs, 1924 2,000 pairs, 1933 4,750 pairs, 1940 6,000 pairs, rising to 9,000 pairs in 1949.

It was Colonel Morrey-Salmon, bird photographer and ornithologist extraordinaire of Cardiff, who pioneered the use of aerial photographs for counting sea-birds, his subject the Grassholm gannetry, as far back as 1924. He and Lockley, working independently, estimated around 5,000 nests by this means.

Morrey-Salmon was also around to make a photographic record of the visit of the eighth International Ornithological Congress to Skokholm in 1934 when a hundred and eighty delegates were transported thither by two destroyers of the Home Fleet! Like Ronald Lockley, this ornithological war horse lived well into his nineties.

Since this time counting has become more difficult, but is still attempted. In 1956, when only twenty puffins were seen, there were reckoned to be around 10,550 gannet pairs. In 1969 16,000, in 1986 over 28,000 leading on to the 1998 estimate of 33,300.

In June 1930 and August 1936 fires were started by picnickers and put out by volunteers of the Pembrokeshire RSPB coast watchers. The military bombing for target practice was carried out in August 1945 when World War II was effectively over and the exercise seemed more than a little redundant, particularly as the gannet breeding season was still in full swing.

Gannet chicks, development of down and feathers.

Ornithologists had become concerned for the island's welfare when officers of HMS *Sir Richard Fletcher* went ashore and slaughtered adult and young gannets resulting in the first court case under the recently enacted Wild Birds Protection Act.

In 1948, the year of my initial visit, Grassholm was bought by the Royal Society for the Protection of Birds, so the fiftieth anniversary of this important reserve was celebrated in 1998. That the gannets are still going from strength to strength, says much for their successful management.

In 1986 the island was designated by the government as a Special Protection Area under the 1979 European Community Birds Directive. Up to that time the UK had designated only eighteen of the hundred and fifty-one sites identified as eligible.

Gannets or solan geese must take priority of place as the most individually splendid of our British sea-birds, as well as bunching together in the most spectacular colonies. They are certainly the largest, questionably the noisiest, at least by day, and with plumage as outstanding as any.

Birds so fiercely aggressive need to hide behind no camouflage. Their worst tormentors are their neighbours, yet they like to nest cheek by jowl, as shown by the clear demarcation between massed nests and bare ground, when there was so much room for them to spread out to gain easier take-off and landing facilities during the mid twentieth century

Grassholm gannets cannot be approached very closely without marginal ones taking off and exposing their eggs and chicks to gull predation. In this wariness they are very different from South African gannets, which are distinguished only by the black tail feathers retained through adulthood.

Those do not make way for intruders but jab viciously at shins and ankles of anyone walking through their colony, even after the young have left the nests in late summer. So unconcerned are they that I have stroked the back of one fast asleep on a boulder, head tucked into the shoulder feathers, without waking it. Yet those are pushed around by teams of workers going through with spades and brooms scraping up the guano at the end of the nesting season, when most adults and a few tardy young are still on site.

Grassholm gannet eggs were greatly prized during the nineteenth century and fishermen would throw soiled eggs into the sea to persuade the birds to lay fresh ones in readiness for their next visit. Lort-Phillips found only twenty nests in 1883 when he visited the island to see if a former colony of roseate terns was still breeding there – alongside the 'thousands of puffins' which occupied almost the entire island. After choosing the emptiest looking patch for his small tent, he was awakened at about 3 a.m. by a curious grunting sound under his pillow and "There was Mr. or Mrs. Puffin, with a very grieved expression, sitting at the entrance of a burrow."

The timidity shown by Grassholm birds may be a legacy from this unhappier past, when they were establishing themselves. Robert Drane, founder member of the Cardiff Naturalists' Society, took a party to Grassholm in 1898 more than a century ago. In *Trans. Cardiff Nats.* xxxiii, 1900-1901, he writes as follows:

"On Grassholm the gannets had been raided by rapacious egg collectors, so that in one of their colonies there was nothing but deserted and rotting nests. Not a bird, not an egg was to be seen there. This was on June 7th and the following notes were made. It would seem that, generally speaking, the first week in June was too late for getting their eggs, which were now nearly all hatched, or about to be; many chicks were just breaking out of the shells, others, lately excluded, were lying in their nests, naked, leaden-black and ugly; others, further advanced, were covered with white down but still small, while some were as large as ducklings a month or five weeks old. This difference in age and development is striking, but becomes moreso when the fact that this state continues from the beginning of May to the end of August is realised."

Gannets diving.

He goes on to report that:

> "A certain person who collects eggs for dealers and had many times exhibited his brutal cruelty and indifference asked to join the party. When refused he asked one of the party to bring him a dozen or two eggs. When given only six he said he would go himself and if he could 'find no eggs he would chuck every young gannet into the sea!'"

Not very conducive to future anticipated harvests!

Wild birds still suffer from egg collectors in this enlightened age, but the gannet populations, at least, have got safely away. Drane refers to "one of their colonies", so it seems that they did not nest en masse in one block in the early days, despite their reluctance to nest beyond the bounds of the existing agglomeration, where each nest is but a pecking distance from the next. Some gannets which I have visited in the New World and the Antipodes, however, do occasionally space their nets quite widely with healthy green plant life intervening between them.

Rather than approach too closely, we liked to perch on the Grassholm summit, with wisps of moulted down settling on our persons like blown thistle heads, and watch the spectacular mass flights and meteoric dives for fish from heights of as much as thirty metres. The birds folded their wings as they descended, from a span of nearly two metres to a slender arrowhead as they entered the water – air sacs in the breast inflated to cushion the impact.

The pristine state of their feathers was maintained by careful preening and a prolonged bathing session on offshore waters when they came off duty from the increasingly fouled nests. Newly laid, pristine white eggs soon became soiled and brown.

Chicks which hatch are incredibly ugly at first, but in their initial naked phase they are brooded under the parent's big flat feet in contact with whatever lies below. Like the larger penguins, gannets lack the usual brood patch. By the time the white down sprouts, they are big enough to come out and face what the world has to offer in the way of weather, so a few become seriously fouled at this stage. The next plumage phase is a dark chequerboard except for the white belly.

By the first summer the head and neck are white. By the second the main wing and tail feathers are black with piebald contour feathers on wings and black flecks on the back. It takes four to five years for them to attain full adult plumage, when only the wingtips are black, the head a light yellow and the beak and eyes a cold china blue, the dark feathers getting fewer year by year, as in wandering albatrosses. With all the plumage variations, the tapered torpedo shape is quite characteristic. There is no mistaking a gannet.

Juvenile and adult birds may stay around the colony after the breeding season if the fishing is good, but Grassholm gannets have been recorded on summer food flights of as much as eighty, a hundred and forty and a hundred and sixty miles away from their island.

Recent work on the Bass Rock gannetry in the Firth of Forth has shown that the larger the colony, the further the component members

Juvenile Gannets, first and second year plumage.

have to go on their fishing trips. Prey fish may retreat outwards, away from the centre of predation, or downwards, below reach. As the Bass colony has expanded in numbers, the duration of fishing trips has increased from fewer than ten hours away to more than fifteen hours in the larger colony of the year 2001 (Sue Lewis, *BBC Wildlife Magazine*, February, 2002).

Only when we visited late in the season did we see the plump young gannets sitting around on the sea looking somewhat forlorn. They were too buoyant to submerge to chase fish and too portly to fly aloft to gain the impetus to dive for them, like their parents. Their early days away from the nest were hard until they lost enough weight to get airborne. Soon after finding out how to feed themselves, they were likely to be heading for African waters.

In contrast to their personal good looks, the colony was the last word in sea-bird slums, with no blade of grass surviving between the noisesome piles to relieve the squalor. Unlike some bird species, this seems not to worry them. When over-population in the foregoing puffin slum came to a head, the occupants had to move out, as gulls and others which like a modicum of plant cover have to when pressure of numbers destroys this.

Gannets need no cover and it seems likely that they will go on occupying their area until numbers are such that some have to leave because of lack of space. It is easy to picture a rogue gale sneaking into the cheek-by-jowl entrances to the puffin burrows and lifting the fragile roofs. Gannets add to their substrate rather than detracting from it. Nests can be up to half a metre high, the grassy building material and increasingly now, seaweeds, becoming incorporated into a cement-like, wind-resistant mass with the guano. The resulting soil is white and spongy, sinking underfoot, with apparently little of the fibrous plant material surviving decay for long.

Soil of the Puffin Pompei examined in the 1940s was much peatier, with forty-five per cent of combustible matter in air-dried samples Sea salt and other mineral nutrients were high, concentrated during the summer droughts of 1949 and 1950, to levels lethal to most plants. Seedlings of orache and a little residual fescue were the only ones found in the early years. In deeper marginal burrows and larger bomb craters in 1951 others survived – rock spurrey, dwarf mouse-ear chickweed, Yorkshire fog and the special succulent variety of buck's-horn plantain. This last is much the most remarkable of Grassholm's land plants and

Puffin Pompei in the early 1950s.

was referred to in chapter two, on our visit to the Skokholm Stack. It romps away on Grassholm, unhindered by grazing animals, its fleshy 25-35cm high leaves overtopped by tall flower spikes. The plant map shows it as dominant in the south, but individual plants are scattered throughout. In good growing seasons leaves can be 5.5cm wide and 0.33cm thick, their tips like the prow of a boat and sometimes hooded., but in dry years they are smaller and fruit earlier. None of the common hairy buck's-horn plantain occurs.

The red fescue (*Festuca rubra ssp. duriuscula*) areas shown on the 1950 Grassholm map are virtually monocultures, with few other species present and these in very small amounts. On Skokholm, the same fescue, closely grazed, is still dominant in parts and might be mapped similarly, but is dominant only by virtue of covering a third of the ground. Its twenty or thirty associates are all less abundant and few, it seems, would be able to persist if the fescue was allowed to grow un-checked. That is dominance by default – the superior species rigorously curtailed but curtailed just that much less than its competitors.

Thick woolly mats of Yorkshire fog grass, Grassholm's second com-monest species, fill the hollows, including the old bomb craters. These are often in the lee of basalt outcrops, on which English stonecrop is

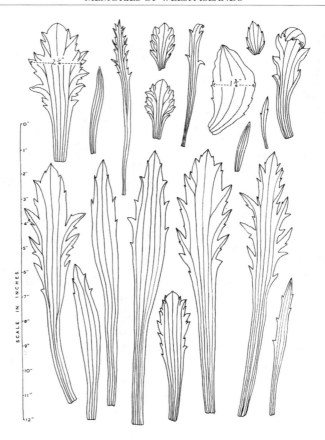

Succulent Buck's-horn Plantain, outsize leaves.

spared harassment by the more robust. Babington's orache is a late summer annual, appearing in June. It does a Box and Cox act with common and Danish scurvy grass, which come to fruition early in the year and then die down. Spurrey and chickweed take the brunt of the flying spray.

Toad rush, the only true marsh plant, is excluded from the north-western seepage by the high mineral content and huddles among the fog, with curled dock, another of wetland habitats. Tree mallow flowers well, at over a metre high in the east, but seldom advances beyond the four-leaf stage in the exposed west.

Only twelve species of higher plants found were of any importance in those early years and probably fewer now. Surprisingly I found no thrift, which would have dominated this sort of site had there been grazing to check the smothering fescue. Heavy puffin or shearwater traffic also favours thrift and Ronald Lockley had recorded "a few sea pinks" prior to 1947, so it was not a matter of non-availability of seed.

Other plants were casuals, mostly on the gull feeding grounds where seeds from the mainland could have been coughed up in crop pellets. These were buttercup, scarlet pimpernel, knot grass, greater plantain, sea mayweed, sow thistle and annual meadow grass. Inevitably there were flowerless plants. Mosses included *Dicranella heteromalla*, *Eurhynchium praelongun* and *Webera sp*. Among the lichens were *Ramalina cuspidata*,

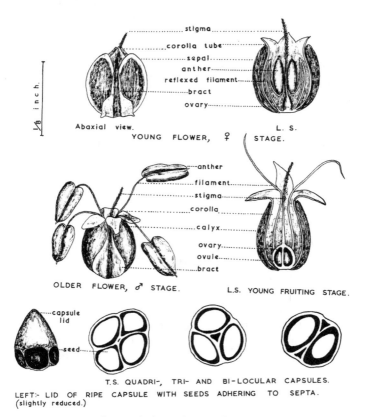

Succulent Buck's-horn Plantain, flower structure.

Cladonia pyxidata, Buellia canescens, Evernia, Lecanora, Lecidea and *Parmelia,* as well as the black and orange species of the splash zone.

The orange belt is particularly well marked, with the pimply Caloplaca cleaving tightly to the rock throughout the lower levels and the wavy-edged fronds of Xanthoria, slightly raised from the surface and more ebullient, further from the splash zone. Both genera benefit from guano spilled by passing birds.

This land vegetation is historically significant as the interim stage between the Puffin Pompei that had been and the gargantuan gannetry that was to come. Great Britain and Ireland host most of Europe's share of North Atlantic gannets, many of which are around Scotland. Grassholm is the only colony in Wales while the one English site, unusually, is not on an offshore island but on Yorkshire's Bempton Cliffs.

After gazing our fill on the heaving, caterwauling metropolis, we would disperse to see what else the island had to offer. The area round the West Tump was rich in razorbills and guillemots, in more accessible places than usual. Chicks escaped an approaching hand by trying to climb the wall behind, instead of pecking at the intrusion like the more human-orientated Skokholm birds.

Both shags and cormorants were plentiful. Kittiwakes, absent from Skokholm at that time, were again in more accessible sites, often on flat slabs. Many in the west were closely associated with lush but necessarily damaged scurvy grass nourished by past and present excreta soaked into the substance of the grassy nests. More flourished at the foot of the breeding cliffs, the smaller Danish scurvy grass as guano-tolerant as the larger one.

Crisply frilled Prasiola algae, spurrey and orache completed this community, while fouled drainage pools swarmed with motile yellow-green Euglenoid organisms, which sometimes became aggregated into star-shaped clusters floating on the fouled brown water.

All three of the larger gulls were present, the herring gulls seeming to be the main predators on the gannet colony, breaking and consuming eggs on the spot. When making a hurried exodus, the gannets would regurgitate their last meal to lighten the load for take-off. Neither chick nor returned adult would re-ingest these fish, which remained as another incentive to attract marauding gulls. As with many others, a fish has to be swimming to appear as prey and trigger the correct response. Gulls are among the most intelligent and adaptable of birds and are not held back by any such inhibitions.

Great black-backs occupied dominating positions on the high ground, standing among a litter of fish bones, crab carapaces and mollusc shells left over from recent meals. Around five pairs of oyster-catchers were seen most summers, these carrying limpet shells up from below the breeding cliffs, and it was not uncommon to come upon their delightful fluffy youngsters, which cooperated so well with photographers by 'freezing' in response to warning parental calls.

A pair of rock pipits was usually present, the nest tucked into a crevice. Shearwaters, although not breeding, were usually to be seen winging over the sea with their inimitable swaying flight, showing first black and then white as they wheeled in unison, their wingtips shearing the waves.

Seaweeds are very much those of exposed coasts, even on the lee shore and in the eastern guts where it was easiest to search for them. The narrow, wingless wrack, *Fucus anceps*, stood in for other wracks in turbulence even wilder than that tolerated by the bladderless form of bladder wrack.

Edible Scottish tang, Irish carragheen (only Gigartina) and Welsh laver grew thickly among the upper fingered oarweed. Thongweed (*Himanthalea elongata* or *lorea*) was common, as on the inner islands, some of the plants here having the vegetative 'buttons' inflated into walnut-sized hollow spheres instead of the usual dummy shape. Yellow rather than brown, their gaseous centres caused these rubbery 'ping pong balls' to pop to the surface if detached. Those collecting as drift showed no sign of having given rise to the usual vegetative thongs. My list from fifty years ago included seventeen of the larger brown weeds and fourteen reds.

Particularly abundant in the rock cracks were beadlet anemones. Dahlia anemones (*Taelia felina*), common Aurelia jellyfish, mussells and Sertularia firweed or whiteweed, which are colonial animals, were much in evidence.

And then, of course, there were the grey Atlantic seals, usually between twenty and thirty. These too favoured the western shore for pulling out to sun themselves, where they remained, even when well aware that there were strangers on their seagirt stronghold. On a 1949 visit there were twenty-three on the north-west corner and two youngsters about nine months old on the rocks where we landed.

Some in the water were bottling, remaining quite erect with nose pointing straight up as they slept. I never tired of watching how they hung so demurely, swaying only gently as big swells passed them by to

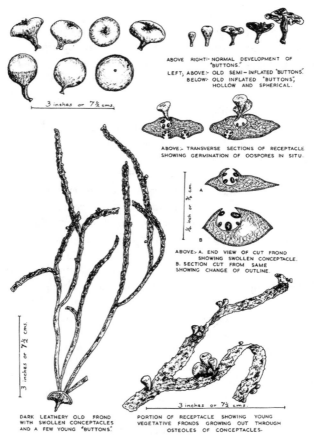

ABOVE RIGHT:- NORMAL DEVELOPMENT OF 'BUTTONS.'
LEFT, ABOVE:- OLD SEMI-INFLATED 'BUTTONS'.
BELOW:- OLD INFLATED 'BUTTONS', HOLLOW AND SPHERICAL.

3 inches or 7½ cms.

ABOVE:- TRANSVERSE SECTIONS OF RECEPTACLE SHOWING GERMINATION OF OOSPORES IN SITU.

¼ inch or ⅔ cm.

A

B

ABOVE:- A. END VIEW OF CUT FROND SHOWING SWOLLEN CONCEPTACLE.
B. SECTION CUT FROM SAME SHOWING CHANGE OF OUTLINE.

3 inches or 7½ cms.

3 inches or 7½ cms.

DARK LEATHERY OLD FROND WITH SWOLLEN CONCEPTACLES AND A FEW YOUNG 'BUTTONS'.

PORTION OF RECEPTACLE SHOWING YOUNG VEGETATIVE FRONDS GROWING OUT THROUGH OSTEOLES OF CONCEPTACLES.

Thongweed with inflated 'buttons'.

crash on the rocks beyond. A few years later, on board the *Rangitoto* en route for New Zealand, I discovered their secret. In heavy seas water in the ship's swimming pool slopped from side to side, swishing up the edges to rain down on the centre. Hanging vertically, like the seals, I maintained position amidships with no trouble. When I came up to the horizontal, like a rudderless dinghy, I was swept sideways and in danger of hitting the walls. I had learned something, but how I wished I could emulate the seals' dexterity in twisting and turning under water. That, I fear, was not to be.

9.

SKOMER: VISITS, HISTORY, MAMMALS AND SEA-BIRDS

Skomer is, to all intents and purposes, a larger version of Skokholm. Lying off the end of the Marloes Peninsula, it is visible from the coast to both north and south. Stand on the great empty stretch of Newgale Sands and the view to the south-west is beguiling in the extreme. Half-way along, some six miles away, are the impressive stacks at the south end of St. Brides Bay. Another five miles reveals the Old Deer Park to seaward of Martin's Haven, with the dot of Middleholm between this and the enticing land mass of Skomer, just asking to be visited.

Middleholm at 21.5 acres is about the same size as Grassholm. Skomer occupies 720 acres (292 hectares), as opposed to Skokholm's 262 acres. Although the two larger islands have a lot in common as regards their plants and animals, Skomer's colours are more subdued. The rock is a cold, grey basalt instead of the warm red sandstone of the other, which contrasts so brilliantly with the blue of the sea below and the encircling orange belt of lichens above the tide mark.

The larger island is known to more people, because of the long tradition of day trips available over the last four decades, sometimes three boatloads of tourists being landed in a single day. A 1999 publication stated that as many as 250 visitors can be landed on busy days!

It is possible to stay for longer periods, self-catering in the 'chalets' of the derelict farm, but the close community spirit experienced on Skokholm is never quite as warm. This may be because of the repeated invasion of day trippers or because the warden's house on the clifftop is almost a mile from the residential block in the old stables or cow byres by the farmyard, and there is no cook bringing everyone together at meals, each pair of stable mates fending for itself.

I, too, have been a day tripper, but never able to do the island justice in so brief a visit. The lesser sister island is just the right size to get a good idea of the lie of the land in a single day. Skomer needs a lot longer. Such opportunities I have enjoyed on a number of occasions when taking

Peter Conder's 'Sea Swallow' off North Skokholm.

parties across for a week or a long weekend during the 1960s and 1970s, these visits the more exciting because of my long acquaintance with the other, providing opportunity to compare and contrast. The prospect of visiting was so popular, that I often had to double up on any trip advertised in Cardiff.

In the early days we sailed from Dale Fort, as for Skokholm, but in later years from Martin's Haven with Alf Knowles – a shorter journey to Skomer's North Haven and avoiding the hazards of Jack Sound. Sometimes we went direct from Skokholm. On one occasion I had the privilege of sailing there with Peter Conder in his new twelve foot sailing dinghy, the *Sea Swallow*.

Possession of this was a dream come true for him, but it was a relatively short-lived one. The sea was seldom smooth enough to take the fragile craft out and the business of heaving her to a safe distance above hungrily licking waves was a constant worry. Even in sheltered havens boat owners seem to spend more time painting, polishing and preening their craft ashore than out on the briny. Peter, as warden, had other things to occupy his time.

On Sunday, 19th July, 1953, the weather seemed right for him to attempt his first landing at a place other than our South Haven, so we set off early, hauling *Sea Swallow* in from her fair weather mooring on a circular rope between the two walls of the Haven. Peter rigged the tackle while I hung on and he rowed well out from the rocks before erecting the jib and mainsail.

Wind and tide were in our favour and we sailed serenely along the south side of the Neck, rounded the Stack and set off across the two mile wide Broad Sound. The Atlantic swell was uncharacteristically gentle and we made Skomer's South Haven without mishap. Landing here proved not so easy that we could leave the boat unattended, so Peter decided to stay aboard for his spell of puffin watching. Ominous clouds were gathering inexorably on the western horizon and the wind was freshening. He gave me until four o'clock ashore unless I saw the weather deteriorating or his signal of a hoisted jib calling me back. I jumped ashore with sandwiches, thermos and notebook and scrambled up through the puffin burrows and bracken to the narrow isthmus that separated the main island plateau from the eastern Neck.

With one eye on the wind, I hastened westwards, nose to ground, as is the way with botanists, writing and listing furiously. My time ashore was obviously going to be foreshortened so I abandoned the idea of lunch, concentrating on the regeneration of the old ploughlands and a recently burned heather heath. Where the two communities converged, it was interesting to see heather colonising the old plough ridges and marsh thistle the furrows between. Fortunately my head was bent to the task in hand and not assessing the gathering clouds when a lesser black-backed gull scored a direct hit, which whitened my hair, the offending matter washed off by rain and spray during our return voyage.

Soon after 2 p.m. I realised my time was up and returned to see Peter hauling up the jib. The increased swell was very apparent when he rowed in to collect me. He decided we should run for it with the outboard motor, as it would be too tricky to sail. I took over the oars while he got the motor up and running and then settled to a bite of lunch.

Just clear of the Haven the outboard popped ominously and petered out, as outboards will, and it continued to do so as often as the skipper got it started again, due, he thought, to an obstruction in the petrol feed. He primed and reprimed, but we progressed only about half a mile in the next half hour, in short stages of 25-50 yards. All was well when we were moving but the frequent spells of idle rolling put me right off the idea of lunch. Peter's mal de mer was delayed until after we got ashore when he complained that immovable objects were going up and down.

The possibility of drifting back to Skomer had its attractions, but the idea of a derelict farmhouse on an uninhabited island and a depression which looked likely to linger for as much as a week, took the gilt off that option. There was nothing for it but to sail.

Puffins among peat mounds.

While Peter swapped outboard for rudder and put down the centre board, I hoisted the jib, lost such lunch as I had managed to swallow and helped to take a second reef in the mainsail. We elevated it as little as possible but could get the sail area no smaller. There were times when the crest of a wave was coming in on the windward side as a trough was entering on the leeward.

We were being blown well off course and had to tack back westwards repeatedly to make up the leeway. Twice Peter decided we should have to run the gauntlet of Jack Sound and make for Martin's Haven, but each time we tried again and made a little headway. Had we gone to the mainland, it would have been a week before we could get back to the island without a craft a lot stouter than *Sea Swallow*.

It rained, of course, and we were soon drenched with a mixture of fresh and salt water, hands so frozen that I obeyed instructions to haul as tightly as possible with difficulty. Peter talked of hot baths and hot crumpets as the water streamed down inside our collars. Half a kettle of hot water each was all that we could hope for on the first count. The crumpets didn't interest me at the time.

At one point we found ourselves unable to avoid a string of lobster pots which we picked up on the centre board and trailed along like a sea anchor, but managed to lose by slowing down and getting busy with the boat hook.

It was clear that if we tried to round the Skokholm Stack to make South Haven we might well finish up on Gateholm or St. Ann's, so we tacked into the north coast. Letting the two sails down simultaneously in a confused heap, Peter rowed hard for the shore while I shipped centre board and rudder. We ran in among the boulders near North Haven and I hopped out and guided our gallant little craft in. She was moored temporarily and a team came down with extra ropes at the turn of the tide to make her more secure.

We would certainly not have been spending the night on Skokholm if I had lingered on the other island till four. It was bliss to be warm and dry and fed again, but not for the world would I have missed our little adventure. My first sailing lesson was one to remember and now, reading my journal, it seems but yesterday.

I was with a friend at Solva on Regatta day a while later to cheer Peter in with *Sea Swallow*. He had hoped to get a lift from Skokholm but the *Cubango* had failed to materialise. Most other contestants had come from Fishguard or Little Haven, the crimson sails of the West of England redwings in the majority. The St. David's lifeboat joined in the fun, decorated from stem to stern with flags and with the crewmen's wives and families aboard.

*   *   *

My impressions of Skomer were acquired piecemeal over the next thirty years, when Cardiff groups took over the old cow byres and enjoyed alfresco living to the full. Memories range from kicking a football round the rabbit-mown farmyard (to the consternation of the resident hens) to the crooning of soft nothings at the seals gathered about the Garland Stone in the north, to be answered in kind.

Most members of my parties were new to island life and it was gratifying to see how delightedly they responded to it, with never a misfit hankering after the 'civilisation' left behind. That island magic was not

Football in the Skomer farmyard. The author in the 1970s.

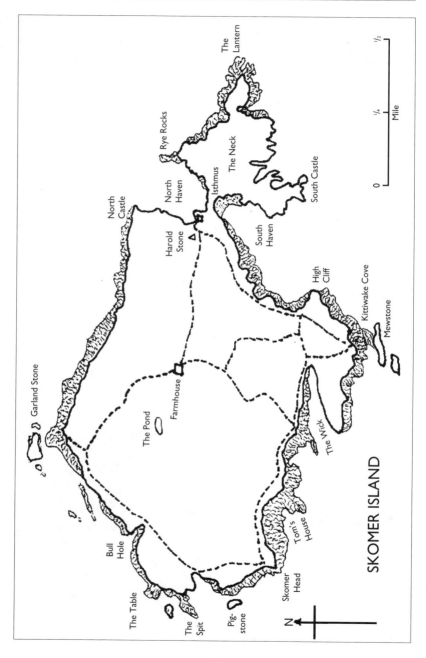

SKOMER ISLAND

The Lantern

Rye Rocks

The Neck

North Castle

North Haven

Isthmus

South Castle

Harold Stone

South Haven

High Cliff

Kittiwake Cove

Garland Stone

Mewstone

The Pond

Farmhouse

The Wick

Bull Hole

Tom's House

The Table

Skomer Head

The Spit

Pig-stone

N

0   ¼   ½
Mile

wholly confined to Skokholm and Grassholm. Had those who lived here as far back as Neolithic times felt it, or had they been too busy wresting a living from its green acres and the sea around? Skomer, being the more accessible, was settled earlier than Skokholm and has been cited as probably the largest unmolested prehistoric site in Great Britain. Robert Drane of Cardiff Naturalists' Society fame, who seems to have made quite a habit of visiting the islands, excavated a prehistoric hutment in the North Valley in 1906.

Professor Grimes delved further into the island's past during the 1940s and John Evans of Cardiff University's Archaeology Department followed up on his findings, leading exploratory digs of the stone circles that lay scarcely hidden among the bracken and wood sage. (J. G. Evans (1986) *Prehistoric Farmers of Skomer Island*. W.W.N.T.). He remarked that the wide scatter of 100,000 pairs of burrowing shearwaters was a hindrance rather than a help, but he undertook his investigations before the onset of the nesting season.

In Palaeolithic times Jack Sound, between Middleholm and the mainland would have been dry land – just part of the long ridge of igneous rock stretching west from Pembrokeshire. Most of this is now a submerged reef, culminating in the Smalls, fifteen miles west of Skomer, with their impregnable lighthouse. The Hats and Barrels are upstanding sections of the reef between the Smalls and Grassholm. They break surface at low tide but are an invisible hazard to shipping at high. Old Red Sandstone flanks this intrusion to north and south, as shown by the red cliffs to either side of the Deer Park.

In Neolithic times Skomer and Middleholm were cut off by rising sea level, as a plateau some two hundred feet high. (The vertical cliff of the Wick is said to be two hundred feet itself.) Any aurochs (oxen), red deer or others stranded on the newly severed land would either have retreated to the mainland or died eventually of starvation or inbreeding. Middleholm broke away from Skomer much later and a promontory fort was constructed on the tip of the Skomer Neck facing towards the mainland, a strategic lookout point.

The imposing block of the Harold Stone which visitors pass on their way up from the most commonly used landing place of North Haven, is something of an enigma. Its date is unknown, but John Evans thinks it was likely to have been erected as a sea mark to guide early navigators into the haven.

Iron Age and Romano-British sheep shears have been found, so the early shepherds were cutting wool rather than rooing it, suggesting that at least some of their sheep were neither the Soay nor the Shetland breed. Seven prehistoric dams have been located across the streams, creating reservoirs. Experts are divided as to whether these were from the Iron Age or the earlier Bronze Age.

Two-thirds of the periphery of the island was not cultivated in the nineteenth and twentieth centuries, but there are traces of old field systems among the ancient hut circles there from an Iron Age community that must have numbered about two hundred souls. Natural rock outcrops run from east to west across the plateau and were incorporated in the old walls. Soil alongside these is necessarily shallower and poorer, but that of the cultivated fields was treated with lime, burned in kilns on the island, and is a rich, deep loam.

Peat is present in the valleys, but contains no recognisable plant remains and cannot be used for pollen analysis, but was no doubt dug for fuel. If scrub oak or other substantial woody plants ever existed they are unlikely to have cohabited with the livestock for very long. So-called 'woodland relict' plants like bluebell and red campion now grow in the old fields, not where any marginal woods are likely to have been.

As on Skokholm, the island was a rabbit farm from the early fourteenth century, rabbits having been introduced in the thirteenth. Ferrets were employed in the catching and the colonial sea-birds and their eggs would also have been exploited.

Working mainly from aerial photos, John Evans thought that the northern stream valley was probably commonland and never ploughed up for crops, current vegetation of about a hundred acres being of purple moor grass, suggesting a soil water content above optimum for cultivation. The two artificial ponds are unaltered since prehistoric times. Similar artefacts are present in the east, west and south, strengthening the belief that only the centre was farmed during the last two centuries.

By the middle of the twentieth century the big old farmhouse in the island centre was in ruins, but it is thought to have been the nucleus of up to about twenty residents in the middle of the nineteenth century. Reuben Codd, later the Dale Fort boatman, was the last to farm on the island, but his endeavours ceased in 1950, although sheep continued to graze the salted acres. A great storm in 1954 damaged the farmhouse roof and the building was out of bounds on safety grounds after that.

There were plenty of major projects achieved over the years, as well as the usual chores like chopping wood, clearing nettles, mending traps and burning rubbish. A task force from Aberystwyth spent a week in 1981 working on the footpaths, repairing the tractor track from harbour to farmhouse and re-fencing rabbit exclosures.

Personnel from the naval-air station at RAF Brawdy on the nearby mainland spent three weeks of that April mending the quay in North Haven with thirty tons of sand and aggregates bagged up for shipment by boys from 'Community Industry'. Brawdy volunteers had been instrumental in renovating it sixteen years earlier, in September 1965, carrying ashore six tons of cement and sand in forty pound bags during neap tides, when the concrete was least likely to wash away before setting.

The six visitor chalets prepared by Reuben Codd in the farm outbuildings for visitors, are said to have been replaced by two small rooms accommodating six people by the mid-1990s, and an 'Information room' has materialised.

A major rebuilding programme was inaugurated in 1999. The hundred and fifty-year-old buildings, of which little more than the outer, slate-faced, stone walls remained, were to be renovated with traditional local stone and slate, but necessary building materials would have to be flown in by helicopter this time. The limited water supply and absence of mains electricity would be no help.

Because of erosion on the isthmus above North Haven, the warden's timber house would have to be moved back ten metres. The instability was accentuated by a cliff fall above the landing in the winter of 2001-2.

*   *   *

The only other livestock on the island around 1964-66 were a small flock of Soay sheep, Amos and Amy, the pet goats which hovered around the warden's house and a bony, long legged horse, very different from the dumpling Sugarback of Skokholm. Soay sheep have minds of their own: they are wild animals, impossible to herd and are said to be enough to break a sheep dog's heart!

An example of selective grazing by Amos, the Billy, was when he pushed open the warden's door, spotted a reprint of my *Effects of Grazing Animals on Vegetation*, pulled it down and started chewing jubilantly. I had said a few hard things about the omnivorous propensities of goats in that paper. It seemed he was getting his own back.

Amos, two and a half years old in 1966, was shaggy coated and piebald, making up for his lack of horns with an extra long beard. His spouse, Amy, was smooth coated and white, as Skokholm's Rowena was to her

Skomer Vole and Ground Ivy.

shaggy consort, Ivanhoe. They were tethered by day and turned loose at night, remaining around the house unless they went walkabout with David Saunders, the current warden and later director of the West Wales (Dyfed) Wildlife Trust for the fourteen years from 1976 to 1999 and still chief of the 'Friends of Skokholm and Skomer' in 2002.

Part of his 1966 household was a six-month-old ginger kitten, who would come through the window in the early morning, shaking the dew from his paws onto my bed when I was billeted there, and leaving to spreadeagle himself on the warden's table in the sunshine. He spent a lot of time puffin watching, but turned tail if an inquisitive bird came too close. A menace only to voles, he would play with the ones he caught quite gently, but would growl ominously at those who rescued them from his capers.

Only semi-domesticated were the non message carrying carrier pigeons which cadged food around the chalets and sheltered by the Elsans. A lingering memory of those chalets is the slowness of the Calor gas stove by which we cooked. Light it on rising in the morning and the kettle would boil for early morning tea an hour and a half later!

Rabbits are at an all time high on Skomer, as on most other islands except for occasional checks – as Reuben Codd, who farmed it from 1930 to 1950, knew only too well. It is on record that he and his lurcher bitch, Bella, caught a hundred and ninety rabbits in one night by lamping – from 6.30 p.m. to 5.30 a.m. How could any man have that amount of stamina?

Skomer Vole's nest.

Skomer's rabbits, unlike Skokholm's, harbour rabbit fleas, the vectors of Myxomatosis, so they suffered the same catastrophic mortality as mainland animals in the mid 1950s. As always, enough survived to build up to a comfortable level of food availability and they had taken over the island grazings again in a big way by 1963.

Some twelve years later a large rabbit exclosure was fenced off in the west between Skomer Head and the Pigstone. By 1976 the original thrift inside had been overrun in all but the south-west corner which sloped into the prevailing wind. Most was smothered by two foot high flowering red fescue grass with a little common sorrel and Yorkshire fog. The lushness inside the fence seemed the more dramatic because all around had been bleached to the colour of straw by the 1976 drought – which was a repeat of the 1975 one. A few years later rabbits broke in and the mattress of dead fescue was not replenished.

Rabbits seemed to be at the maximum holding capacity of their individual territories in many areas, but patches of decent plant cover survived in between, accentuating their strong home ties. Those left unscathed by the disease built up an immunity, so subsequent Myxomatosis outbreaks lay low only the few. The rabbit story is no less complex here than anywhere else.

The small creature with the greatest claim to fame on this island is the Skomer vole, about which a number of scientific papers have been published, not least the one by Fullager, Jewell, Lockley and Rowlands in *Proc. Zool. Soc. Lond.,* V 140, March 1963.

These authors caught similar numbers of Skomer voles and long-tailed field mice in their live traps – two hundred and thirty voles and two hundred and twenty mice – and found that voles favoured the denser cover of tall bracken and the borders of old walls, while mice were more numerous in open sites, on cliffs and bluffs,

Robert Drane was the first to point out the difference of the vole from the mainland type, and he is credited with its discovery. He set out to prove that it was a distinct species and opinion is still somewhat divided as to whether it is specifically or only sub-specifically different.

During his 1898 lecture to the Cardiff Naturalists' Society referred to in the Grassholm chapter, he produced some live animals, pointing out that the five specimens he had brought back from his last visit to Skomer had increased to forty-seven, and proved exceptionally tame. He also produced the corpse of a female, with five seven day old youngsters attached to her nipples. He waxed poetical regarding these, in the language of his time.

"They were in a truly pitiful plight. I felt it would be useless to attempt to rear them and therefore administered chloroform. Try to visualise this pathetic scene. There was the dead mother at her maternal post and there the hapless young. Could human mother have done more?"

In spite of all those eggs collected and specimens shot in the name of science, he had a soft spot.

Clethrionomys skomerensis differs from the bank vole of the mainland principally in its larger size and heavier skull. Island animals proved a third heavier than mainland ones. Sexually mature females weigh 24gm and 14gm respectively, while the maximum weight of adult males is 39gm and 30gm – much less (22gm and 12gm) at the end of winter.

Size and reproduction were studied by I. W. Rowlands during eight years of the 1960s (*Nature in Wales*, 11, 4, 1969). The fact that island voles start to breed two to three weeks later than mainland ones was not regarded as significant, the reproductive capacity of both being similar. Before taking samples (25 females and 15 males per month between March and November in 1961) he estimated the population and found it to exceed twenty thousand animals, leaving a safe margin for investigation.

Young animals are small and grey, the characteristic red-brown fur and more robust dimensions being their breeding finery. Females give birth from late May to late August, some conceiving their next litter while still suckling the one before. If doing this throughout the year, one dam could produce a maximum of five litters averaging four young each and totalling twenty. This number is halved if conception is delayed until after weaning, giving a total of only nine young. Gestation lasts nineteen to twenty days, slightly more if this starts before weaning of the last, with an estimated nine to fourteen young per year.

Sexual activity continues until the end of October, but there is no implantation of the embryos after the end of August. Youngsters born early in the season can produce a litter of their own before winter clamps down. Late arrivals have to overwinter and bear their first brood when their older siblings are bearing their second. This reproductive regime, set against the natural hazards of predation and other mishaps, serves to keep numbers steady, with none of the lemming style population explosions seen in some other vole species.

Skomer voles are not hard to see. I seldom went to the mossy well near the farmhouse to collect drinking water without spying one in the dripping undergrowth nearby. Place cupped hands in one of their surface runs (which are used also by shrews) when a vole was approaching and it was likely to keep going and snuggle into the warm haven so formed.

The red-brown waif sitting in the palm of my hand preening his whiskers like the most beguiling kitten, seemed much too innocent to take the blame for gnawing the hole in my rucksack to get at the Mars bar secreted within. That, surely, must have been the work of the sharper-nosed, perky-eared field mouse.

Plenty of both species scuttled round the farmyard, sharing the corn and other goodies intended for the free range poultry. Good cover was afforded among the nettles by the big rain water tank where we took our enamel bowls for morning ablutions – a shady site under the low-swept boughs of the black poplar that huddled in the shelter of the buildings.

Poking among the plants further afield, as was my wont, I came upon a cosy vole's nest tucked against the base of a bluebell clump, Bright brown eyes peered up at me from behind the bristly nose, but there was no attempt to flee.

Like his kind elsewhere, the Skomer vole eats green plant matter as well as seeds and fruits. A surprising favourite on Skomer is said to be ground ivy, a plant which thrives under bracken and is particularly abundant in rabbit warrens, where it is patently not eaten by the rabbits. It appears coarse and hairy, the hairs holding on to dust and soil from scuffling animals, making it seem even more unpalatable than others of its dead nettle family with their aromatic and usually distasteful oils. Some say it is rich in protein.

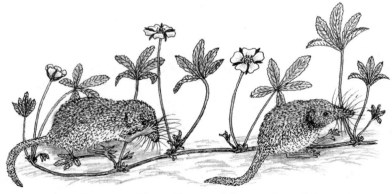

Common and Pygmy Shrews and Creeping Cinquefoil.

A vole caught in a Longworth live trap in 2001 gave birth to her litter there. The door was left open for her to take the naked pink morsels somewhere more appropriate. The breed's apparent tameness seems to be an adaptation to the sort of predation to which animals are subjected. On the mainland a vole's worst foes are stoat, weasel, mink and fox, which smell them out, so that their best strategy is to escape as fast as their little legs will carry them.

On Skomer there are no mammalian predators. The chief enemies are owls and kestrels, which are alerted by movement, so the best strategy is to lie still, even in the palm of a potential enemy's hand. Has the resulting saving in energy contributed to their larger size, one wonders? The voles do not fight as readily as do the more nimble field mice, as those who have handled both know only too well.

In the 1960s four pairs of short-eared owls nested on Skomer, though in many years it is fewer. There are other owls and diurnal birds of prey but the buzzards prefer the heartier meals supplied by young rabbits – the ecological tool controlling their habitat.

In 1973 Colin Plant made a study of the winter diet of the barn owl on Skomer. He deduced that the bird did not make feeding forays to the mainland or Skokholm but gained all its prey on Skomer. An analysis of forty-six owl pellets showed remains of fifty-five Skomer voles, twenty-three frogs, eleven common shrews, ten pygmy shrews, five field mice and three starlings.

The frogs were particularly thick on the ground around North Pond at spawning time in February and March where the owl was often seen hunting. This is a nice example of opportunist feeding, but the cool coating of slime seems a poor substitute for the furry or feathery roughage said to be an essential component in the feeding of captive owls.

The diet changes seasonally. A previous 1971 analysis by Twigg of summer barn owl pellets revealed prey items as a hundred and eighty-nine Skomer voles, sixty-seven field mice and eighteen common shrews. The absence of house mice (the only small rodents present on Skokholm but absent from Skomer) and of the mainland bank and short-tailed field voles show that the owl was adequately sustained on the island, despite competition from other owls and kestrels.

Other potential prey present on Skomer are toads, palmate newts – seven of which were sometime present together in the well – slow worms, common lizards and small ground birds. A good place to seek both Skomer voles and slow worms is under discarded sheets of corrugated iron, which have built-in tunnels of the right size and trap the sun's warmth.

*   *   *

Skomer life is becoming more high tech of late. Skomer voles are being radio-tracked in the previous privacy of their runways. Shearwaters and storm petrels are having tape-recorded messages in their own language played at the mouth of their burrows, to see if they are at home. Only the males respond, so this is not a very reliable census tool.

Nest boxes are being supplied for both species to facilitate monitoring. Sixteen shearwater boxes were in place in the warden's cellar as early as 1959 but only four were used. Viewing them in 1963, I was told that the same birds had been in residence each year so far except for one change of partner. Only three were in use in 1969. Later the boxes were removed and the birds had the run of the cellar – their nocturnal whoops a distraction to the folk trying to sleep above.

Others nested in dark outbuildings near the farmhouse, crowing loudly on moonlight nights and no doubt wondering why their partners did not appears, thinking that it was 'dark as usual'. No puffins used the warden's nest boxes, but they were not averse to using artificial holes – as witnessed by the startled bird that came clattering down his chimney on one occasion. In the Welsh Valleys, my home territory, it is jackdaws which do this.

1999 saw the fullest survey yet of petrel numbers. The Manx shearwater population was confirmed at around 150,000 pairs or 75% of the world population, divided between the three islands, with 102,000 on Skomer, 46,000 on Skokholm and 3,000 on Middleholm. One of the most visually delightful shearwater colonies on Skomer is among the deep flowering thrift at the eastern head of the Wick Gully, with puffins covering the rounded slope to the north and guillemots, razorbills and kittiwakes plastering the vertical face to the south.

Storm petrels, flitting bat-like along the walls before the main influx of returning shearwaters, are far fewer on Skomer than Skokholm, at around seventy-five pairs in the early sixties, but increasing.

Birkhead and Ashcroft (*Nature in Wales*, 14, 4, 1975) recorded a general decline in guillemot and razorbill populations between 1963 and 1974 on Skomer, with puffins fewer than they had been thirty to fifty years before. Guillemot numbers hovered just below the five thousand

Kittiwakes, adult and two juveniles.

mark (individuals, not pairs) from 1963 to 1967, plummeting to below two thousand three hundred in 1969, with recovery to less than four thousand. Razorbill pairs numbered two thousand or more from 1963 to 1965 and around fifteen hundred from then to 1974.

I was interested to come across two light phase razorbills with medium brown plumage and buff throat in both 1963 and 1964, by the Garland Stone and further along the north coast. They were accepted by their fellows with no scuffling

We are so used to seeing nesting pairs of fulmar petrels scattered along mainland cliffs nowadays, in fairly public sites that could never accommodate auks, that we tend to take them for granted. It was not always so. In my early days around the islands none were nesting, although pairs were prospecting along the mainland cliffs from the 1930s (Fisher, *The Fulmar*, 1952).

The first fulmar egg seen was on Skomer in 1949, the first chick known to hatch was reported by John Fursdon on the north coast near Mathry in 1950, the year when Ronald Lockley saw an egg on the south coast. By the 1960s fulmars were a familiar sight patrolling off the Garland Stone. By 1976 there were breeding colonies in seventeen ten kilometre squares (Sharrock, *Atlas of Breeding Birds of GB and Ireland*, 1976).

Six pairs brought off chicks successfully on Skomer in 1958, subsequent increases monitored by the warden, David Saunders, who saw twenty-one chicks fledged in 1963 and twenty-five in 1965. A hundred and three pairs were nesting by 1973, two hundred and eighteen pairs by 1976 and a hundred and ninety pairs by 1977.

The first fulmar was not seen ashore on Skokholm until 1965, the number of breeding pairs reaching only to sixteen by 1976 (*Skokholm Annual Bird Observatory Reports*).

There was a small cormorant colony in Skomer's south-west in the early 1960s and erratic nesting on the Mewstone. A few shags nest on cliffs and spread their wings to dry on sea-washed rocks after fishing forays in home waters.

While the three big gulls are regarded as shore-birds rather than sea-birds and black-headed gulls often nest far inland, kittiwakes are very much birds of the ocean. They build their nests on peripheral cliffs, as close to the sea as they can get, and their only sojourns on land are to gather nest material from the grassy clifftops.

They are much less widespread, with none on Skokholm during my early years there, so it is interesting that Buxton and Lockley in *Island of Skomer*, 1950, stated kittiwakes to be twice as abundant on Skomer as the other gulls. There were one and a half times as many kittiwakes as lesser black-backs in 1945 and twice as many in 1946, this increase being from fifteen

Fulmar Petrels at nest.

hundred to one thousand nine hundred and nine. At that time there were six hundred to seven hundred herring gulls and forty to sixty great black-backs.

My particular fascination with the kittiwakes' hemispherical nests glued so seemingly precariously to the tiniest ledges on sheer faces was the occasional occurrence of associated plant life. In Kittiwake Cove I saw ten different species growing around the paired chicks. These included, mayweed, cat's-ear and chickweeds, as well as the usual halo-phytes or salt-lovers.

The nests seemed to be fairly permanent fixtures, repaired and added to each year. Breeding starts late and birds were still venturing onto land collecting substantial beakfuls of grass to add to them in mid June 1964. Most would make several circuits over the sea (to shake off the taint of such unfamiliar terrain?) before bringing the offering to their mate on the nest, this accepted after a vociferous greeting ceremony.

This association of plants and kittiwakes occurred also in Tom's Hole on the south coast, both birds and plants favouring a narrow lava flow a few feet wide. This rock had a slaty cleavage which produced horizontal fissures a few inches apart. Birds built on the shelves between, plants were rooted in the crevices, with neither able to obtain purchase on the more massive igneous rocks above and below, where there were few cracks.

Razorbills on the north-west face of the Skomer Neck were also more involved with plant life than those on Skokholm. Some were standing around well up on a closed sward of grass, thrift, sea campion and plantain, others even among taller mayweed, red campion and sea beet. Even guillemots nested close to scraps of vegetation in Bull Hole.

Owned by the Countryside Council for Wales, Skomer has been leased to the West Wales Wildlife Trust since 1959, when it was designated as a National Nature Reserve, as well as an SSSI and a Special Protection Area under European law. In 1990, after years of controversy and delay, the surrounding seas were designated as a Marine Nature Reserve, to safeguard food supplies for the sea-birds, which are the island's chief claim to fame.

10.

SKOMER: LAND BIRDS, FLORA, MARINE LIFE AND MIDDLEHOLM

Sea-birds inevitably steal the show on the islands because we see them so seldom on the mainland, but there is a great deal more here on the ornithological front. A stroll from the Narcissus-bordered farmyard in any direction can be full of interest.

Stonechat.

Wheatears commonly flirt among spikes of wall pennywort erupting from the big old stone gateposts, or bring food to their fledgelings on mats of English stonecrop with fleshy vermilion leaves and starry rose pink flowers. Dapper cock stonechats broadcast their chinking calls from looping bramble stems in parts where there is none of their favourite gorse to bear them aloft.

Stand quietly and an alighting skylark may drop into a hole in the top of a grass tuft and into a nest below. I have stumbled across a meadow pipit's nest in hogweed and a rock pipit's under a displaced basalt slab. In the early 1960s there were some sixty pairs of meadow pipits and thirty pairs of rock pipits nesting, the latter seldom coming up to forage over the plateau until after their young had fledged on the cliffs. The odd pied wagtail can be seen quartering rabbit-nibbled turf almost as smooth as their favourite lawns and putting greens.

Blackbirds are versatile, making do with minimal cover for their nurseries, usually bramble, sometimes blackthorn – a nesting habitat which they sometimes share with dunnocks. Plantings of blackthorn and conifers near the central buildings should enable their offspring to choose more typical sites.

A small hump on a wall top materialises into a little owl as I approach and stands its ground, watching me with fierce yellow eyes under frowning brows, its body motionless but its head turning through a hundred

Little Owl.

and eighty degrees as I pass. Two choughs come dawdling across from the Neck and a raven cronks in the blue void.

Once I watched a wren feeding its diminutive chick on a baulk of driftwood wedged in a gully by a storm wave. Down on the rocks were purple sandpipers and mottle-backed turnstones. A curlew chick scuttles from cover near North Pond and a lapwing chick comes bowling past, with more speed than caution.

Skomer, being larger and closer to the mainland than Skokholm, supports a wider variety of land birds. Nesting passerines include robin, starling, linnet, reed bunting, yellowhammer and whitethroats. Bramble, a popular nest cover, scarcely occurs on Skokholm except on a few over-grown cliffs.

Three pretty sights enjoyed on a 1978 visit were a spotted flycatcher on the chalet-dwellers' clothes line, a pied flycatcher on the stable roof and a passing short-eared owl carrying a shrew. When the peregrine took one of this owl pair later in the year, the other failed to cope alone and the brood was lost.

Lapwing were most often sighted on rabbit-induced barrens, snipe could be watched in aerial chases, spurting from invisible hide-outs among purple moor grass. Cock pheasants crowed as raucously as in the arable East; mallard nested by the ponds and curlews in rushy places, their streaky chicks sometimes flushed from among bordering bluebells and fog grass. Once in a while there was a whimbrel and often a couple of dunlin pottering by the pond, and incredibly tame.

When I watched from the North Pond hide in May 1978 the resident curlew circled constantly, awing or afoot, coming to within two metres of the hide and peering in, then retreating to land with a splosh in the pond and peck around for a while before taking up her agitated 'Go way' call again. Her mate was perched unconcernedly on a bank a hundred metres away, rising only occasionally with the evocative bubbling call that I associate with high Welsh moors. I left and later, when I put two others into the hide and walked away, the hen was much less agitated, obviously unable to count. A person or persons signified one and the same – disturbance.

The green woodpecker which I watched in undulating flight during a feeding bout on North Haven anthills in 1964 was the first record during David Saunder's tenure as warden.

Mike Harris of Swansea University crossed to Skomer in the bitter winter of 1962 to see how birds fleeing the snow and ice of the East were faring in this western seascape. He found a stricken host of passerines, unable or unwilling to move on to an anticipated haven across the Irish Sea. He writes in *British Birds*, 55, 1962:

> "It was virtually impossible for these birds to obtain food and water because the whole island was frozen hard and many of them were dying from starvation or cold. A search of boulders and beaches . . . revealed five hundred and sixty-four recently dead corpses . . . A few live birds were caught and ringed, but some of these died within the next twenty-four hours . . . Many other birds were killed by predators such as buzzards, a hen harrier, a peregrine, a tawny owl and carrion crows."

Corpses were weighed, sexed, measured and examined for parasites, their weights found to be down to as little as half the normal but parasites not at a critical level. Redwings had suffered most (two hundred and forty-five dead), all but two of those that were in good enough condition for examination being first year birds. Starling corpses numbered a hundred and twenty-nine, ninety-two of these first year birds.

Thirty-six dead fieldfares weighed half the norm, song thrushes a little over half and meadow pipits two thirds. Other casualties were chaffinches, lapwings and wrens, while species suffering apparently little were skylark, blackbird, snipe, woodcock and curlew. Blackbirds benefit by their habit of scratching away surface debris, like barnyard fowls, to find what lies beneath.

There are always strangers arriving at migration time: – bluethroat, red-backed shrike, ortolan bunting, wryneck and spotted crake, seeking such scant cover as they can find, ferruginous duck and red-throated diver on the water and sabines gulls coasting along the cliffs. The list accumulated over the years' of skilled observation is huge.

*   *   *

Not all is roses, however, in this wild garden of the Irish Sea. A great black-back passes with the hind quarters of a baby rabbit dangling from its powerfully efficient bill, a buzzard pauses in its languid circling, then drops to strike. A gull chasing a peregrine falcon may find the tables turned, a crow pestering a curlew may have its own tail feathers tweaked out, but most victims of harassment have few defences.

The biggest menace are the gulls, more bellicose and numerous than any. Several thousand shearwaters are killed by great black-backed gulls each season, their carcases littered all over the island, particularly near fresh water. These marauders seize adult puffins at their burrow entrances and grab razorbill and guillemot chicks from their ledges, while certain herring gulls become specialist egg thieves among the cliff-nesting auks.

There has been a tradition of egg collecting over the centuries, indiscriminately in some cases, as we saw on Grassholm. This practice, or the pricking of eggs to render them infertile, continues legitimately with gulls, but is not enough to show immediate results in lowering the numbers, because eggs allowed to hatch would not add to the breeding population until the chicks were four to five years old and mature enough to return to the colony to produce more.

Eventual reduction in numbers arising from egg pricking in lesser black backs' nests in earlier years led to a drop in chick production in 1969 of eighty-five per cent over the 1968 figures, but clearly more immediate measures were called for. Wire cages over great black backs' nests employed for ringing and monitoring were brought into use for culling as well, leading to 1969 seeing thirty-five fewer pairs of these larger birds than 1968. A hundred of the more accessible gulls' nests were 'subjected to control measures', which is a nice way of saying that a hundred and forty-five birds were removed from a possible two hundred.

Catchers found it more profitable to concentrate their blitz on a limited area rather than cull indiscriminately. If only one of a pair was taken, the bereaved would select another mate from the big mob of 'also rans' that was inevitably standing around somewhere like labourers in a market place waiting to be hired. Take both of a pair and it would be longer before the site was reoccupied by complete newcomers. In the early 1960s upwards of two hundred and fifty gulls had been killed annually to produce more immediate results.

Buxton and Lockley in *Island of Skomer*, 1950, reported sixty pairs of great black-backs on Skomer and a surprising hundred pairs on Middle-holm, this before the sudden increase that occurred over a wide area during the subsequent decade.

Steve Sutcliffe, reviewing the changes in gull numbers in *The Welsh Ornithological Newsletter*, 10, 1993, forty-three years later, reckoned there to be two hundred and eighty pairs on Skomer and over a hundred pairs on Middleholm, with sixty pairs on Skokholm. He links their fluctuating fortunes to outbreaks of botulism and human persecution on the negative side and boosts from fisheries waste on the positive. The figures quoted he regards as the lowest for half a century (although obviously not specifically on Skomer) and part of a widespread decrease after the earlier population explosion.

Sutcliffe reports that herring gulls increased to a peak in the 1970s, nourished on offal from Milford fish docks and mainland refuse tips. Then fermentation in the black trash bags gave rise to outbreaks of botulism and some eighty per cent of herring gulls breeding round the Pembrokeshire coast died within five years. Poor recruitment of juveniles since the 1980s led to a stabilising of numbers.

Lesser black-backed gulls are restricted almost entirely in Pembroke-shire to Skomer and Skokholm, where nearly fifteen per cent of the European race was breeding in the mid 1990s. A fairly stable population was depleted after World War II, when there was extensive egg collecting, their colonies being usually more accessible than those of other gulls. These made the meagre rations go further and supplemented the flavourless egg powder that we had become accustomed to.

Numbers rose in the decade from the mid 1960s with abundant food and good breeding success. Fluctuations have occurred from year to year since with no dramatic changes. Lesser black-backs are more likely to feed at sea than herring gulls and birds have found it increasingly difficult to find sufficient food since 1987 because of changes in off-shore fishing practices. It is the young which have suffered rather than the long-lived adults, so a considerable decline in colony replenishment was expected during the 1990s – except on Cardigan Island, where the population was rising and had reached three thousand pairs.

Corvids are as innovative as always. Ravens and crows are traditional egg thieves and are an expected part of the ecosystem. Most evocative are the choughs, those delightfully aerobatic red-legged daws, that attack few organisms any larger than ground dwelling grubs. The finding of a lidded magpie's nest only a metre above the ground was a novel expe-

Jackdaw stealing Guillemot's fish.

rience, the search for the preferred tall tree or unkempt hedge obviously a non-starter.

Jackdaws are the *bêtes noires* among birds for those of us who live in the Welsh Valleys. They drop piles of sticks or hardware from landfill sites down our chimneys, driving other birds from the feeders and quartering the skies throughout the year in noisy flocks of forty to eighty. During the last few decades an overspill has been taking up residence on the islands.

As far back as 1963 we watched an advance party of these rapscallions pirating puffins, harrying them, skua fashion, to give up their hard won fish. They must have been watching the gulls! These two groups are regarded as among the most intelligent of birds, their capacity to learn new tricks geared only to their personal welfare.

The warden was shooting jackdaws then, but they were still very numerous, stealing burrows as well as fish from their victims, many of these along the isthmus leading to the Neck. As hole nesters, there was nothing to stop them walking into a puffin burrow to steal egg or chick, and we would see them flying off with a whole egg in their bill, to consume at leisure elsewhere.

On one occasion I watched a puffin holding twelve sand eels just behind the gills, the bodies dangling neatly on alternate sides, being chased into its burrow by a jackdaw. This stood at the entrance looking in with seemingly endless patience before giving up. Maybe the chick was too large or the parental bill too fearsome in so confined a space. More often they prevent the puffin from homing, causing it to circle back over the sea with the undelivered goods. T. R. Birkhead (*Nature in Wales*, 13.3, 1973 and 14.1, 1974), made a study of these in 1972, when he observed them harrying guillemots on their ledges as well as puffins. In 1946 there were thought to have been only twenty pairs of jackdaws on Skomer. By 1964 these had risen to around two hundred pairs, but they stabilised at about this number. His observations were made on ledges near Bull Hole in the north-west which held seven hundred adult guillemots and a hundred and seventy-five chicks.

Jackdaws patrolled the ledges even more frequently than did the various gulls, their forays occurring at any time of day, their target the herring fry, sprats and pilchards brought in by the guillemots. They would alight beside a returning bird, sometimes, but by no means always, frightening it into dropping its fish. Often the marauder would nip in to scavenge a whole or part fish from beside a chick.

Two hundred and fourteen jackdaw nests were monitored in 1973 but the number of birds involved in this piracy was modest and not regarded as a significant threat to the guillemots. The Nature Conservancy Council controlled daw numbers from 1962 to 1971, killing up to eighty-eight a year to keep the population at the two hundred ceiling.

Jackdaws from the Neck were observed flying to the mainland to feed. Maybe it was the plethora of potential breeding burrows that attracted them to the island, their principal food of grubs and other invertebrates hauled from the ground being more easily obtained on mainland farms. Surprisingly jackdaw breeding success was low, few pairs rearing more than one young per brood, possibly because of the distance to mainland feeding sites. On our 1976 visit researchers from the Edward Grey Institute were following this up.

Two each of two broods housed in cardboard boxes were being supplied with special food prepared for insect eaters, the dog food used initially having proved unsuitable. Each time one squawked food was pushed into the open beak with a finger, accompanied by water from a fountain pen filler as a substitute for parental saliva. If squawks were not forthcoming, the carer chacked, as a good parent should, and the bill would open in response.

As they grew the fledgelings got cheeky, as tame jackdaws will, walk-

Great Black-backed Gull food remains.

ing about on their surrogate parents and tweaking their hair. They were not quite ready to fly when we left the island. It was not until the number of daws breeding on Skomer had stabilised at about two hundred pairs that breeding had started on Skokholm. Here, too, the increase was rapid, to about fifty-five pairs in 1974, bringing the density of nests during the late 1970s to about the same level – or one and a half to two pairs per hectare on both islands. These were in rabbit or puffin burrows and rock crevices in the absence of their more usual tree holes and chimney pots.

An American couple working on pipits had pitfall traps scattered across the island in an attempt to assess the invertebrate food potential. There were glossy green and slender bronze leaf beetles, smaller versions of the devil's coach horse type, wearing their wing cases as short waistcoats, minotaurs and other ground beetles. Red-tailed and white-tailed bumble bees sipped from the abundance of flowers, while seasonal swarms of St. Marks flies with long black legs dangled in the spring sunlight. Always there was a wealth of yellow field ants and other food items.

Available prey included the caterpillars of brown silver lines, yellow shell and angleshade moths, along with many more caught in moth traps at night. The hordes of tiger-striped cinnabars on the ragwort and burnets on the legumes were probably too toxic. Breeding butterflies included peacocks, tortoiseshells, graylings, meadow browns, wall browns, small heaths, ringlets, small coppers, common blues, dark green fritillaries, orange tips and the other whites.

*　　　*　　　*

Joe Sadd, a fellow student from Aberystwyth, was the first to map the Skomer vegetation, his 1947 map appearing in Buxton and Lockley's *Island of Skomer*, 1950. Peter Panting's map of 1959 indicated a spread of bracken following the cessation of farming. Others, such as A. D. Jones in 1974, refined these early land-based efforts with the help of aerial photographs.

Of the many wild flowers present on Skomer the ones which commend themselves most to notice in early summer, apart from the obvious thrift, are the bluebells and red campion. The magnificence of the first on Skokholm has already been mentioned. On Skomer these are even more magnificent, transforming some of the less exposed tracts into a knee-deep carpet of blue, dotted with the sparkling black and white forms of nesting gulls – the two converging because of their dual need for the bracken which sprouts later in the year.

An interesting exercise on Skokholm carried out by E. Long and G. Crofts in 1949 was the counting of the number of flowers on two thousand bluebell stems. The commonest number per spike was twelve, four hundred and sixty-one having ten to twelve flowers. Two spikes contained forty-two flowers and twenty had anomalously long leafy bracts up to fourteen centimetres in length. Thirty-two plants of their sample bore white flowers. Skomer's plants are no less splendid.

On a broader front both bluebells and campion are centred on the cooler damper parts of North-west Europe. Both seek late summer protection from direct sunlight, but the campion is the more north-westerly of the two. It cleaves to coastal regions and is boosted by sea bird guano, although intolerant of overdoses of sea spray. I later found it to be an important feature of Fair Isle's puffin and fulmar colonies and Ailsa Craig's gannetry in Scotland, and there is a specially robust form, *Silene dioica var. Zetlandicum,* on the cold damp slopes of the Orkneys and Shetlands.

Bluebells and Red Campion.

Its fluctuations, from all embracing to almost nil on Skomer seemed more closely tied to temperature and rainfall than to grazing. With regard to rabbits, its tolerance resembles that of the often associated Yorkshire fog grass. Rabbits eat it down to ground level only if they cannot find anything more acceptable, but normally leave it strictly alone. It was rare on Skokholm, but can be as eye-catching as the white sea campion on Skomer in some years.

The wet summer of 1963 was such a year, when my colour photos show sheets of pink where there had been none during the 1969 drought. In fact the plants were recovering in 1961 from a more severe setback in an earlier autumnal drought, but had not yet reached the flowering stage. By 1963 large areas of the Neck, where rabbit regeneration after Myxomatosis had been slow, as well as the northern slopes and the eastern gull colonies, were a blaze of pink flowers. In 1964 this feature was accentuated, with more diffuse hazes of colour occurring elsewhere.

There seems little doubt that the spectacular rise to dominance was the product of the two cool moist summers of 1962 and 1963, following the two arctic, Shetland style, winters of those early sixties. No parallel rise occurred on Skokholm, where the species was rare, but plants introduced to the garden there began to spread outside.

Many Skomer plants stood five feet high during the wet summer of 1964. This was a particularly good year for the flowering of the equally cyclic biennial ragwort, which replaced the rose coloured sheets with brilliant yellow in autumn – topping the late season bracken fronds and the maturing capsules of bluebells and campion which they sheltered. 1975 was another exceptionally good ragwort year.

The spread of bracken is being curtailed by repeated flailing to starve it out, but there is no danger that such activities could seriously damage the benefits it provides by standing in for the absent tree cover. In the limited areas where flailing was effective, the new generation comprised mainly wood sage with a creeping understorey of ground ivy and plenteous spikes of golden rod. These still supplied cover for rabbit warrens, as the bracken had done, but little more sustenance.

Bracken is the climatic climax vegetation here, where salty winds suppress woody plants. It has been advancing inexorably over the old field systems since the island was purchased as a nature reserve in 1959. Although destroyed by ploughing or trampling livestock in the main body of the fields, there was plenty clustered along walls and bluffs with bluebells, foxgloves and other lovers of cover, including Skomer voles.

Wood Sage and Golden Rod.

As the bracken spread out from the walls, it became populated by lesser black-backs, which build their nests long before the fronds expand, in the expectation that they surely will. Huge gull colonies of over a hundred acres overlap with the shearwaters on which they prey. It is necessary to keep the fern in check to maintain the diversity of the grass, heather and other communities.

Herbicide use is a last resort in nature reserves. Winter ploughing, followed by a cultivator to rip out the underground rhizomes and expose them to frost, cannot be achieved without destroying the shearwater burrows. Resort has been made to the use of a potato haulm flail, lopping the bracken in two fields but leaving strips around the boundaries. With the flail set high, low growing competitors remain fairly undamaged. By ripping rather than cutting, more injured surfaces are exposed for infection by pathogens.

There was little regrowth after two years of this treatment, the new fronds being widely spaced and a quarter of their former height. The formerly starved underlying sward thickened up, with more plants than before, and with them more birds, butterflies and moths.

The number of plant species increased from seven to twenty-one, the number of breeding birds from two to seven and of those feeding across the area from four to twelve. Under tall bracken there had been only shearwater, curlew and meadow pipit, those moving in were oyster-catcher, wheatear, skylark and cuckoo. Butterflies recorded included meadow brown, common blue and green-veined white, along with the usual day-flying moths, cinnabars, burnets and yellow shells, and visiting humming bird hawk moths hovering over the marsh thistle flowers.

Such inroads into the great swathes of bracken are minimal taking the island as a whole. To eliminate this dominant in an area devoid of trees would be to lose one of the island's greatest glories, the bluebells. No newcomer following the track from North Haven to the farmhouse in May or June could fail to marvel at the counterpane of heavenly blue spread to either side. Even when the light fades the enchantment is carried on by the delicate scent wafting from the pendant blooms.

Firmly imprinted on my mind are the occasions when I walked this path at night. Leaving the fugitive honeysuckle scent of the North Haven cliff slopes, the more overpowering aura of bluebell aromatics took over. Specks of green luminescence bordered the way, the twinkling lights of glow worms calling soundlessly to potential mates. On still dark nights the points of light shone brighter, studding the darkness – a more dispersed version of the phosphorescence that we had awakened by trailing our fingers through the sea water down in the Haven.

This was the time of night when toads were abroad, big flabby, plopping forms displacing the dewdrops held on the hairy leaves of the fog grass. If they had a penchant for the big black *Arion ater* slugs they would feed to repletion, those repulsive yet vaguely ornamental shining animals being everywhere. Frogs and palmate newts were abroad at night too, but harder to find. It is the magic of the luminous beetles that we choose to call glow worms that lives on for me.

There is an average range of water plants scattered through the wet-

Rock Pipit, Barnacles and Carragheen.

land habitats. Lesser spearwort, buttercups and lady's smock give way to purple loosestrife and meadowsweet in midsummer and these to water mint and hemlock water dropwort as the season advances, forget-me-nots and marsh bedstraw taking their chance in the shade beneath. Both skullcaps are here, the greater blue and the lesser pink. Leaves of bistort and floating pondweed on the ponds become massed with gull feathers shed during the post nuptial moult.

There are few pastimes more relaxing than to settle in the bird hide between farmhouse and pond. In May and June the distant slope is awash with bluebells, in August and September the foreground is clothed in low heather or ling, with the deeper purple of fine-leaved heath and yellow specks of tormentil.

The streams, although quite small and partially ephemeral, nurture a variety of water creatures – water beetles, caddis flies, leeches, worms and the like. It is interesting to note that the two laver spire shell snails recorded by D. and N. Williams (*Nature in Wales*, 16, 2, 1978) are not the Jenkin's spire shell, the member of this trio which has shown an increasing affinity for fresh water since 1893, but the two species of brackish water, *Hydrobia ulvae* and *Hydrobia ventrosa*.

The first of these is characteristic of the Bristol Channel mudflats, where it is an important food source for shelduck and other birds at low tide. The second was an important component of the fauna of brackish or salty pools on the Rhymney Mouth saltings at Cardiff before these were largely destroyed by rubbish dumping. Another salt lover in the Skomer streams is the sand hopper, *Gammarus duebeni*, which is usually found in brackish lagoons and saltmarsh pools.

Hyde and Wade of the National Museum of Wales had sticky microscope slides collecting blown pollen on Skomer as well as on Skokholm, their collections contributing to a study of the incidence of asthma and hay fever. Most of their catches was grass pollen, but in smaller quantities than from equivalent areas on the mainland unless an east wind was blowing. Much of that caught was local in origin, but there was also tree pollen which must have blown across from the mainland.

*   *   *

With the offshore waters seldom still, there were few opportunities to explore the lower littoral zone. More often we were pottering on rocks in the splash zone, among scuttling sea slaters (*Ligea oceanica*) and more slender bristletails (*Petrobius maritimus*). Tiny insects with the bloom of a blue plum walked on upshore pools, supported by surface tension – these springtails (*Lipura maritima*). There was always weedy flotsam and shelly jetsam to sift through.

Velvety purple-red mats of *Rhodochorton rothii* infiltrated into cave entrances and crept up moist shady faces to as much as fifty feet above high water in places, trapping sand to cushion hands and feet. The only semblance of a sandy beach was in South Haven and it was known that there were stretches of sand in the sub-littoral here, supporting lugworms (*Arenicola marina*).

Long brown cords of bootlace weed (*Chorda filum*) wafted back and forth in the quieter bays, but even there were likely to be ripped free by the sort of turbulence favoured by the Gigartina element of carragheen. Gelatinous purple-red fronds of *Nemalion multifidum* were able to cling to wave-swept faces which could support little but acorn barnacles. These were mainly *Chthamalus stellatus* upshore and *Balanus balanoides* downshore, along with the dog whelks which feed by boring into them.

Shell gathering sorties brought to light two of the little British cowrie shells, *Trivia arctica* in North Haven and *Trivia europaea* in South Haven, where the opalet or snakelocks anemones (*Anemone sulcata*) were among the offshore gems.

In rock pools lined with crusty pink Lithothamnion, which had been scoured clean of all algae by grazing limpets, it was entertaining to see green gutweed and sea lettuce and brown Scytosiphon thriving on the backs of the limpets that so enjoyed eating them. Their hosts could not reach them there and none grazed over another's shell, so they were quite safe – as a 'limpet island flora'.

The many limpet shells brought onto the island plateau by foraging oyster-catchers were part of a study by Dr. Uriel Safriel of the University of Jerusalem in 1975 on Skokholm, when I was there with a party from the Merthyr Naturalists' Society. This was one of the many useful contacts emerging from island life, as he was instrumental in arranging a visit for some of us to his home territory along the shores of the Dead Sea in Israel – a very different type of shoreline.

During a week on Skomer in 1964 we shared the island with a party of skin divers from Cambridge. Their collections, ranging from metal lobster pot floats to a live lobster, were displayed on the clifftop. Particularly attractive were the big edible mauve sea urchins, gorgonid sea fans, big half scallop shells and sponges.

My only incursion into the depths of North Haven was during a spell on the island in 1976 with Arthur and Jennifer Gaines of the Woods Hole Marine Institute in Massachussets, New England. Arthur had spent two years on the staff of Atlantic College in Glamorgan, during which time he had taught Jennifer and me the rudiments of scuba diving, along with his students. Furnished with flippers, wetsuits and all the necessaries, this was too good an opportunity to miss.

The highlight for me was, not the marine life, but swimming under the idling flocks of puffins on the surface and watching the paddling of countless little red feet under plumage spangled with adherent air bubbles. Feeling our way along rock walls draped with thongweed and pimpled with gelatinous brown blobs of *Leathesia difformis*, our best finds were starfish and brittle stars. Sadly a suspension of algae limited visibility more than a few feet down.

Back in the late 1940s Bassindale recognised scarlet and gold star coral (*Balanophylia regia*) and a common temperate water coral, *Caryophyllia smithii*. These two contributed in no small way to the recognition of Skomer's offshore waters as something rather special.

The island has been a National Nature Reserve since 1959 for land organisms. When it transpired that it lay on the convergence of warm water and cold, the richness of its marine communities was realised. The idea of basing a marine nature reserve here was inaugurated in the mid 1970s. Legislation proved very complex, but a steering committee was set up in 1974, incorporating no less than ten official bodies, detailed in the *WWNT Bulletin 21*, Oct. 1977.

By that time the reserve boundaries were defined, embracing the sea bed around Skomer, Middleholm and the Marloes Peninsula. Rules were laid down regarding collection of specimens and avoidance of disturbance of the nesting sea-birds, but there was no legal basis for these so compliance relied on the cooperation of divers and boatmen until official designation in the 1990s.

This worked, a typical exercise being the convergence of twenty-one divers in May 2001 to survey fish occupying territories in the inshore waters. Ten main species were investigated, one, the shining blue cuckoo wrasse with red patterning, being of special interest. When the leading male wrasse dies or moves away, the largest female in the shoal changes sex and takes his place! Some of the wrasse and the gobies were found to make nests and tend their eggs.

There are other, more reprehensible, ways in which fish can change their sexual potential. Media news in March 2002 pointed out that there is so much synthetic oestrogen, from pesticides and contraceptive pills, polluting our rivers, that more than a third of the male roach population are producing little or no sperm, eggs appearing in the roe alongside such flawed spermatozoids as exist. Fewer fish are being fertilised and stocks are dwindling as a result.

The media were most interested in the fact that many people's drinking water comes from rivers and the chemical is 'exquisitely potent'. As most of the world's troubles stem from over population, the feared diminution of Homo might be an asset.

Very little line fishing takes place from the shore, this usually when fishermen's fish move into one of the havens in pursuit of fry, their presence indicated by an excited flurry of fishing kittiwakes. In 1966 Ainsley Harrison and Jimmy Lewis of Penarth managed to catch two large bream, a rainbow wrasse with colourful spots on its belly and a rather bony common wrasse. The first three made good eating when brewed up on the slow motion calor gas in the chalets.

Sadly no amount of keeping to the prescribed code of conduct by users can prevent the most disastrous damage of all, that of oil pollution. With Milford Haven regarded as Britain's largest oil port in the 1970s, there is a big traffic in tankers in and out around St. Ann's Head, as well as rogue navigators cleaning out their tanks at sea.

In January 1977 the damaged Greek tanker *Chryssi P. Goulandris* created a spill in Milford Haven resulting in the death of almost the entire swan population. This incident led to the establishment of the

Oil Pollution Research Unit at the Field Studies Council Centre in Orielton House, South Pembrokeshire, to investigate the effect of oil on marine life and methods of cleaning birds.

In March of that year Pembrokeshire saw the much greater disaster of the *Torrey Canyon*, when hundreds of miles of beaches were fouled and thousands of sea-birds killed. Researchers found that almost all the birds' internal systems were affected, through swallowing, preening and penetration of oil into the lungs. Many died a slow and painful death through emaciation and cold arising from loss of insulation.

Swans, ducks and gulls were the only species likely to live after cleaning by hand. Others, released as clean, were still dying after three hundred days at sea. Orielton staff were as much concerned with the health of seashore life in general as with the rehabilitation of sea-birds.

The most toxic elements in the oil are said to be aromatic compounds which are volatile and discharged to the air, so old oil spills are less lethal than new ones, but the cloying nature of the mass remains. Detergents used on beaches polluted by the *Torrey Canyon* proved more poisonous than the oil. The best practice is to destroy the slicks at sea before they reach the beaches.

1974 saw an oiling incident affecting some of Skomer's southern beaches from 9th September. Most sea-birds had left the island by then but the seals were at the height of their breeding. Nothing could be done for the adults but a number of pups were cleaned, these and others irretrievably oiled, kept under observation for six days.

Cow seals came in to feed both clean and oiled pups, which were weighed at intervals to monitor their progress. Sadly, the faithful mothers were transferring oil from their own bodies to the pups, destroying the 'oil team's' cleansing efforts. Happily those pups lying on a clean beach were able to shed their coating of oil with the first moult of their baby fur, before swimming off to sea at about three weeks old.

Sixty pups were born on Skomer in that year of 1974, four of them stillborn, and fourteen others died on the beaches. Most had their hind flippers tagged in the hope of further sightings. 1973 had also seen the birth of sixty pups, of which nine died during their first week. The warden, John Davis, reported that the totally blind seal which had given birth on this same beach for the past few years, returned again in 1973 and reared a fat, healthy pup. As he writes in the Winter 1973 *West Wales Naturalists' Trust Bulletin*, "How does she do it?" Skomer and Ramsey Islands are the main seal breeding grounds in West Wales.

In 1978 the tanker *Christos Bitas* ran aground on the treacherous Hats and Barrels at low water and was floated off at high water, continuing on her way with oil streaming from a hole in her hull! Storm winds brought some of this into North Haven, where three seal cows which had pups ashore there seemed to be suffering from oil burning their eyes.

The smallest pup, only a few days old, was soon exhausted trying to hold its head above the treacly brown mass and sank into it to asphyxiate. The medium sized pup, barely visible in the mass, managed to keep her head above it until rescued and taken to an animal hospital on the mainland, but died a few days later. The oldest pup fared better, holdings its own until moved to a clean bit of the beach and the worst of the mess scraped off. The rest was shed at the moult. After treatment of an oil-induced abscess, it went off to sea as normal.

September 1980 saw ten tons of heavy fuel oil washed ashore in South Haven, this cleared up by the island staff helped by RAF Brawdy. A London laboratory needing weathered oil for research purposes, paid to have it taken away, although getting the stuff into bags designed for fertiliser proved no picnic.

On 16th June 1985, just seven years after the *Christos Bitas* fiasco, on a calm fine evening, another tanker, the *Bridgenss*, took a lazy short cut and was holed on the Hats and Barrels, spilling oil off Grassholm and threatening the gannets and the Skomer sea-birds at the height of their breeding season. Providentially the wind drove the oil north, away from the islands, and broke it up into slicks, saving the gannets, but proving catastrophic for over two thousand nesting guillemots, razorbills and puffins.

Many swam to their home islands and clambered out onto the rocks but died there of starvation and cold. Most of the ninety birds rescued from Grassholm died subsequently. No rescues were attempted of the thousands of oiled birds on Skomer, because of the inevitable disturbance to breeders which had escaped. Six hundred corpses were collected by the National Museum staff around Pembrokeshire, no lesson having been learned from the *Christos Bitas* scandal.

Happily the seals do not always have to suffer the tribulation of oil spills. 2003 was a particularly good year, with few autumn storms washing pups from the breeding beaches. the number born was around average, but higher survival rates made this a special year.

In the marine nature reserve as a whole 223 pups were born and more than 185 of these survived. Between tweny and twenty-five per cent are lost during an average year. In 2003 the mortality rate was down to sixteen per cent.

*   *   *

Middleholm or Midland Isle's 21.5 acres was cut off from Skomer subsequent to the separation of the two from the mainland. The Skomer isthmus between North and South Haven has been getting progressively narrower since and will be the next to be cut through, leaving the Skomer Neck as a third island, between Midland and the parent body, with Little Sound to the east and a littler sound to the west.

Little Sound is currently about eighty yards wide at low water. The current swirls through at a rate of knots, as was only too apparent from the smaller island when Reuben Codd was hovering there to pick us up with the Middleholm goats for Skokholm.

Common porpoises enjoy breasting this current – to test their physique? Common dolphins are fewer but sometimes join them. Larger cetaceans are seen only further offshore. Jack Sound between Middleholm and the Old Deer Park on the headland protecting Martin's Haven is notorious

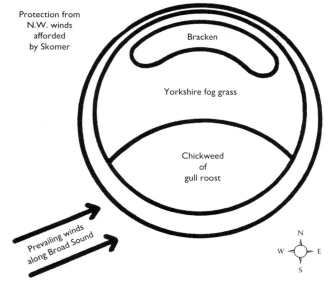

Diagrammatic Plant Map of Middleholm.

for its fierce tidal swirl over submerged rocks at both high and low water, but provides a slightly easier passage between the two.

Although Soay sheep, the odd few goats and a population of rabbits were present on Middleholm, the fescue swards fell between those of the heavily grazed larger islands and the ungrazed Grassholm of equal size, in both quantity and quality.

While 80-90% of the fescue swards consisted of fescue on Grassholm, 60-80% were fescue on Middleholm and only 30-45% on Skokholm. These figures vary, depending on drought and other factors, but comparably on the three.

The general layout of the vegetation is expressed diagrammatically and illustrates the overriding effect of gulls in modifying the plant cover. Not only were there more great black-backs breeding on Middleholm than Skomer, a hundred pairs as opposed to sixty pairs despite their size discrepancy, but many gulls roosted there, flying in from the Milford Fish Docks after a day of gluttony, where they were sufficiently well provided with fish waste to be able to refuse the bonier, less succulent morsels.

Chickweed, which dominates the gull roost, thrives on areas bared by animal traffic and enriched by their dung, so long as conditions are cool and damp. This was graphically shown by Fraser-Darling on the island of North Rona, where Atlantic seals hauled ashore, scouring the soil bare and producing an aftermath of several acres of almost pure chickweed.

The surrounding Yorkshire fog may be an interim phase between chickweed and the expected more mixed sward – big gull roosts on the Neck of Skomer sporting the blue-green of fog grass when viewed from afar off, in a sea of dark green or salt-bronzed bracken. It seems likely that gull pressure destroys the bracken in the first instance and subsequent roosters prefer the bare area because of the lack of impedimenta.

The pioneer naturalists occupying Skomer during the latter years of the 1940s collected as many as fifty gulls' eggs a day during May and June, the equivalent of some three thousand eggs, this inevitably reducing the population, in spite of re-laying. Some were transported to fisherfolk and farmers on the mainland, who had traditionally collected eggs on Middleholm, hoping to relieve disturbance of the auks there. Eggs were still rationed in those post war years and great black backed gulls' eggs, even the fish flavoured ones, were a great improvement on the prevalent egg powder.

The Skomerites used the standard lobster pot style wire traps placed over gull's nests for either culling or ringing adults. Gulls soon found their way back in through the hole in the top, but failed to find their way out. A removed bird would not return for a while, but its mate might well do so, allowing both to be dealt with in a matter of a few hours and the trap moved on.

Kittiwakes, which are so abundant on Skomer, with around a thousand pairs on the Wick alone, only started to nest on Middleholm in the late 1940s. They breed later than the other gulls. Although prospecting the nesting cliffs in March, they do not usually start gathering nest material until the end of May and are gone by late August. Fulmars started moving in during the fifties and sixties. Shearwaters were shown to number three thousand pairs in the 1999 census.

Ten to a dozen shags nested in dark cliff crevices on Middleholm, about the same number as on Skomer. Strangely, both these and cormorants are rare nesters, although frequently seen fishing offshore.

Not only the Middleholm gulls are independent of their home island for food. The remains of a mole, which must have come from the mainland, was found in the crop pellets of the local buzzard. It is but a short hop for choughs, ravens, crows, daws and others to wing across to the Old Deer Park to feed.

Shag's nest with three eggs.

Marine Hopper, Orchestia gammarella, *150 feet above the sea.*

Perhaps the most remarkable find on Middleholm was made by R. Bassindale (*Proc. Bristol Nats. Soc.,* XXVII.II, 1946). This was a sand-hopper, *Orchestia gammarella,* which normally inhabits the upper and mid littoral zone, but was found on Middleholm a hundred and fifty feet above sea level, in the dusty mouth of a rabbit burrow. This reddish or greenish-brown crustacean also leads a terrestrial life on Grassholm and Skokholm, hopping skittishly over a habitat very different from the damp sand, shingle or rotting seaweeds of its more conventional haunts. The animals, like tiny shrimps, reach to only 2cm long, a handy snack, one imagines, for a chough.

Few landings are made on Middleholm, so Nature is able to take its course there. Much the same can be said of the Neck of Skomer, which is out of bounds to the public and visited infrequently by the residents. With so many visitors landing, this is a necessary precaution, as is their restriction to the paths, which lead to all the best viewing sites and avoid the collapse of myriad burrows under myriad feed.

Large numbers of researchers, particularly from Oxford's Edward Grey Institute of Ornithology, were working on both Skomer and Skokholm during the middle decades of the twentieth century, with many of the birds' underground nesting chambers furnished with lids, the gulls' nests trapped and plots of ground fenced off. I was working in Exeter University during the mid 1950s and it was not wholly unexpected, as I set off for the islands on one occasion, that my professor should remark scathingly:

"I shouldn't think there's any ecology left there now, with you lot tramping around!"

He could have been right. The environment certainly lost its pristine freshness, but its intrinsic charm never waned, even for the hoary old-timers. However well intentioned we are, the encroachment into other creatures' terrain must always be disruptive, and alter the very situation that we try to study. Fortunately newcomers accept things at face value, paying little heed to other people's laments as to how things were "in the good old days".

It would be selfish for the few to deny such splendid wildlife spectacles to the many, so long as a code of conduct is adhered to and we tread as lightly as we may on the enchanted acres.

*　　　*　　　*

Our residential Skomer parties were often pretty wet on arrival in Martin's Haven. Twenty-second of May 1966 was such a day. The manly strength of Alf Knowles, the boatman, straining on the rope that he had managed to get through the iron mooring ring was supplemented by that of the ocean. The ring broke loose, still attached to the top of the boulder which came down heavily on his foot. With his shoe oozing blood, he issued a volley of instructions to the still able-bodied.

Poyntz, the chemist from Chepstow, was flat on his back in the shallows by then with a coil of rope on his chest. Bill Boulton, steel worker from Risca, was up to his waist in the sea, saying how glad he was he'd put his waterproof trousers on! Bob Richards from Ebbw Vale was shipping oars and clearing impedimenta. His cobber, Phelps, made a gallant rescue with the boat hook of Watkin Davies' rather smart hat which was drifting out on the ebb.

Betty Hughes, the teacher from Bridgend, was manning the ropes, up to her shins in bilge water. A happy hefty lass was Betty, with a lovely sense of humour. When Alf requested 'more humanity' to get the baggage ashore, she presented herself with the comment, "Bags of it." Berenice Davis, PE Inspector from Cardiff, and about half her size, was plunging through the waves under a rucksack full of cine equipment almost as big as herself. Someone else was being sick over the side.

When all were safely gathered in, we took it in turns to change into dry togs in the lobster shed. Our bath mats were plastic sacks sprinkled with mouse droppings, our bathroom stools were lobster pots. A yacht had been wrecked a little to the north a few days before, so some had feared the worst, but all was well, except for Alf's toes. My parties always remembered their visits to Skomer and none regretted them. Most chose to return.

When I visited Martin's Haven in 1994 everything had changed. The upper part of the loberstermen's shed – formerly a pair of cottages – was by then a marine nature reserve museum and the middle part offices of the Countryside Council for Wales. Wet travellers were catered for with public toilets and running water and wildlife reaped a few fringe benefits. A family of baby swallows peered down at us from their mud nest and a yellowhammer perched on the roof.

Later, we walked along the coastal path and encountered a happy 'accident' on the cliffs of the Marloes Peninsula, where man's activities had boosted the maritime flora. This was in the early days of 'setasides', the new word for 'fallows', and a twenty-acre oatfield had been set aside, unsown, two years earlier.

Instead of the usual thistles and weeds of the early phases of neglect, the land had been colonised by neat little mounds of thrift – pincushions for upstanding pink flower heads – plus some of the usual associates, spurrey, storksbill, sea campion and plantains.

This field, on Runwayskiln Farm, illustrated the spontaneity with which the beauty of the islands can take hold on the mainland if given the chance. The National Trust owns the land and the Countryside Council for Wales is helping the farmer, who had already won a Countryside Caretaker's Award for creating a pool and wetland, to boost the natural regeneration with light sheep grazing in lieu of arable cropping.

It is a joy to those who walk the coast path along its outer edge. To seaward is a fine view of the islands and it is bordered by two SSSIs. Management includes clearing gorse and rooting out thistles, to do the work of seering salt winds in keeping these more boisterous invaders from ousting the poorer competitors of lower stature.

Local choughs, recently feeding on gleanings of the corn crop, will be able to change back to their natural diet of grubs and insects as the low flowery sward develops.

11.

RAMSEY: CRAGGY HEATH AND POOLS, CHOUGHS AND SEALS

In travelling around St. Brides Bay to Ramsey, the next island to the north, we are moving from the 'Little England beyond Wales' of South Pembrokeshire to the Welsh Wales of North Pembrokeshire. Or, as John Barret of Dale Fort Field Centre would have it: to North Pembrokeshire where the people speak Welsh and go to chapel from South Pembrokeshire where they speak English and don't go to church! He was one of the English who did, forming the mainstay of the choir in the little Dale church.

Ramsey was always a more contained island than Skomer, seldom visited except by a few ornithologists when it came under the jurisdiction of the Royal Society for the Protection of Birds from 1965 to 1975. Their tenure lapsed, but it was finally bought by the society in 1992 and it is now possible for the public to visit or sail around its rugged periphery viewing the sea-bird colonies.

Active farming continued for longer and Ramsey has not been a hive of research activity for students and scientists like the southern islands. It is a place to go to unwind and take in the integrated picture of rocky capes, clamorous sea-birds and placid hay meadows. I took only two residential parties, one in May 1969, when George Critchley from Lancashire was warden, and one in 1971 when Peter Frost from South Africa was in charge.

We were a mixed lot, twelve the first time – two solicitors, two engineers, a company director, a gardener and a bevy of teachers – and seventeen the second time – some of the same, plus surgeon, bank manager, steel worker and medical secretary. In other words, a typical cross section of general observers with no-one aspiring to do any research or pursue any special hobby horse. Half of us set up our menage in the old farmhouse and half in the bungalow under the shadow of Carn Ysgubor in the north-west, a dwelling built in 1908 and renovated in 1963.

Ramsey boasts some splendid maritime heath and a wealth of sea-bird cliffs, but her chief wildlife claims to fame are her choughs and her seals. Choughs or red-legged daws, with their striking crimson bills, have always been rare, unlike the yellow billed mountain daws which congregate over tourist hot spots in the Alps.

Choughs.

As far back as 1896 the owner of Ramsey was jealously guarding his small colony of the birds, allowing no-one to land without his permission (Robert Drane, *Trans. Cardiff Nats.*, XXXIII, 1900-1901). A small population persisted in Wales after they had become extinct in the West Country and numbers are now slowly building up.

Most islands regard four to five pairs as a 'high'. Ian Bullock, an early warden after the 1992 purchase of the island, recorded seven to eight pairs breeding there, with a flock of around twenty during late summer. Charles Martin, warden in 2001, also reported eight breeding pairs, each with three young, totalling forty birds with the resident non-breeders. He laughingly referred to the island as a chough factory, supplying other sites.

Recent years have seen choughs on Gower and at Ogmore in Glamorgan. Are these some of the overspill? They arrived under their own steam, as did those of Cornwall in 2001 after an absence of nearly half a century – forestalling the dedicated 'Chough Reintroduction Group' by a short head.

Most of the North Atlantic's grey seals breed around Great Britain and Ireland and South Pembrokeshire is special in being near the southern limit of their geographical range. In the final years of the millennium

Young Atlantic Grey Seal and Wracks.

more than one thousand three hundred grey seal pups were being born annually along the southern half of the West Wales coast, from Tenby to Aberystwyth, thus excluding Bardsey

This was the 1996 figure, published after a four year survey, before the *Sea Empress* oil spill. The trend was for a 1.5% rise in the number of births each year, with the seal population reckoned to be about five thousand. Ramsey has the greatest concentration of seals in Southern Britain, averaging five hundred and five pups a year, with Skomer coming second. More were found in small groups along the mainland coast, however, than on these two islands together.

Ramsey pups can be dropped on any of the island beaches, mostly between August and November, but the two big western bays, Aber Mawr and Port Llavog, harbour most and are out of bounds, as seal sanctuaries.

*   *   *

Ramsey is hillier and more rugged than the southern islands, with two high points and a patchwork of different rock types leading to uneven weathering. Carn Llundain towards the south-west rises to six hundred and forty-six feet (136m), towering above the general plateau level, which is around a hundred and fifty feet. The distance from north to south is nearly two miles (3km) and the acreage is six hundred and ninety-five (282 hectares). Three sizable islets and five lesser ones trail off the southern end, while the Bishops and Clerks Islands lie to the west.

Just as Middleholm, Skomer and Grassholm are the eroded remnants of a ridge of hard rocks protruding from the mainland, so is Ramsey the continuation of a headland reaching west through St. David's Head.

The lighthouse which warned navigators of the rocky peril before the days of radar was built on the South Bishop, as welcome in its time as the one on the Smalls, which failed to keep the tankers off the Hats and Barrels.

Softer coalfield rocks between the two headlands have been eroded back to form St. Brides Bay, these bordered by some fine sandy beaches from Newgale Sands in the north, through Nolton and Druidston, to Broadhaven and Little Haven in the south. Headlands protruding from Pembrokeshire's sea-flattened peneplain north to Strumble Head are of resistant igneous rocks, the bays between of softer sedimentary ones.

Some outcrops are of the oldest rocks known, the pre-Cambrian and Cambrian, these used as building stones through the centuries. It is the

Cambrian sandstones that give the attractive purple sheen to the walls of St. David's Cathedral, built in the hollow to seaward of Wales' smallest city, in the vain hope that it might escape the sharp eyes of the marauding Vikings.

The bones of these ancient rocks stick up through the smoothly nibbled skin of turf on Ramsey. Carn Ysgubor behind the bungalow is a basic intrusion of particularly hard rock. The more southerly hill is of Ordovician volcanic rocks with acid intrusions to the south and east. The Ordovician rocks do not differ greatly from the Cambrian, the volcanic suite on Ramsey consisting of a sequence of rhyolitic ashes, tuffs and lavas. These lie towards or on top of the Bifidus zone of the Didymograptus shales, the name derived from the fossil Graptolites, *Didymograptus bifidus*, which are shaped like an open or closed tuning fork with serrations along the inside edges.

Many fossils occur in the softer shales of the little bays eroded into the east coast between the harder, more resistant masses of quartz porphyry. This gentler coast is subject to water flow north and south along the coast; the more rugged west side has to stand up to the direct force of the Atlantic swells and is more deeply eroded into inlets and caves, forming some of the highest cliffs in Wales.

Basal conglomerates containing fossil *Bolophora undosa*, are followed by highly fossiliferous grey mudstones with lamp shells (brachiopods), molluscs, trilobites, crinoids and starfish. Trilobites are crab relatives resembling segmented sea slaters flattened onto the rock surface. Crinoids are early sea lilies, animals having a tubular stem with a bunch of splaying branches at the tip. Ramsey has produced the oldest crinoids known anywhere in the world, one of these bearing the name of *Ramseyocrinus cambrensis*.

Some rather fine fossils had been lined up beside the entrance to the bungalow during one of our visits, but have no doubt been moved on to safer quarters. My only prize find was an orthid brachiopod, identified as *Lenorthis alata*, from the lowermost layers of the Ordovician.

Beaches are of pebbles rather than sand, these in various colours depending on their origin in the black, white or red layers of ancient volcanic ash or volcanic breccia, with quartz, feldspar and porphyry. The island is categorised as a Geological Conservation Site, an SSSI and a Special Area of Conservation, as well as lying within the Pembrokeshire National Park.

*   *   *

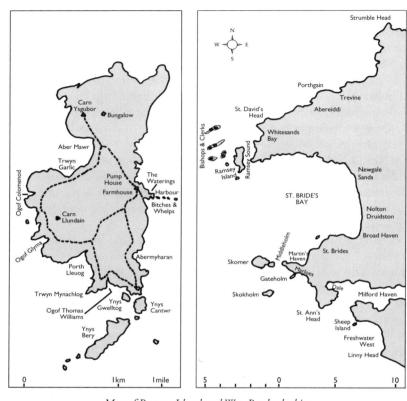

Mao of Ramsey Island and West Pembrokeshire

Like the other South Pembrokeshire Islands and despite the roaring waters around the landing place before construction of the modern wharf, Ramsey was inhabited from earliest times. Recent repairs of dry stone walls brought to light flint flakes thought to stem from early Neolithic inhabitants, as well as gin traps, clay pipes and antediluvian bottles from the old rabbit catchers. Bronze Age people of two thousand BC left cairns and constructed the earliest walls, which were maintained by the Iron Age folk who succeeded them. The name is said to be Viking.

Lying so close to St. David's and the cathedral dedicated to the patron saint of Wales, and bearing in mind the ancient holy men's predilection for 'getting away from it all' on remote islands, it is inevitable that there should have been early ecclesiastical settlements here.

St. Devynog, Tyfanog or Devanus was the first of these, establishing a monastic building near the eastern landing. Stone coffins have been unearthed here, near the present farmhouse. He was followed by St. Justinian, who used the island as a retreat in the fifth and sixth centuries AD and gave his name to the point of embarkation on the adjacent mainland, which now houses the lifeboat station.

Two chapels were erected, one dedicated to each of these saints, and Ynys Tyfanog is the old Welsh name of the island. Later St. David came along and the name was changed to Ynys Dewi. For centuries after Justinian was beheaded by his henchmen, who found him too strict a disciplinarian for their liking, the island was held by the bishop of St. David's and later transferred to the Church in Wales.

It was stocked with cattle, sheep and goats in the thirteenth century and cereals were grown. Rabbits had been introduced by this time and were a winter source of income. A series of holding ponds was dug to power a grist mill, with an overshot wheel fourteen feet in diameter and a lime kiln was constructed, its stones coming in useful later for building the quay. Archives refer to pirates raiding the island in 1633 and making off with cheeses and sheep (Roscoe Howells, *Across the Sounds*, Gomer, 1972).

The old farmhouse was built around 1822 and was in a bad state of repair by the 1960s. Whitehead bought the island in 1935 and achieved the massive task of building a seaworthy wall from the Axe (the innermost of the line of reefs known as the Bitches and Whelps) to the shore of the island. This excluded the tidal rush through the intervening gully, the hazards of which were described by Ronald Lockley when he first visited Ramsey in the *Shearwater* on his honeymoon in 1928 (Lockley, *I Know an Island*, 1938).

This massive structure comprised a quay facing north with a wall to the south, turning the northern embayment from a maelstrom to a millpond. During the earlier tenure of Williams from 1867 to 1891, small coastal traders used to shelter during storms north of the rocky straggle of the Bitches. This bay was known as the Waterings, because of the freshwater springs bubbling out there – springs which are still the island's main water supply.

The seamen came ashore to replenish their freshwater barrels and the still functional pumphouse was installed just above the hundred foot contour. Some of the boats brought coal and lime for the kilns and took off the surplus grain harvest, most of which was sold as seed corn. At this time the island accommodated eighty head of horned stock, including twenty-four cows, six horses and a fluctuating population of pigs, as well as geese.

Sadly, Whitehead died in 1938, only three years after building the quay. Bert Griffiths, foreman of the masons, stayed on as bailiff and then master farmer. He grew a hundred and fifty acres of corn, fenced against the rabbits, which were a pest rather than an asset by then, continuing as thick on the ground as ever into the new millennium. Flax and potatoes were other crops grown, with the help of a tractor imported in pieces and lifted ashore by winch to be assembled on the island. Self sufficiency was the order of the day, even to rope making, as well as general repairs, the making of bread and butter and curing of hams (see Roscoe Howells).

Bert Griffiths went to the mainland to farm from 1947. Phil Davies, who took over, left the island in 1963. In 1961 the queen and her family landed on one of the western beaches from the Royal Yacht *Britannia* for a picnic – the only visit by a reigning monarch to a Pembrokeshire Island.

Later K. Allpress bought Ramsey to dedicate to the RSPB. He repaired the farmhouse for a potential farmer and the bungalow for an RSPB warden, but sadly, he too died young, in 1968. Richard Alison was the last to try marrying farming and conservation on the island but his tenure was short-lived, the poor level of agricultural returns, aggravated by the difficulty of getting farm produce ashore, proving too much.

Current farming by the RSPB is used as a conservation tool, the chief grazers now being red deer, left over from a former spell as a venison farm, supplemented by some fifty sheep and the thriving rabbit population. Land fenced against the latter is clustered in the north and amounts to a hundred and ninety-eight acres (80 hectares)

The animal dung supplies enough nutrients to nurture flowery pastures and, most vital in the ornithological context, a wealth of burrowing beetles and dung flies for choughs and others. Five hectares is planted with spring oats – more for the winter stubbles to supply finches, buntings and larks with gleanings and weed seeds than for the grain. A half hectare of linseed grown in the late 1990s attracted a flock of three hundred linnets. Efforts are being made to entice lapwings back to breed. In decline everywhere, they dropped from twenty-five pairs at the start of the decade to a mere fragment at its end.

The farmhouse was only in partial use in the late sixties, but other buildings, the yard, sheep culling pens and sheep dips were in good condition. Water was pumped by diesel engine from the pump house and warden George, who had been short of both diesel and calor gas in his time, had his own way of conserving water. He would take a long bath on a Friday evening, leaving his towel and working garb soaking in the bath over the weekend, announcing sweetly:

"No-one will be wanting the bath for the next couple of nights – I'll do these later!"

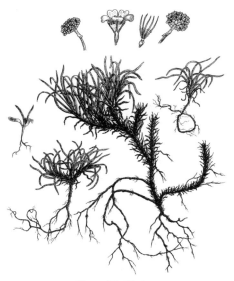

Young Thrift plants.

*   *   *

Ian Bullock's vegetation maps accompanying his chough survey, published in *Nature in Wales*, Winter, 1986-87, show interesting changes. In 1966-68 most was mapped as grass, a legacy from the era of farming. With the alleviation of grazing heather had made a big comeback right across the south by 1974, apart from a grassed strip along the exposed west and south-west cliffs. By 1982 a swathe of grass had returned through the centre of this heathland, bordered to both west and east by bracken, which was making considerable inroads in the south-east, being otherwise concentrated in the lee of the two hills and the sheltered north-east cliffs.

As May passed into June in 1969 the spring flowers were at their best. We all fell under the spell of the humpy 'prairies' of thrift in various shades of pink that spread across clifftops flecked with the blue of spring squill and white sea campion. The squill was particularly abundant in the north and was a great favourite with bumble bees. The old mounded walls were just as colourful, with rock spurrey, English stonecrop and plantains tucked between the tufts of thrift.

Fairy Ring Champignons and Bovista Puffballs.

May is not the most propitious season for fungi, but several fine fairy rings on the maritime turf caught our eye after we had brought the gear up the ladder to the quay and started the trek inland. These broken circles of fairy ring fungi are *Marasmius oreades*, and are particularly partial to maritime turf throughout Wales, although occurring also inland. As the underground mycelium spread from the central starting point here it was boosting the grass in the normal way to form the extra bright green ring, but was killing off the heather clumps.

Other May fungi were white puffballs, *Bovista nigrescens*, the outer skin gathered into the base instead of rising from a basal sterile column as in many puffballs. Their attachment to the threadlike rhizoids which bore them was fragile, so that they soon became detached and went bowling off across the slopes in the wind, shedding their myriad purple-brown spores as they bounced along.

Associated with the fairy rings near the landing were white campion and white dead nettle, both more characteristic of farmland than sea cliffs. More in keeping with the overall habitat were the sheltered gullies full of Scottish heather or ling and fine-leaved heath or bell heather and the ridges above, where the heather clumps were dead on the windward side with sea campion trailing over the moribund twigs as though to shelter the remains from the worst of the blast.

Another woody plant escaping from the gales was noticed here by Robert Drane in 1898, a prostrate subspecies of broom, which creeps along the ground both here and at Martin's Haven, *Cytisus scoparius ssp. prostratus.* The prostrate stems produce short shoots and tiny leaves, both covered with silky hairs. The only sites recorded in the official British flora of 1948 were cliffs in West Cornwall and on the Channel Islands. Drane had found it also on Rathlin Island in Northern Ireland.

He also discovered a Ramsey giant puffball, of which he writes:

RAMSEY II

'Lenorthis alata', Ordovician fossils, 1969.

Gorse topiarised by Rabbits and thickly sprinkled with their pellets.

Escape to Utopia, Sea Campion.

Massed Gorse among Bluebells.

BARDSEY I

Lighthouse beyond old lime kiln at hay time, 1984.

Nibbled Gorse by Old School House and Cristin.

Connemara Ponies.

Sheep maintained the closely rabbit-grazed turf after the 1983 Myxomatosis.

BARDSEY II

English Stonecrop invades among burned Gorse.

Sheep explore the new barricade on the Narrows.

Little Big Foot, the egg-shaped Bunny.

Foxgloves, a later stage after Gorse burning.

Honeysuckle on the 'Mountain'.

PUFFIN I

Three newly fledged Kittiwakes.

Puffin on Puffin Island limestone.

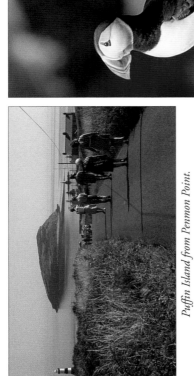

Puffin Island from Penmon Point.

Garden Tiger Moths from elders by ruined Norman church.

"We took it home, sliced it, fried it and ate it for breakfast, much to the doubt if not the disgust of the natives, who, finding that we suffered no harm, regarded us as gods and partook of one which we afterwards found on Skomer, and said that it was good."

Gorse was compact, as always by the sea, the moreso for the nibbling of the soft young shoots in spring by the rabbits instigating multiple branching just behind the tips. Sheep have the same effect in the Welsh Uplands, but there was only one sheep on Ramsey during our 1969 visit. So dense were the gorse bushes that even those that had attained to more than a metre high were used as meeting platforms and were covered with rabbit pellets, where bunnies scampered up the sides and sat atop the domes passing the time of day and exchanging pheromones as others do on anthills or mossy tree stumps.

These gorse bushes bore few flowers, and these below the level of the close-set spines. This is contrary to the norm, typical seaside gorse bushes, as in South-west Ireland and the Scillies, being far and away more floriferous than inland plants, forming veritable mounds of golden blossom and filling the air with their heady scent of pineapple with undertones of coconut and almond.

Rabbits and topiarised Heather.

Some of the Ramsey gorse clumps became undercut with the traffic of rabbits tunnelling beneath. These were the ones which 'got away', the basal gap preventing the rabbits from getting aboard. Free from their nibbling incisors, these shrubs produced gangling branches, showing that the mounded form was not caused by wind trimming but by rabbit trimming.

The same goes for the heathers. Wind trimming of these leaves only a straggle of dead, dried-out stems on the windward side, all new shoots growing to leeward so that the clumps move gradually away from the nip of the gales. Rabbit nibbling does not kill, but stimulates a dense, cushion-like growth of new shoots from ground level, over the top of those necessarily lower domes, as neat as any garden topiary. This is until and unless pressure becomes too great and the heather gives way to grass or bracken, as on many an overgrazed island or mountainside.

Between the tumps of gorse and heather are small unassuming plants such as doves-foot cranesbill, sea storksbill, sorrels, mouse-ear chickweeds, pearlworts, scorpion grasses (which are forget-me-nots) and real grasses, including the inevitable, distasteful fog. A small rare treasure here is the yellow centaury (*Cicendia filiformis*), a very local plant of cliff swards in the South-west, including Pembroke and South-west Ireland.

A legacy from the old rabbit farming days was the presence of piebald, grey, black and long-haired individuals, a presumed outcome of introduction of domestic stock. These dived into the 'air raid shelters' under the leggier gorse bushes when the outline of a cruising buzzard was spotted. Some had made short escape holes in the sides of anthills.

Our quarters at the bungalow were infiltrated by domestic fowl. Jemima, the duck, had a nest under a gorse bush, where she was assiduously incubating twenty infertile duck eggs (having no spouse to fertilise them) and one fertile goose egg. When George came to feed her she waddled, quacking matily, to the pond to meet him, but never let on where the nest was, wandering nonchalantly around until he was out of sight before returning. This instinct for secrecy had been retained through generations of domestication.

The geese were feral, a gaggle of females with a single, over protective, gander. One white goose and one brown were incubating eggs (hopefully fertile) on opposite sides of the same bramble bush. The gander and another brown goose, his current consort, spent a lot of time foraging together in a freshwater seepage.

There were plenty of wetland communities around the island, each differing slightly from the others. Jemima's pool, enriched by the droppings of Jemima and her friends, was characterised by duckweed – what else? Alongside were thickets of water starwort, beset with little green disc fruits although early in the season for these. The corner receiving seepage from the goose nest was occupied by watercress (not recommended for human consumption) and water blinks.

The golden orbs of the kingcups had changed to circlets of capsules as the leaves expanded to the strengthening sun, their place taken in the water by fool's watercress and marginally by the wispy flowers of ragged robin. Carnation sedge was flowering; yellow sedge about to, but queen of all the plants under Jemima's surveillance was the noble clump of royal fern among bordering brambles.

A larger pond not too far off had fronds of alternate-flowered water milfoil permeating the water with feathered leaves and fragile spikes of pink flowers breaking the surface in midsummer. More substantial were the pink flower spikes of water bistort pushing up between floating leaves. Fighting for space in the surrounding thicket of hemlock water dropwort were elegant plants of water speedwell with opposite branches bearing pale blue flowers.

Two tiny moorland pools at the south end of the island where the lapwings nested were filled with a thick vegetable soup of mosses and water starwort. Shoreweed crowded the shoreline, as on Skokholm and Skomer, the outermost, up-shore plants flowering. These pools had only the starwort in common with Jemima's well fertilised, eutrophic home waters.

Incorporated in the soup was water purslane; creeping among the shoreweed was marsh pennywort. Eleocharis spike-rush and lesser spear-wort merged with the sedges and soft rush, while pink-flowered lousewort infiltrated outwards among the heather.

A larger moorland pond and its satellite pools contained all the above plus the floating leaves of bog pond-weed (*Potamogeton polygonifolius*) and the hair-like submerged ones of small pond-weed (*Potamogeton berchtoldii*), also ivy-leaved mud crowfoot (*Ranunculus hederaceus*) with little white buttercup flowers.

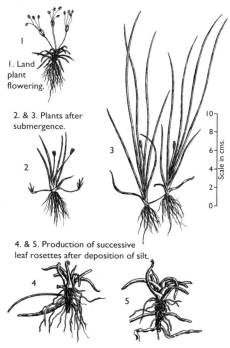

1. Land plant flowering.

2. & 3. Plants after submergence.

4. & 5. Production of successive leaf rosettes after deposition of silt.

Shoreweed, different growth phases.

195

Feathery-leaved lesser marshwort was exclusively dominant in one of the smaller pools where water was nearly half a metre deep, while tiny bristle sedge (*Isolepis [Scirpus] cernuus*) covered the bed of another the same size which had almost dried out.

Twenty-seven species occurred here, not counting the heather, which seemed to be dead by drowning on the little islets amidships. Early lady's smock was succeeded by delicate bog pimpernel and bog stitchwort, with marsh bedstraw, flote grass and bulbous rush. It was interesting to see the blue spikes of bugle pushing up through the surrounding heather, as this is usually a woodland plant and rabbits were not going to allow the heather to grow up and shelter it as bracken would have done.

A nearby ditch nourished a strip of sharp-flowered rush, spearwort and silverweed. Marginal colour was supplied by greater birds-foot trefoil, creeping buttercup and marsh forget-me-not, the whole drowsing in an aroma of water mint. Bordering the standing water were common sorrel and purple moor grass.

The acid nature of all these aquatic floras apart from Jemima's Pool showed how necessary that well-used lime kiln was to get decent crops and nutritious grass to grow on these acid volcanic tuffs.

*   *   *

Small mammals finding cover on moorland and farmland were common shrews and bank voles, the voles the same as those tunnelling in mossy woodland banks on the mainland. Only Skomer has the big bank vole with heftier skull and kindlier temperament. It has been suggested that these may be the remains of a formerly more widespread population, pushed back to that island by the more agile common bank vole. Either that or that it had evolved on Skomer, but, whichever way, why not also on the other islands?

Brown rats came ashore in the 1800s from a grain ship which foundered just off the island, and proceeded to decimate the large puffin colony and threaten any shearwaters that may have been present then. An archive of 1717 says of the puffins – "Vast numbers . . . living on fish and having a very fishy taste so that they were always allowed to be eaten in lent". A flimsy excuse is better than none. Today's puffins are restricted to a small group on the North Bishop, with none left on the main island.

The rats apparently remained mostly around the farm buildings, but they continued to pose a threat to the shearwaters. These last were not very obvious at that time, but about a thousand pairs were thought to be breeding around the cliffs and on the hills in 2000, these rafting impressively on offshore waters prior to their evening homecoming. They were first proved nesting in 1968, when four eggs were seen. By our second visit in 1971 twenty occupied burrows had been found. These were hidden among bracken and bluebells on the western cliff-top, well away from the farm-based rats, which had evidently decreased when the grain store and poultry feed were no longer available. (The ducks and geese were free range grazers and not grain dependant.)

Plant growth seemed so thick as to impede the shearwaters in their comings and goings until more moved in to open up the habitat, but at least the peaty soil provided a soft digging medium. A two month survey in the late 1990s resulted in the recording of 13,098 burrows on the island. Many of these would belong to rabbits, but in 1999 volunteers went round a representative sample playing a recorded version of shearwater calls, to register the number of responses from male birds within.

At the turn of the century a blitz was launched against the rats and this proved completely successful. Fourteen hundred tubes containing the bait blocks were set out at close intervals around the island and fifteen thousand of the blocks were taken. By the time Charles Martin arrived on Ramsey in July 2001, there was no evidence of continuing rat activity on the island. A beneficial spin-off was an increase in the number of ground-nesting wheatears. Cats, too, had supposedly been exterminated, but one was seen in June 2002.

Much of our 1969 sea-bird watching centred around the south-easterly headland between Abermyharan and Foel Fawr, where we could also watch choughs probing in the turf for grubs, as green woodpeckers probe anthills for ants, sometimes flicking their heads back to send a davit of turf flying. A botanical bonus was a cluster of the big island form of fleshy buck's-horn plantain.

A count of guillemots in 1998 yielded 3,240 birds – a welcome increase of ten per cent over the previous count. Razorbills were fewer, kittiwakes were associated with the plethora of islets lying to the south, as well as being part of the island's finest sea-bird spectacle on the four hundred foot high cliffs of Trwyn Bendro in the middle west. Here kittiwakes nested closest to the sea, razorbills and guillemots on the main face and the shoreline gulls near the summit. Fulmars sailed by, fearlessly close, casting inquisitive glances in our direction at each passing.

Two unexpected members of this family of tube-nosed birds, the Procellariiformes, turned up on Ramsey later, in 1979. These were a black-browed albatross and a sooty shearwater, the first wide-ranging over the Southern Ocean, the second the subject of the Maori mutton bird industry in New Zealand. Had they travelled from the Southern Hemisphere together, or been wafted in on the same winds? They were in a very different category from other specialists turning up that year, like the osprey, the wryneck and the Richard's pipit

Shags were present, particularly in the west, where they were associated with the caves, nesting above these on shady north faces, with the choughs nesting on ledges inside and foraging above in groups of four or five. The inevitable three large gull species were present in modest numbers, while fulmars were clustered on the south side of Aber Mawr and oyster-catchers scattered throughout. There were no storm petrels, but we had offshore sightings of tysties or black guillemots, gannets and terns.

Curlew, whimbrel and dunlin came to the ponds to forage and we also saw stock doves. The domestic pigeons were kept constantly on the move by the peregrines, a pair of which quartered the island. The 1969 warden had not seen these falcons for a month but the boatman maintained that they were nesting. Eight gulls were harrying one, like bombers attacking a fighter which easily out-manoeuvred them. The falcon sometimes turned upside down, presenting its talons to attackers from above and putting them to rout.

Buzzards are meek by nature and resort to no such tactics. Two white fluffy chicks were present in their cliff face nest at the end of May, their parents often mobbed by the ravens, whose young had flown from their twiggy cliff face nest long since, one with tail and wing feathers now missing. Young carrion crows in their cliff nests were near to fledging. Jackdaws were breeding in holes all round the cliffs so we could not see what stage their young had reached. Kestrels concentrated their hunting flights over the west coast.

Four nestlings cheeped urgently from the pied wagtail's nest tucked into a niche in the old farmhouse wall. A turret of pennywort bells sprouted from the crevice immediately above, making a pretty picture when the black and white parent arrived with food.

The usual rock and meadow pipits, wheatears and skylarks were about, along with more homely birds like blackbird, dunnock, stonechat, linnet and three pairs of reed buntings. All three hirundines graced the scene, including sand martins, these joined by swifts at the end of May.

*   *   *

In 1971 we enjoyed a boat trip round the island, which enabled us to peer deep into the western caves and obtain panoramic views of the bird colonies from the sea. Choughs' nests were not visible, but there was a bird on watch outside each breeding cave, alert for danger.

A sparrow hawk had built its bulky nest of sticks for the first time low down in an old elder by a spreading clump of willow near the farm. Swooping off to slip unobtrusively down a cliff gully, it revealed four whitish mottled eggs. These birds need large feeding territories and it is unlikely that the island could hold more than two pairs.

We watched two cuckoos being seen off by a meadow pipit, with good reason, and had a rare opportunity to sort out the difference between predator and parasite, which could seem so similar if they failed to call.

Three pairs of buzzards shared the island hunting, these requiring smaller territories than bird-eating falcons, when rabbits were as thick

Sparrow Hawk's nest near the bungalow.

on the ground as here. One nest, tucked below a clump of triquetrous garlic, contained a single chick in down. A young, unpaired bird was prospecting in the south of the island, as though intent on setting up a fourth homeland. These are cliff nesters, like the ravens and carrion crows, not relishing the brief cover that the sparrow hawk was risking. A batch of young ravens started leaving their nest on 30th May, with one less at home each day.

The hovering kestrel that dropped onto prey, shrew or vole, outside the bungalow, took its catch to a nearby rock, holding it underfoot to tear it to pieces. The sun that highlighted its yellow legs was backlighting a family of rabbits, changing their ears to a transparent pink atop a halo of light.

A pair of short-eared owls was nesting on the steep inland slope of the middle western knoll, apparently a first for recent years, and we had splendid views of a third, a paler intruder. Only once did we see a lapwing mobbing one of these owls, although they would rise to chase everything else off, even a passing buzzard. Little owls were about and shags ogled up at us from a nest a metre or so away.

Oyster-catcher nests among thrift clumps still contained their trios of eggs, as did a skylark's nest found among tussocky red fescue. Stonechats were breeding, the whinchat just passing through. Stories of wrens eating fish had always been pooh-poohed until someone produced a photograph of one holding a minnow!

Robert Drane (*Trans. CNS XXXIII*, 1900-1901) reported the fate of some of the small passerines on the Bishop's lighthouse. He visited the rock on June 10th, 1898 and questioned the lighthouse keepers about these. Fatalities occurred in spring and autumn when the migrants were passing through. The men regularly found reed warblers, spotted flycatchers, wheatears and lesser redpolls to be victims. In May whitethroats sometimes died, night after night. Nightjars in August and one swallow had come to grief on 20th March. In thick fog storm petrel and guillemot had fallen foul of the lantern, but sea-birds normally stayed clear.

Ramsey, with its average of five hundred and five Atlantic grey seal pups born each year, is the leading seal nursery in West Wales. Eighteen pups were branded with a W here on 26th October, 1946, these the first to be so marked in the UK. Of these two bulls were recovered at Ramsey, one as a twelve-year-old and one at fourteen years old, with a cow on Skomer in 1967, by then twenty-one years old.

*Atlantic Grey Seals,
cow and pup.*

Examination of three hundred marked grey seals in later years showed the oldest cow to be thirty-four and the oldest bull twenty-three. Nearly two hundred pups were marked by the West Wales Field Society prior to 1966. The 1973 count recorded one thousand two hundred and fifty adult seals in Pembrokeshire – only half the 1994 count of four thousand.

Common seals have dished faces and are very rare on this coast, with one record for Skokholm in 1963 and one with a hundred and forty Atlantic seals on a mainland beach in 1967.

I always enjoyed watching them feed, a leisurely business that could last a full hour when they were tackling a big skate, two feet across in both directions. They were not very good at holding onto their catch, which skated frequently from their foreflippers, causing them to dive to retrieve it as it floated down. Were they, perhaps, just playing, cat fashion? Fastidious feeders, they made a very neat job of it. The meal over, the backbone, tail and fins would remain connected to the skin of the fish's back, with all the flesh eaten cleanly away.

Two oiling incidents affected Ramsey in 1975, these harming birds rather than seals. She received the worst of a slick from the *Esso Tenby* on 13th April, when a hundred and fifty-five auks, mainly guillemots, were badly oiled and presumed to have died, with six hundred and fifty others, including kittiwakes, more lightly oiled.

Anangel Friendship caused a spillage at the end of May, leaking oil in Milford Haven and mooring the following day in St. Brides Bay. The Department of Trade and Industry sent a tug out with dispersants and the casualties were few, but the closeness of these two incidents shows how vulnerable the wildlife is to this scourge.

*   *   *

It was good to be able to renew my acquaintance with Ramsey on a long weekend with the Cardiff Naturalists' Society in mid June 1994. Our departure from St. Justinian's, the port of embarkation, was delayed by a practice launching of the St. David's lifeboat, an interesting experience, as it swooshed down the long slipway to create a fine bow wave on entering the sea.

We crossed the turbulent Ramsey Sound in *Sea Vixen II*, moving in along the north side of the Bitches and Whelps to the now so tranquil harbour, where gulls idled on placid waters that would once have sent them bowling out to sea on the six knot current. Sue Ward, warden during the nine years from 1988 to 1996, came to welcome us ashore. It was evident that the island was much more geared to visitors now, with a little shop at the farmhouse selling leaflets, postcards and refreshments and hiring out binoculars.

Traditional farming had ceased by this time and there had been no sheep for a while, but a small flock of mountain and downland breeds

had been introduced recently to help the rabbits in keeping the swards down to chough-friendly and wheatear-friendly levels. The only grazers we saw were little groups of red deer, survivors from the former production of venison, fearlessly grazing the greener northern fields or lolling among the fern.

A charming plant still to be found in the bracken understorey, was climbing Corydalis, a relative

Red Deer.

of the pink-flowered fumitories, but with pale lemon flowers and sprawling habit. Sheep's-bit grew particularly tall, each globose head resembling a small scabious. Thrift and bluebells were past their prime, but spring squills still flowered on the windy hilltops, although mainland plants had dried up long since.

Tracts of heather had recently been burned, leaving bare ground which had been colonised by English stonecrop, the leaves and stems a dark red, suggesting water stress. Some of the gorse formed a level but spiky ground cover, possibly regenerating after an earlier fire. It behoved us to study the ground carefully before we sat down. Preferable resting places were the banks where the wild thyme grew.

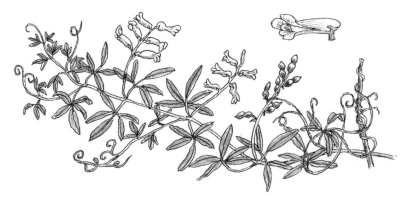

Climbing Corydalis or Fumitory.

Subsidiary species were a mixture of heathland and dune plants, tormentil, heath speedwell and milkwort in the first category, dewberry, burnet rose and lady's finger or kidney vetch in the second. Clifftops boasted swards of sea plantain as well as buck's-horn plantain. Most spectacular at this season were the showy spikes of foxgloves which speared skywards on both maritime heath and farmland. Rarities which we failed to see were subterranean clover and fiddle dock.

Some of the seven to eight pairs of choughs put on a fine display of tumbling flight, exploiting the fickle winds in what could only have been play. A kestrel passed above them, then a peregrine in pursuit of a rabble of feral pigeons. Twelve pairs of lapwing had bred this year, the last of the chicks just hatched. Now that these birds are so scarce throughout the UK compared with a decade ago, this is the last surviving lapwing colony in Pembrokeshire.

Wheatears, dapper as ever in their breeding plumage, were rather thin on the ground, their numbers checked by the rats. When those were eliminated a few years later, the population responded, rising from forty-two territory holders in the year 2000 to seventy-two in 2001.

Time ashore in 1994 did not allow for full exploration, so some of us kept to the more natural southern end. This was an area of contrast, with quite thick scrub clinging to the cliffs of Abermyharan, mostly spiky blackthorn, but with hawthorn, elder and wild privet, as well as the small scrub-dwelling passerines that go with them. This possible relic vegetation from a distant past, grades out through bracken to heather heathland, with sea campion looking oddly out of keeping.

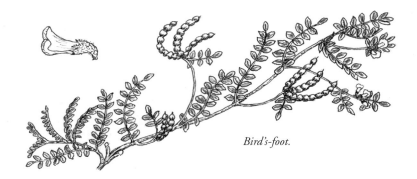

Bird's-foot.

More to be expected, although generally rare, were the little bird's-foot (*Ornithopus perpusillus*) and small-flowered buttercup.

Scrambling up the cone-shaped tump of Foel Fawr in the far south, we gazed our fill at the forbidding shapes of the southern islets, with the sea surging between them. Sheep and rabbits were formerly quartered there, despite the difficulties of harvesting the fleeces and pelts, but they have been ungrazed for many years now. A cacaphonous colony of lesser black-backed and herring gulls occupied the summit of the largest, Ynys Bery, which is Welsh for the Island of Peregrines.

We had arrived at low water, mounting tall intertidal steps, and left at high water, descending wooden stairs to the lower quay. Both ways were an improvement on the ladder of our earlier visits, but were soon to be superceded by massive works producing a series of four broad concrete platforms to gain the upper levels. This new low tide landing stage took three months to build and was completed in October 2001.

Rock chiselled from the cliff to make way for the slabs was bagged up and taken by boat to the inner harbour to strengthen the sea defences. A flight of steps now leads from the uppermost platform to a new galvanised steel boardwalk with safety handrails shaped to follow the curve of the rock.

In past years we would have scoffed at so much pandering to comfort, detracting from the spirit of adventure engendered by this sort of life. Now that we old timers are waxing more decrepit with time but are still functional, we welcome them. The magic of the islands has not faded for the aging population that served its apprenticeship on Skokholm and Skomer in the middle of the last century!

*　　　*　　　*

As an octogenarian in June 2002 I was, indeed, able to sample these new landing facilities. We arrived at high water, mounting the same slatted stairway in the walled off gully as before, but left at low water from the new concrete slabs laid with such determination during the brief intervals of the ebb.

Hovering on the brink until the boat rose to the appropriate level on a rolling pulse of water funnelling through the bottleneck and stepping onto the gunwhale was no problem. Organising unresponsive limbs into the bowells of the craft was accomplished with less elegance and a wave of nostalgia for the days of long ago, when everything was in good working order.

Stalwarts ashore and afloat were adepts at bundling the less agile aboard and ashore across the gap with no mishaps, but I couldn't help contrasting these public excursions with others run by the American Audubon Society in New England. There almost any undulations of the sea had been regarded as a hazard for our Cardiff party and landing was cancelled. Maybe the prevailing westerlies left their side of the Atlantic quieter than ours, where such a degree of caution is impractical.

The wind was spiteful on this 15th June, drawing tears from the eyes as we waited on the St. Justinian's lifeboat slip before ever we scrambled aboard to the sound of scrunching paintwork and headed into it. Our seaworthy little craft hugged the mainland coast to the south at first, branching out across the channel at its narrowest point, where cattle had been swum across in the past.

It was one of those grey days with intermittent showers which seem to dog our present summers, with no break in the blanket of low cloud and the breeze failing to dispel the mist that veiled what should have been a fine panorama of St. David's Head and Whitesands Bay. The advertised schedule was one and a half hours around the island and three hours ashore, but the wizened boatman warned us that the first might have to be curtailed.

Desultory gulls coasted above the sullen waves, dipping occasionally to retrieve some abandoned morsel. A gannet came volplaning past, joy-riding on the wind, to be lifted again on rigid wings. Another followed, off duty from the Grassholm colony away to the south. Then there was a little party of kittiwakes, in aerial balet above the dancing, white-flecked wavelets of the broken water to leeward of the Bitches and Whelps.

We drew into the less agitated sea under the island cliffs, headed for Abermyharan, where clear ultramarine water slid smoothly past the vertical pre-Cambrian faces. In better weather these would have reflected the blue of the sky: today they were a deep bottle-green, grading to turquoise as they slapped against our hull, and seemingly bottomless.

Denied the best of the sea-bird cliffs on the western side, we nosed in close to a small nesting site under Foel Fawr. Razorbills zoomed on and off their breeding ledges, small, rapidly flapping wings keeping their plump bodies on courses straight as arrows. Their chicks were still quite small and barely visible among the shadows on the ancient rocks. They were close above the sea and would not have far to fall when their time came to leave.

On a ledge above, like china ornaments on a mantelpiece overlooking the bustle of activity below, was a row of dusky brown guillemots. Fulmars swept past on rigid wings and a shag spread similarly still but angled wings to dry on an offshore rock.

We backed out and moved on, to peer through the gap between the main island and Ynys Cantwr ('Chanter'), first of the southern islets. The peak of Ynys Gwelltog ('Grassy') just beyond obscured part of the view, but we caught a glimpse of the lighthouse on the South Bishop, faintly visible through the cloying mist.

Then we were moving along in the lee of Ynys Bery ('Peregrine'), largest and most distant of the outliers. A mixed flock of herring and lesser black-backed gulls frolicked in the playful south-westerly breasting the slopes which they no longer shared with sheep. It was only on ungrazed cliffs such as these that the lemon-yellow kidney vetch and harebell-blue sheep's-bit reached their full potential.

The skipper emerged from the forrard cabin to confirm that the sea was too lively to proceed this way, so we would back-track and get as far round the northern end as possible. A shame. I had hoped very much to peer into those dark western caves where the choughs nest.

The tide was falling and more of the Bitches and Whelps were above water, stretching almost half way across the sound into the six knot current of the main channel. We passed alarmingly close to the outermost. Obviously there was deep water here, as there was beside the innermost around which we later sidled into port.

Just beyond was a veritable jacuzzi of froth and bubble, where gulls seemed to be profiting from the shoals of little fish near the surface. An oyster-catcher on a rock newly emerged from the tide, ceased its probing for shellfish to voice its oft-repeated, slightly panic-stricken bad tidings to the passing boat.

Although fresh water is traditionally short on islands and Ramsey depended on its own catchment, there was no problem at present. Recent downpours had replenished the bogs and springs and settled in puddles across the paths. At the Waterings a lively little waterfall was tumbling down the cliff and wasting its precious contents in the ocean. Had we been putting in to replenish our water barrels, we should not have needed to bail.

A little beyond was a deep declivity, Chapel Cove?, and then the yellow-orange scar of an old stone quarry in the upper cliff, the split surfaces unsoftened by colonising plants. Grassy slopes to either side, pocked with inumerable rabbit holes and alive with frisking bunnies, slithered down to the cliff brink.

Soon we were rounding the north-east point and able to breath deeply of clean sea air. On the way up the coast diesel fumes from the exhaust had destroyed any illusions about the quality of the briny atmosphere. This is one of the paradoxes of travel in open power boats. The following wind was travelling faster than we were and overtaking, with its burden of fumes. Or was it our fault for occupying the stern seat under the immoderately flapping red ensign?

A headland under the northern height was composed of massive sedimentary beds displaced almost to the vertical by a volcanic intrusion pushing up into the inlet behind – one of those striking geological phenomena where naturalists pray for sunshine and reach for their cameras.

Then there was the great storm beach of Aber Mawr, where waves have piled the cobbles above tide level, allowing a good proportion of Ramsey's five hundred plus breeding cow seals to pull out and drop their pups. This would not be until August and September and we saw only two today, regarding us with interest from the water. With no sunshine there was little point in hauling out to bask on sun-warmed seaweed.

A little path zig-zagged down to the southern end of the beach, part amidships lost to erosion. This is where seal workers descend to monitor, measure and mark the pups. The circular track for the public followed this section of the clifftop and a line of trippers with rucksacks paused in their passage along it to peer down. We were the only human element in their vista of open sea, as they were in our view of the empty landscape.

We finally turned back where the coast bulges westwards around the

Ramsey Farmhouse in May 2002.

high point of Carn Llundain about halfway down the west side, far enough out to be able to glimpse the South Bishop lighthouse again crouched, like its fellow islands, almost invisible on a nebulous horizon. Speeding back across the sound, we dropped a few passengers at the lifeboat station and roared back to the island landing.

This last lap, headed into the wind, was bitterly cold, every layer of garments welcome, and it was good to see the notice "Hot Coffee" as we trudged up from the warden's welcoming spiel towards the farmhouse. The others set off on the island circuit, but warden Simon, the only staff member here today, brewed us a welcome cuppa before haring off about his business. We adjourned to savour the brew on a seat placed strategically out of the wind and dedicated to Sue Ward, who had been in charge here on my last visit eight years before. Could it be all that while ago? How time flies!

We lingered over our sandwiches, well entertained by the local birds. First and foremost was the chough, rollicking along the fenceline bounding the home paddock, our views of these from the boat having been somewhat fleeting. The red bill is preceded by a yellow-orange one in young birds.

Then there were the wheatears, engaged in their relentless search for victuals over grass mown shorter by the rabbits than could have been achieved by any mower. A quick run, a jab into the turf and then onto the next rock, where they drew themselves up to their full height, as depicted in many of the bird books, to spy out the next sign of movement. There were seventy pairs of wheatears on the island at present, this thought to be the largest collection in Wales. A pipit perched for a while on the fence but left the foraging to the wheatears.

Setting off on our amble to the south, we were soon brought up short by the frenetic activity of a family of whitethroats in a thorn bush at the further end of the garden. Two birds were constantly crossing from there to the bracken-filled valley of the little stream, perching in passing on the wire, and we thought they must be feeding young. Coming abreast of the bramble and thorn we saw more, so the family had fledged and was playing hide and seek among the branches. A blackbird was singing in the ferny hollow. It was good to see these homely hedgerow birds infiltrating the harsher terrain of the ocean-goers.

The garden, with its cabbage plants and protective marigold patch, was double-fenced, by the original hedge and an inner layer of rabbit-proof wire netting. Peter Rabbit and some of Beatrix Potter's other characters were exploring hopefully between the two, but with no joy. Outside the hedge their contemporaries were everywhere, hipperty-hopping in, over and under all and sundry. My companion, Clive, was suitably impressed, not having been on this sort of island before.

The Normans, who brought the first rabbits in from Morocco and Spain a few years after the battle of Hastings, could have had no idea what they were starting – not that they were likely to have cared. The estimated population of rabbits on Ramsey in the year of our lord 2002 was sixty to eighty thousand.

A fully grown white one sat his ground on a slope so distant that the normal brown ones could only be picked out from the dun-coloured moorland with binoculars. If the black ones we had seen from the boat had stood out like sore thumbs, this one stood out like one with an extra large bandage. The only likely predators were the island buzzards, but Alice's white rabbit remained unperturbed, contemplating the world at large on the open hillside, which was, in fact, riddled with handy bolt holes, like all the rest.

Peregrines, kestrels and ravens also nested here, as potential hazards, but it was the magpies and carrion crows that were keeping the lapwing numbers down. We passed the notice "Track closed. Lapwings nesting" to give the survivors a sporting chance. Only five young had fledged successfully from the seven pairs, early broods having been decimated by the two egg-thieving Corvids. There were too many of both, as also of jackdaws. Linnets and stonechats were the only others to put in an appearance in this nibbled, trampled and wind-shorn wilderness. Not even a skylark had defied the greyness to lift its voice in song.

A few fawns had been born to the red deer herd but these were very secretive and remained hidden. I was intrigued, as always, by the rabbit-induced topiary of the gorse bushes. Some were cut back to simple domes, most to more complex mounded forms like cumulus clouds viewed from a 'plane. Shorn so tightly, the myriad new stem spines had to remain parallel if they were to emerge at all. All seemed much the same length, so none protruded to inflict injury. The result was a sturdy cushion as cosy as the bristly doormat enjoyed by my feral cats.

To judge by the scattered rabbit pellets on top, they were well used. I was minded of a rabbit population I had worked with on an island in Saldanah Bay off South Africa, where rabbits hopped up a stairway of massed cormorant nests to graze the succulent tops of the Zygophyllum bushes (Gillham, *Salt Wind from the Cape*, 2004).

Some of Ramsey's rabbit meeting sites were undercut, affording escape from winged predators. Plants beneath were limited to three main species, wood sage, ground ivy and foxglove, the last not flowering, although there were plenty around the island that were. These, along with red campion, carried the pink banner over the hiatus from the spring swards of thrift to the autumn ones of heather – this also largely topiarised and unlikely to throw the noble flowering shoots of mainland stands.

Before returning to the quay we explored the renovated farm buildings clustered around a yard floored by bedrock in situ. The stonework and stone troughs were masterpieces of craftsmanship but we were most intrigued by the row of pigsties along the western boundary.

The stout stone, wind-excluding walls of these were too high for the pig to look out or the pig keeper to look in. They were adorned with fleshy spikes of wall pennywort, pink bouquets of English stonecrop and swathes of pellitory-of-the-wall. These last had shed their seeds to generate a thick fringe of pellitory seedlings along the wall bases. Occupying crevices were elegant maidenhair spleenwort ferns and chunky sea spleenwort, this last seldom found away from sea cliffs. Cushioning all was an impressive array of lichens.

Along one side wall of each sty was a long stone feeding trough and

Stone chute leading into pigsty trough, with Wall Pennywort.

a chute led in from a hole in the front wall, independent of this. The problem was solved when we found a chute with a smaller, squarer trough below – one for liquids and one for solids? The untrodden cobbled floors bore flat rosettes of sea storksbill and tufts of scorpion grass peppered with tiny blue forget-me-not flowers.

Up some new wooden stairs in the last renovated room of the backing barn was an eco-friendly public loo – no water, no smell, all achieved by aerobic digestion. The former reign of island Elsans had bowed out in favour of all mod cons, with emphasis on the mod.

12

BARDSEY: UPLAND, FARMLAND, WETLAND AND SHORE

Bardsey Island, lying off the tip of the delightfully rural and scenic Lleyn Peninsula, is a must for all Welsh island-goers. It is the only one of the island nature reserves with a full time warden which is not managed by an 'official' body.

The idea of a Bardsey Island Field and Bird Observatory was mooted in 1951 and in 1953 an observatory committee was formed representing the inhabitants, the West Wales Field Society, the West Midlands Bird Club and other interested parties, under the guidance of the late William Condry, naturalist, writer, broadcaster and teacher.

Cristin Farmhouse, the future bird observatory, was rented, a permanent summer warden installed and four Heligoland bird traps erected. When the island came up for sale in 1975 for the second time in five years, this collection of dedicated people set about raising the necessary £200,000 to buy and maintain it, in the hope of preventing possible destruction or development of this valuable SSSI. In 1977 the Bardsey Island Trust Ltd. was incorporated and registered as a charity. Funds accrued and the island was bought, hopefully for posterity.

Although not so far west as the Pembrokeshire Islands, it is literally out on a limb, just missed by most of the road maps. Bardsey Sound, like the other 'Sounds between', is subject to the whims of unruly tides and currents of up to six knots, but the island is open, by arrangement, to visitors, for single day or longer term stays.

It is possible to cross from Aberdaron near the tip of the Lleyn in half an hour when conditions are good. As depicted by rather horrendous footage on the TV news of a boat trying to reach the stranded islanders in one of the many winter storms of early 2002, however, conditions are not always good.

A more popular voyage is from Pwllheli on the south-facing coast. This takes three hours, the first part heading south past Llanbedrog and Abersoch to the twinned St. Tudwall's Islands, the second part west round

Trwyn Cilan Head and across Hell's Mouth, with Rhiw and Aberdaron and so across the sound.

This last, like Jack Sound and Ramsey Sound, is the passage created when the island was nipped from the tip of a headland extending out

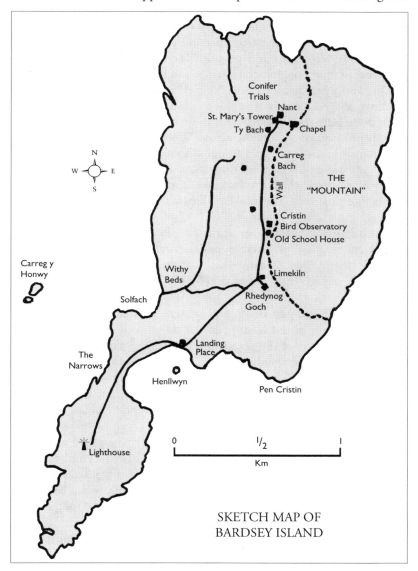

SKETCH MAP OF
BARDSEY ISLAND

into the Irish Sea. This one is the northern arm of Cardigan Bay, which forms the West Wales coastline right down to Pembrokeshire. As with the Smalls, Bardsey represents the last gasp of its parental peninsula before that finally surrenders to the sea.

Its rocks, like those of Ramsey, are some of the oldest known – pre-Cambrian – laid down some 580-610 million years ago. Some are sedimentary, some volcanic, partly metamorphosed and intruded at later dates by various basalts and granites. Here are volcanic tuffs, basalts, quartzite, marble, conglomerate, jasper and much more.

One and three quarter miles (2.8km) from end to end, the island is saucepan shaped, balanced on a long thin handle pointing south. The main body bulging eastward, with the more substantial highland at its base, is just over one kilometre across. Where the pan handle meets the pan is an isthmus less than a hundred feet (30m) from shore to shore. This, unlike the cliffy Skomer isthmus, is only a few feet above sea level and is of sand and clay, so vulnerable to marine erosion. Excluding the weedy intertidal zone, the total land area is four hundred and forty acres (178ha).

Much has been written about the people and natural history of the island, culminating in Peter Hope-Jones' definitive hardback pulling together the findings of naturalists over the years in his excellent *The Natural History of Bardsey* published by the National Museum of Wales in 1985.

The ecclesiastical past is also well known, the legend of twenty thousand saints being buried in its hallowed acres much quoted. Bearing in mind the sparseness of the population in monkish times, and its degree of unlawfulness, one wonders how so many corpses of holy men could have been rounded up and shipped across the stormy waters to peace at last north-west of the island 'mountain'! Nevertheless, the tall Celtic Cross at Nant nearby, was erected in their memory. Perhaps the qualifications for sainthood were a little elastic?

St. Cadfan is the name associated with the first monastic settlement on Bardsey, this in the fifth century. St. Mary's Abbey or Friary is attributed to both the eighth and the thirteenth century by different writers. It is thought to have been built by Augustinian monks when the Celtic Church was giving way to Catholicism. The still impressive ruined tower is all that now remains.

This account centres around the observations and impressions gained by a Cardiff party which spent a week on the island at the end of June

1984. That was not a typical week, being at the height of a long drought with much of the vegetation withered and the ponds dried out. While plant life was under stress, there was still enough moisture to keep the nectar-seeking butterflies dancing in the sunshine, while panting sea-birds could drop off the cliffs into the ocean to cool down, leaving others sheltered in their burrows.

We embarked from Pwllheli, the St. Tudwall's Islands looming on the horizon like a couple of hump-back whales, their mounded shapes outlined against a hazy purple background of the Snowdonia Mountains. White lighthouse buildings topped the higher hump of the more westerly – so far above the waves, that we wondered how often its warning beacon was eclipsed by cloud or mist.

Passing alongside, we had fine views of the parallel strata set at an angle of forty-five degrees to the waves creaming gently along the cliff base. The oblique ledges created a dark divide between the parched turf above and the similarly pale barnacle zone below. These rocks are part of the ancient system that crops up again on Anglesey to the north.

Common Dolphins.

We crossed the two mile wide Bardsey Sound on the gentlest of swells. Some say that it was the facing of the possible perils of this crossing that earned the pilgrims of old as much merit from three pilgrimages to Bardsey as from one to Rome. We earned no merit on that account today. The island's Welsh name, Ynys Enlli, translates as 'Island in the tide race'. Harbour porpoises and four species of dolphins, common, bottle-nosed, Rissos and beaked, are seen in these waters, but we sought them in vain.

The landing is at the little harbour where the coast dips into the eastern bay near the junction of the narrow and the more lumpy part. Our salt-crusted craft edged into a long inlet between weed-covered reefs. Low sea walls backed by pebbles reinforced the natural shoreline and a couple of boats were drawn up below the big rusting winch.

As we carried the gear up the concrete slipway we had our first close-up view of the ancient contorted rocks. Knowing these to be acid, it was a surprise to see the lime-loving yellow stonecrop growing alongside the acid-loving pink English stonecrop – which is so much commoner in Wales and Scotland than in England, despite the misnomer. The anomaly was solved when we were told that this was the spot where the heli-copter servicing the island had dropped a load of lime.

The one lane leads north to the monastic remains and dwellings and south to the lighthouse. We headed north, half of us bedding down in the Bird Obsevatory at Cristin, just beyond the old stone schoolhouse, and the others in houses further along. The island is virtually treeless apart from withy beds and walled gardens, but the densest tree growth was in the Cristin garden, where the bird-ringers erected their mist nets.

From the back garden wall, skirted by drifts of foxgloves, rose 'the mountain', which only qualifies for half of that designation by reaching to five hundred and forty-eight feet (168m) before dropping precipi-tously to the western shore of the sound.

*   *   *

Here, on the backbone of the island, we enjoyed Nature in the raw, scarcely influenced by the farming that used the rest and displaying ribs of naked rock with some unexpected plants couched in the crevices. They were as secure from marauding sheep and rabbits there as those which grow in the grikes of the very different limestone pavements of other islands, such as the Arans of County Clare.

Beyond these hideouts a combination of drought and grazing pro-duced a baldness on the shallow soil lapping against the rock faces that accentuated the lushness of the crevice plants. These escaped direct sun-light and drying winds as well as gnawing incisors and must have posed a sore temptation to the grazers nimble enough to get close.

Robust growths of orpine or live-long (*Sedum telephium*) were tucked into crannies of the steep east face just under the summit. Turgid suc-culent leaves with scalloped edges fell half way between those of the sturdy ice plants that lure so many butterflies to our gardens and the roseroot of Aran's grikes.

All three are Sedums, but very different from the creeping stonecrops

The Orpine or Livelong.

that typify that genus for most of us. While roseroot is a plant of the limestone, orpine has wider tolerances, its rare occurrences in Glamorgan ranging from the limestones of the Gower cliffs to the acid coalfield crags at the top of the Rhondda Valleys. The spreading pink flower heads that unfurl from June to September push up among soft green hart's-tongue ferns, buttercups and Poa meadow grasses. According to the botany books, they are woodland plants, as are so many of the grike and crevice floras which are denied the luxury of woodlands by grazing animals.

Less ebullient, but sprouting likewise from upper vertical faces, was lesser meadow rue (*Thalictrum minus*). The temptation here for hungry herbivores was the delicacy of the foliage, which resembles that of the maidenhair ferns of humid greenhouses rather that the juicy succulence

Lesser Meadow Rue.

of the orpine. The pale yellow flowers were thrust against the backing cliff, frail and wispy, and quite unlike the rest of their buttercup family.

Rigid shining fronds of sea spleenwort were tucked back in nooks well away from the pepperings of spray that most of these ferns receive. The accompanying sea campion was in full flower in late June, whereas most in the open bore only bloated, straw-coloured fruiting calyces.

It was this difference of vigour rather than rarity that characterised most of the crevice plants, two of which were legumes. Bird's-foot trefoil burgeoned out against a matrix of grey-green lichens and kidney vetch pushed from among lax dandelion leaves, which are on the menu for all grazers, including human salad eaters.

Wall pennywort was well represented, as an almost obligate crevice plant. Wood sage might have fared better in the open elsewhere but often chose not to here. Sheeps-bit was doing particularly well on these resistant shining rocks with their criss-crossing veins of quartz. Their tight leaf rosettes and blue globes sprinkled with coral pink anthers on this windy summit contrasted with the orange-brown of the fruiting heads. They bore an overall resemblance to the Globularia of like situations in the European Alps – a case of evolutionary convergence of unrelated plants coping with similar environmental hazards.

A few woody species were rooted in the deeper clefts, principally blackthorn and ivy, along with golden rod, bluebell and even the odd primrose. We failed to find the Wilson's filmy fern (*Hymenophyllum wilsonii*) which is said to grow here. It was interesting to find so many chough feathers, primaries from wings and tails, caught up in these plants. Had they blown here and been intercepted or do the birds moult them on the heights where they can see in all directions and have plenty of wind to take off on their trial flight without them? Seedling wood sage and first year foxglove rosettes were doing their best to stabilise little patches of shifting scree.

Most splendid of the crevice plants, although not a rarity, was the honeysuckle, which flowered in gay profusion in the few spots where it escaped the normal rigours of life. Its powerful scent drew pollinating moths at dusk as the others drew butterflies and bees by day.

Painted lady butterflies were most in evidence, sunning themselves on rock and lichen or taking off into the brisk wind. Strong fliers, these and red admirals are the ones most often seen on breezy heights such as this. Now, in June, these would be migrants, incomers from the Mediterranean – even, perhaps, from the shores of North Africa. Hopefully

*Painted Lady Butterflies
and Sheep's-bit.*

some might stay to breed, as there is a 1977 record of painted lady caterpillars at Solfach, feeding on thistles.

We were about a week too early for the big influx of graylings, which emerge from their chrysalids in mid July and exploit the camouflaged background offered by hill and coast and the rubbly terrain of industrial tips throughout South Wales. A couple of weeks after we left in 1984 the island held an estimated two thousand graylings on the mountain ridge and the path along its western base. Their larval food plants are grasses, so there is no problem there.

The only other butterflies seen in large numbers in that last week of June were green-veined whites in the withy beds. Small magpie moths (*Eurrhypara hortulata*) haunted the nettle beds and Depressaria caterpillars wove silken complications among the hogweed flowers.

Most notable of other insects on the upland were the bumble bees, only three species of which were known on the island at the time. Some refer to these monsters of the bee world as humble bees, but there is nothing humble in the way these brave the worst of the gales as they bumble from one patch of nectar plants to the next. They are abroad on nippy days in late winter, even before the pampered, sugar-fed hive bees: queens who are not too proud to labour alone for the good of their community. Large garden snails were part of the mini ecosystems of the crevices, despite the shortage of lime for shell building.

Craggy undulations rolling away along the summit ridge were a scenic delight during the hot sunny weather that enhanced our stay. Translucent minerals, worn smooth on the ancient weathered outcrops, reflected the rays in a mosaic of silver, while some of the quartz veins wandering vaguely through the dusky matrix stood an inch or so proud of the general level, with micro-habitat for lesser life along either side.

*   *   *

Moving along the steep eastern face below this intriguing mountain top, we encountered more mundane plants. There were few sheep here and no horses, but nowhere was free from rabbits, in spite of an outbreak of Myxomatosis in the previous year of 1983.

Unlike the more fortunate Skokholm population, these bunnies hosted fleas, small Myxomatosis vectors identified as *Psilopsyllus cuniculi*, the specific epithet implying that they are geared to life on *Oryctolagus cuniculus*, the unwilling but prolific host. Flea specialists have been at large on Bardsey since the 1950s and the other three small mammals of the island, long-tailed field mice, house mice and common shrews, have been found to support seven other species of flea between them.

Most flea investigations, however, have centred around the birds, data accumulating since the first batch, killed at the lighthouse, were despatched to a specialist for investigation. These were migrants, showing how parasites can be transported from place to place. Not only fleas were found on these long distance travellers, but flat flies and feather lice.

During the 1960s live birds were investigated by holding them briefly in a vessel containing chloroform, with their heads out in the fresh air. The chemical induced the ecto-parasites to drop off, freeing the former unwilling host of its burden.

Fleas harboured by the Manx shearwaters resident on Bardsey were *Ornithopsylla laetidiae*, as with shearwaters from five other island populations. These parasites were taken from nest material in the burrows. Collections from choughs' nests contained three different species.

The crisp yellow sward of fine dry hill grasses glowed against the cloudless blue vault. Here and there were low dark mounds of heather, bell heather or fine-leaved heath as well as Scottish heather or ling in parts, this already in flower. Errant foxgloves speared up in local shelter but the late June bracken was sparse up here, rising only a few inches from the ground and spurning windward faces.

Catching box of the Cristin Heligoland Trap.

Gorse tumps were low, dense and smooth-sided, as on Ramsey, simulating anthills or vegetated molehills, but there were no moles on Bardsey. Most on the summit adopted a mat form, easy to walk over, but we sat at our peril. Slight alleviation of rabbit pressure allowed flowering of heath bedstraw and tormentil, albeit close to the ground, while starry white flowers of heath pearlwort pushed out through wind-clustered collections of dry rabbit pellets. Almost complete alleviation of rabbit pressure had the opposite effect. Because of repeated outbreaks of Myxomatosis the rabbit population had waxed and waned, these fluctuations reflected in the flora.

Highs and lows were more frequent during the 1990s and no rabbits were seen at all in 1998. Could they possibly have been exterminated?

Peter Howlett of the National Museum of Wales reported that this drastic reduction in rabbits had caused the loss of many of the once familiar small flowers that thrive only in short turf.

Back in 1984 mini swards of eyebright-speckled thyme flaunted pink-purple flowers, protected by the aromatic oils that delight chefs but deter four-footed takers. They were not threatened by the miniscule herbage round about – silvery hair grass, early hair grass, sea fern grass, and stunted versions of brome, fescue and bent.

Shoot tips of thyme bunched together and coated with silvery hairs were the galls caused by mites, *Eriophyes thomasii*. Little apart from sheep's sorrel and tiny patches of lady's bedstraw topped the ground level swards, with their dog violets and heath speedwell.

Much of the low gorse on the mountain was the western species (*Ulex gallii*), already with early flowers although these peak in August, their golden glow bouncing off the deep red-purple of the bell heather.

As we descended towards the bird observatory, the common European gorse took over. Some was topiarised by sheep or rabbits but reached as much as a metre high. Other bushes were quite leggy, with bare soil below. Some formed extensive thickets impossible to walk through. Island farmers formerly used the young gorse shoots for animal fodder and bedding, but the only major check now is fire.

Local gorse burning was practised to encourage new growth from roots undamaged by the flames, these preceded by other, opportunist species. Pioneers on new 1984 ash were English stonecrop, rock spurrey, a few wispy milkwort plants and bright clumps of scarlet pimpernel. Tiny foxglove rosettes were liberated from dormant seeds quite early in the succession, but these need two summers to build up the where-withal for those magnificent spires of pink trumpets that fulfilled the aspirations of the local bumble bees and flaunted their colour above Cristin's grey stone walls.

On several occasions we braved the crisp night air to go out after shearwaters and where better than on the mountain, close to our places of residence? We were not ringing, just enjoying the experience and recording it with flashlight photography. The birds are thought to be most numerous in the deep pockets of soil on the eastern slopes, but are scattered throughout the island, although seldom seen and not even suspected by most day trippers. From around thirty to forty pairs in 1913, they have built up to something between two thousand and four thousand pairs.

Shearwater chick and Sea Storksbill.

A lot have been ringed, most recoveries of ringed birds being local, from around the North Wales coast during the breeding season, with twenty-four getting as far as Scotland and eight to France or Spain. During the northern winter (their duplicated summer) four ringed birds were recovered off Brazil or Uruguay and two in the United States. These records fall within the thirty-two years before our 1984 visit.

Storm petrels have bred on the island sporadically in very small numbers since the 1950s, some found dead in nests of the little owls. One 'stormy' trapped on Bardsey in 1970 had been ringed on Skomer, showing that there is interchange between islands. A few leach's fork-tailed petrels have been spotted moving south past Bardsey during their autumn passage from nesting grounds further north, two of these caught at the lighthouse.

The *Celtic Bird Tours News Letter*, Winter, 2001-02, reported a few leach's petrels in the strong north-westerly wind that brought twenty plus little auks to the Bardsey waters on 31st October, 2001, along with a heavy passage of all three divers. Small numbers were present on other parts of the North Wales coast in early February 2002. A rare phenomenon was the stranding of three hundred and fourteen leach's petrels off Aberaeron in Mid Wales on 6th February, 2002, and with them eighty-one little gulls, an Iceland gull and a great skua.

The *Welsh Bird Report*, 1968, reported at least twenty-five sooty shearwaters (*Procellaria grisea*) off Bardsey on 29th/30th September and a further eleven in October. Other strangers that year were twenty-six Balearic shearwaters (*Procellaria puffinus mauretanicus*) at Bardsey between 27th July and 17th October.

*   *   *

Most of the island is occupied by pasture and hayfield, this punctuated by a few small wetlands and bordered by a varying width of maritime heath. Our birds'-eye view from the mountain in midsummer was a living map of different facets of land devoted to the four hundred or so Welsh Mountain sheep and lively bunch of Connemara ponies and foals which had replaced the former working horses.

Haymaking was in full swing, uncut meadows bloomed with the purple-red of sorrel and grass heads, undulating kaleidoscopes of colour responding to every wayward breeze. Mown ones were denuded yellow aftermaths, which had had too little time to repair the onslaught of the mowers. Paddocks were grazed short and burned beige by the sun, some of the central ones dotted with dark tufts of rushes and some of the marginal ones with darker mounds of gorse.

At the beginning of the twentieth century a hundred to a hundred and twenty people had lived on the island, gaining their living from the land, supplemented by fishing for marine crawfish and lobsters – a familiar pattern of island life around Britain's Atlantic fringes. Bardsey lies at the north of spiny lobster distribution and mackerel and pollack were other sources of income. Now there was only one farming family, the Stricks, but husbandry continued along traditional lines on a more extensive scale. Sometimes referred to as ranch farming, the 1984 lamb crop had averaged two per ewe.

Like island farmers everywhere, the Stricks were proficient at handling boats, with lobsters their main catch. Only their presence on the island made possible the existence of the bird observatory. When an earlier farmer left in 1971 there was no boat transport available and ornithology had to go into abeyance until his successor took over.

His poultry went with him and also the formerly resident house sparrows. Were they missing the human company that this gregarious species always gravitates towards, or was it the grain fed to the poultry? No arable crops have been grown commercially since 1960, the cessation of this practice thought to have triggered the decline of yellow hammers and reed buntings.

With so much grassland we expected more skylarks, but the grass was grazed too closely, leaving few of the tufty growths necessary to conceal nests. (twenty-first century skylarks around Cardiff choose to nest on rubbly urban saltings, derelict dockland or re-seeded landfill sites, where grass and weeds grow unrestricted rather than on the smooth green-swards lauded by the poets.) Meadow pipits have fared rather better on

Bardsey because of their affinity for the rocky tumble of the 'mountain', with its gorse, heather and bracken.

Few plants remained recognisable in the denuded pastures but the meadows were a different kettle of fish, indicating a rich seed bank in soil not soaked in pesticides over the years. Among the brighter yellow of tall meadow buttercups was the paler shade of that sure indicator of ancient grassland, yellow rattle. Hay rattle is perhaps a better name, as the rattle of the loose seeds inside the cockleshell prison of the inflated calyx bladder is most apparent at hay time.

Local but more continuous patches of yellow flowers were flaunted by lady's bedstraw, this in pleasing contrast to the spikes of crimson sorrel and soft mauve sheen of the undulant fog grass plumes. Centaury, clovers, bird's-foot trefoil, and tooth-blunting field horsetails occupied the middle layers of the fragrant tangle. Creeping through at ground level were cinquefoil and small flow-ered buttercup.

The subterranean clover is rare this far north, being the farmers' answer in warmer climes for a

Yellow Rattle and Lady's Bedstraw.

nitrogen-fixing legume in swards too arid for our temperate zone species. Like mini ground nut plants, the seed-bearing stems bend over when the flower fades, to bury the little pods underground out of harm's way.

Peering over the chest-high walls from the sunken lane the profile of the sward was a study in diversity compared with the monocultures of perennial ryegrass which signify hay on today's mainland. Here were wild oat and tall oat, soft and tall meadow grass, soft and sterile brome, cocksfoot, sweet vernal, crested dogstail, bents and fescues to delight the palate of the most fastidious grazer. PRG as it is known in the trade, may have all the vital nutrients, but how terribly unimaginative to deprive the recipients of the gamut of flavours experimented with in the Grassland Research Station at Aberystwyth when I was a student there in the 1940s.

Bardsey field boundaries come in various patterns. Most were flat-topped walled banks with more flowers on the lane side of the topping fence than where questing tongues could reach. The herring bone pattern suiting the flatish slabs of Skokholm's old red mudstone was a non starter here, although some courses of stone were laid obliquely.

The diversity of lichens testified to their antiquity, these a backdrop for rigid wall pennywort and laxer fronds of pellitory-of-the-wall. Gate 'posts' were often massive stone pillars, Pembrokeshire style, some hemispherical in plan view. One of the stiles, near the ruinous, grass-topped lime kiln was a big old wooden reel, which must have been wound about with heavy metal cable in its younger days.

The cheerful chirruping of common field grasshoppers (*Chorthippus brunneus*) emanated from tiny cracks. Hover flies and drone flies were suspended through the lower atmosphere while craneflies tumbled over their long legs among the upper herbage. Ants were everywhere, a feast for the birds. Six species were known here in the eighties.

Scuttling through the rough alongside paddock walls were the well known violet ground beetles (*Carabus violaceus*) and devil's coach horse beetles (*Ocypus olens*). Attracted to horse droppings, as the Skokholm minotaurs are to rabbit droppings, were clumsy bumble dor beetles (*Geotrupes stercorarius*) which dig nesting burrows as much as a foot deep under the offering and roll little dung pellets to feed their larvae hatching within. Ladybirds were not recorded on Bardsey until after the plague years of the 1975-76 heatwaves, this evidently an overspill from the speckled red hordes of the mainland.

The big black slugs ventured forth only at night and came in two forms, the usual all-blacks and a variety with orange sides (*Arion ater salmolateralis*). Abroad then too were dark-lipped hedge snails, some yellow-shelled and some pink. Less desirable were the bracken bugs or harvest mites (*Trombicula autumnalis*) which appear later in the summer, and sheep keds (*Melophagus ovinus*), flat flies that insinuate themselves in woolly fleeces instead of between the feathers of birds.

*　　　*　　　*

Withies, planted where water lay in clayey hollows to be woven into lobster pots, served in these days of plastics principally as a haven for small birds feeding over the farmland. Outliers of nest-concealing willows extended along overgrown field banks and into the walled gardens of the

*Devil's Coach Horse
and
Violet Ground Beetle.*

old grey stone houses. Blackbirds were the most often seen and at least one of these had learned to mimic Jane Strick whistling her dog. The sound was indistinguishable to human ears but the dog was not fooled! More often it is starlings which indulge in mimicry. These were about, centred round the buildings, like the swallows and pied wagtails.

Wrens shared the walls with nesting wheatears. Much the most abundant of the finches was that lover of wide open spaces, the linnet, and of the corvines, that harrier of others, the jackdaw. Wood pigeons, magpies, dunnocks and the odd warbler were likely to find a refuge in the withy beds. A red letter event for ornithologists was when a tiny goldcrest was captured on Bardsey only three weeks after being ringed in Russia!

Blackbirds and Marsh Cudweed.

Oyster-catchers had reached to eighty pairs by 1983 but lapwings stood at only eight. Forty species breed on Bardsey, but well over two hundred and fifty species have been ringed here, mainly during spring and autumn passage of birds following the coast.

Kestrels roosted on one of the chapel window sills in 1978. An analysis of their accumulated crop pellets revealed the leg rings of no less than a hundred and thirty-eight small birds, all ringed on Bardsey except for one chaffinch ringed in Belgium. Some of the victims may have flown only from the bird ringers' mist nets just down the road among the willows and elders of Cristin garden, before being apprehended again, this time with fatal results.

This was the accumulation of years of foraging, as wren rings were found from as far back as 1959. Over the 1978-79 winter another sixty-seven pellets were examined, these containing thirteen bird rings from five species (Roberts, P., *Bird Study*, 27, 1980.)

We think of kestrels as preying on small mammals, but only one pellet from this roost contained the remains of a field mouse, a few others the hard exoskeletons of minotaur and other beetles. Was it the lack of hedgerows and tree cover that allowed the passerines to fall to kestrels rather than sparrow hawks?

It is an unavoidable fact that the ranching of sheep and ponies over the island, as practised since the end of the 1970s, has had a deleterious effect on the amount of cover for wildlife. Livestock is not housed so gorse is not cut for feed and bedding, but bramble cover and Fuchsia hedges, even rushes, nettles and bracken, have diminished under the impact of grazing. With so little cover invertebrate life is most abundant in the withy beds and gardens.

Our visit of 1984 coincided with a severe drought scenario in a summer when the number of overnight visitors at any one time was often over fifty. Hungry sheep moved downshore at low tide to supplement their rations with seaweeds, as on many of the bleaker Scottish islands. Although described at the acquisition of the freehold in 1979 as a Nature Reserve, this savoured somewhat of wishful thinking. There are many aspects of the island's use and culture that have to be reconciled in the intended conservation of its way of life.

*   *   *

In the absence of adequate fencing, standing water was the best deterrent to grazers, but not to the horses, which, as Connemara ponies, were not unduly worried by wet feet. The thickest hedges were those with reasonable ditches alongside, where the grey sallows had enough moisture at their roots to allow them to reach two metres high, where their wispy tips were trimmed by wind rather than livestock. Straggly reeds and gale-nipped tamarisks were associated and there was a fine belt of hedgerow honeysuckle flowering just north of the landing.

Ditches alongside grazing paddocks were badly poached, the tufts of branching bur-reed chomped off at an even ten centimetres or so above ground, their stumpy bases twined about with spindly forget-me-not. A newly shorn mountain ram with fine curling horns forming a double spiral, poked among trampled Iris leaves for any remaining shreds of green, while a possie of ewes huddled about the Pwll Cain depth gauge that rose from bare, cracked clay or scratched their backs on its timbers.

Ditches alongside hay fields were in better form, with flowering watercress overtopping the rampant fools' watercress and a few pale flower spikes of heath spotted orchids. The trefoil leaves of bogbean and discs of kingcups told of former glory and stands of feathery giant horsetail spread inwards from the banks. The humble ivy-leaved mud crowfoot produced its tiny blooms among shining discs of marsh pennywort, where the others thinned to allow them in, but finest of the ground cover was the pink bog pimpernel grading upwards to pepper and salt allseed flecked with blue milkwort.

Wetland species of the Iris bur-reed type might border both sides of a field bank with a pathway of bared soil along the top. Others formed battered islands on dry pond beds where red water purslane shoots languished on a jigsaw of cracked clay among mealy grey sprouts of marsh cudweed. This was the newly excavated pond at Pwll Cain west of the Carreg Fawr withy bed and still holding tenacious sprouts of Eleocharis spike-rush and bulbous rush.

The best bird cover was provided in the willow spinneys proper, where olive-leaved grey sallow (*Salix cinerea ssp. oleifolia*) occurred among the more mundane and flat-topped elder bushes spread canopies of sweetly scented flowers just asking to be made into elder flower cordial.

Along with the expected lacy lady fern arising from the mud beneath were gleaming fronds of broad and hay-scented buckler ferns (*Dryopteris austriaca* and *D. aemula*), already with shiny black spore packets peeping out all round the shield-shaped indusia on the back of the fronds. The attractive, aromatic and crisply crinkled leaves of the hay-scented

White Musk Mallow.

are much rarer than the broad buckler so common in mainland wood-lands. Mauve flowers of tufted vetch and darker ones of woody night-shade coiled their way into bushtops, in one of which was a twiggy crows' nest.

Seven conservation volunteers were working thigh-deep among the yellow irises during our visit, repairing walls around the spinneys with rock and turf and erecting new sheep mesh fences along their tops to give the woody plants a chance to regenerate.

Most of these were tucked safely away in sheep-proofed gardens where, paradoxically, were also the greatest numbers of weeds of cultivation that should have been occupying the wide open spaces. Queen of the bushes around the mist nests in the Cristin thicket was tufty-topped *Fuchsia magellanica* with pendant crimson bells.

Wild hop clambered through willow and elder; tall fennel and wood groundsel grew along the walltops. Corn cockle and meadow cranesbill were cherished as garden plants; borage and bastard fumitory graced the herb garden, common pink mallow and white musk mallow the un-kempt beds between. There was henbit as well as the more cosmo-politan red dead nettle and ebullient sun spurge pushing through a carpet of lesser swine cress. Beaked hawksbeard and charlock provided unsophisticated colour among sterile brome.

A small triangular field had been ploughed and harrowed to see how many of these opportunist 'weeds' might put in an appearance under genuine arable conditions. By 1984 a knee deep sea of yellow flowers, a veritable floral fecundity, was lapping against the stock-proof fence – a pointer to considerable fertility.

It was 1973 when three rectangular plots of sitka spruce trees were planted as shelter belts near the grizzled remains of St. Mary's Priory and the Celtic Cross. Sitkas withstand mountain winds in the forestry plantations of Wales better than do other conifers, but the salt-laden winds of Bardsey proved not to their liking. Few trees survived in two of the plots, so the rest were removed.

The third plot fared only marginally better. Viewed from the eastern end, by flowering elder and wind-tattered thorn bushes, the nine rows of trees got progressively more depleted and dwarfed as they receded westwards. Some of those close to the deciduous scrub were almost two metres high, many of the distant survivors were less than half this.

Gaps were planted with hardwoods and the whole fenced against the inroads of livestock, so that fog and cocksfoot grass grew tall between them, to be shaded out beneath the more robust of the evergreen boughs. Fourteen neatly ridged rows of virus-free potatoes grew in a plot between the eastern trees and the arable plot and looked likely to yield a good crop.

*   *   *

Only on the eastern side of the mountain do high cliffs drop steeply to the sea, as on the other islands covered. Most of the coast is low-lying, with partially naked rock sloping gently down to the water, so that a lot of the narrow maritime fringe spared by agriculture falls within the splash zone. The flora is much the same as on the cliffs, with tiny thrift, plantain and fescue predominating. Livestock aids wind and spray in keeping most at ground level and confining a lot of the rest to crevices.

Bands of white-veined, shaly black rock reach seawards, leaving elongated pools between. In June 1984 the water in some of these was a dark purple-red, possibly from its content of Dinoflagellates. Different viewing angles showed the purple element to be dependent on the reflection of the bluest of blue sky, seen unadulterated in pools free from the soup of micro-organisms. A narrow belt of green sea lettuce and gutweed bordering each pool added a surreal touch.

Flatness of the land was matched by shallowness of the inshore waters. Falling tide revealed expanses of seaweedy rocks off Henllwys, south of the landing. Scattered across this were partially submerged basking seals unusually far from the deep open water into which they could make a hurried escape. They commonly allow themselves to be stranded on the ebb, to enjoy a sunbathe, but usually on steep-sided boulders or rock shelves offering a rapid getaway to their more natural medium if the need arises. It was odd to see them lying in what appeared to be open water, but with most of their bulk above the surface.

The low spread of rocks on both side of the Narrows at the base of the 'panhandle' disappeared underground on the Neck itself, with no outcrops between Solfach on the west and Henllwys on the east. The three types of shoreline seen here – clay clifflets, sandy beaches and pebble flats – do not occur on the other islands.

Sand stretches right across in one part, but there are no sand dunes. Material picked up by the wind did not build up on the narrow isthmus, but wafted out across the Sound, possibly to contribute eventually to some mainland holiday beach.

We found no true dune species, not even the cosmopolitan sea rocket and sea beet which are sometimes present. All were arable weeds, the only 'ornamental' some spreads of golden-flowered silverweed with vermilion tentacles migrating across the sand. Clumps of small nettle (rare on the mainland) were surrounded by drifts of aspiring seedlings. Other colonists on these largely open flats were burdock, slender and creeping thistles.

The only true dune species was growing in crevices on the clayey shores of Henllwys, opposite mainland sands from which dissemminules may have drifted. This was sharp rush (*Juncus acutus*), the spikily tipped leaves fireworking from among the rocks to more than half a metre instead of helping to stabilise shifting sands as on other Welsh shores.

Clay is as vulnerable to erosion as sand, but by slumping rather than blowing. Convex grassy slopes at Solfach in the current drought were scored across with more or less parallel horizontal lines of complex cracks and pits, illustrating soil creep in an advanced state. More level swards backing beaches of grey pebbles had become cleft by vertical splits parallel to the coast, ground on the seaward side collapsing towards hungrily lapping waves at full tide. Sometimes a new fissure would open up behind as the forefront dissolved away, so that several low clay clifflets half a metre or so high were formed.

Sheep converged on these to create the 'sheep lairs' so familiar around

Solfach, new sea defences by bird hide.

many of the Scottish islands. They benefited by complete shelter from land winds and a mitigation of sea winds as these lifted over the brink above their woolly backs. Scraping in under the ceiling of turf produced a modicum of protection from rain. Gobbets of wool got caught up on this grassy fringe and mingled with their droppings on the stony floor, but not in sufficient amounts to compensate for the scuffling away of potential plant colonisers on the newly exposed surfaces.

This sticky gleyed soil is part of the Boulder Clay drift brought down from the North by Irish sea ice many aeons ago – the same impermeable matrix that holds water in the ponds and withy beds in years of normal rainfall.

Displaced clods seep into the stony beach or wash down the gentle rock slopes below, helping to nourish the two orange lichens, the foliose Xanthoria above and crustose Caloplaca below. Clay flooring cliff seepages or stream outlets supports upstanding brookweed and mud rush and creeping sea milkwort and marsh pennywort before seeping away itself.

In each case it was lost to the system, hastening the narrowing of the Narrows. We were not surprised to learn that waves swirl right across this low neck of land in the fiercer storms.

The team of conservation volunteers working on the island during our stay divided their time between gumbooted spells in the Iris swamp and dap-shod spells on the isthmus. Here they were erecting a tide barrier on the western Solfach, side Two rows of posts were sunk deep in the sand at the back of the beach to support solid barriers, the two metre space between infilled with sand. They worked from the low bird-watching hide in the centre to either end of the long curving beach.

As soon as the workers packed up for tea and left a possie of sheep arrived to inspect the changes, rubbing their backs on the posts and hollowing out beds for the night in the sun-warmed sand piled against the seaward flank!

The hide was where we took turns to watch waders foraging along the tideline and turnstones flipping seaweed from the driftline to expose sandhoppers and maggots. Sometimes a chough would join them picking kelp flies delicately from the surface before probing beneath with the elegantly curved scarlet bill.

The flat expanse in the south of the island was dominated by the thirty-metre high tower of the red and white lighthouse, erected in 1821, with its associated white-walled, black-roofed buildings. These were as sprucely painted as lighthouses always are, but there were repeated visits

Lighthouse at south end and helicopter.

one day by the servicing helicopter, dangling loads of paint, ladders and other building aids to smarten them up even further.

The goods were dropped in clearings of the low gorse between the lighthouse and the tall pole carrying the floodlights erected to prevent migrating birds being dazzled by the beam. These were installed in 1979, jointly by Trinity House and the RSPB. At first two and later four five hundred watt bulbs were employed.

The old lighthouse keepers' log for 1919-1920 includes a reference to the removal of two or three dozen dried corpses of birds, mostly willow warblers, sedge warblers and grasshopper warblers, from the trumpet of the foghorn. Annual death tolls varied between sixty-nine and nearly two thousand, averaging three hundred and fifteen before conversion of the light from paraffin to electricity in 1965, and three hundred and sixty-two after, this number greater than at almost any other British lighthouse.

Almost thirty per cent of the casualties over the twenty-five years to 1983 were redwings – amounting to four thousand three hundred and twenty-one birds. Starlings, sedge warblers and willow warblers numbered well over a thousand each; whitethroats, grasshopper warblers and blackbirds over five hundred. Most deaths occurred on cloudy nights when the stars were obscured and birds circled the light in confusion, only sometimes finding perches to avoid impact. Seldom is a resident

Choughs.

Bardsey bird killed, these evidently habituated to the position of the light and with a knowledge of escape routes. Casualties are the migrants passing through, many for the first time.

Floodlighting in the first year brought an estimated four thousand down to rest on the grass in safety on one October night. These were mostly thrushes and starlings. Warblers came down to settle in the gorse or the Hebe hedge of the lighthouse garden.

On some nights birds are transferred to dark roosting boxes, to be ringed in the morning before release, this activity resulting in a host of ringing recoveries from North-west and Southern Europe. Waders migrate high above the ground and are unaffected by the light.

13.

PUFFIN ISLAND, ANGLESEY:
RATS, GULLS AND RANK VEGETATION

Puffin Island occupies 79 acres (32ha) and lies off Penmon Point, where the Menai Strait separating Anglesey from Snowdonia broadens out to the north. Elliptical, tapering to the south-west and north-east, it is 1,100 yards (1,005m) long by 350 yards (320m) wide, rising to 200 feet (60m) at the south-west end, where access can be gained across the narrow channel from Penmon Point on the Anglesey side of the strait.

It is a plateau of Carboniferous limestone, matching that forming the Great and Little Orme along the north coast of the mainland, although more ancient Ordovican rocks surface between the two, with great granite quarries backed by cliffs a thousand feet high along the edge of the land between Llanfairfechan and Penmaenmawr.

Bell Tower Lighthouse on Penmon Point.

*Puffin
and Scurvy-grass.*

The island cliffs are nearly vertical and are composed of massive horizontal beds of limestone, affording useful ledges for nesting sea-birds. Rock platforms extending seawards where waves break on their base show that the land mass has been eroded back from something much larger.

Puffin Island's similarity to the more accessible Holms in the Bristol Channel – Flatholm and Steepholm – is immediately apparent to those who know both. Each rises abruptly from the water and is poor in the lime-loving plants that one might expect, being dominated by coarse weedy herbs, due to over exploitation by nesting gulls.

The trees appearing on all three islands are elders, the species which characterises overworked areas around badger setts, rabbit warrens and human habitations in much of lowland Britain. None of the three are of the calibre that might be an inspiration for a book entitled *Dream Island Days* – one which was so appropriate to Lockley's early account of the much more attractive Skokholm.

Nevertheless, there is a certain element of magic about islands, simply because of their current remoteness. They were by no means remote before the age of railways and adequate road systems, in the days when folk travelled by boat or on foot. Islands then, in any part of the world, were more likely to become populated than inland sites, which later became hubs of communication. Perhaps, like the sea-birds, early settlers favoured their isolation from predators and other hazards of the unknown mainland.

Puffin Island was no exception and its known history stretches back to late fifth or sixth century when St. Seriol settled here. The Welsh name is Ynys Seriol while, from Saxon and Norman times, it has also been known as Priestholm.

The saint's original foundation on the island was laid bare in 968 according to the Welsh Chronicle, and there was a monastery here from the twelfth century, referred to by Gerald de Barri in 1188. All that now remains are the monastic stone footings surrounding the Norman church, with its tower still standing. This sea-girt plot has been owned by the same family for over four hundred years and is now a private nature reserve. In 1957 it was designated as an SSSI, mainly for its sea-bird populations. Some of these have dwindled and its particular biological value now, in the new millennium, is the cormorant colony containing over 750 nesting pairs. This is the largest in Britain.

I had got to know something of Puffin Island when I lived in Bangor for two years during the start of the 1950s. At that time it had excited more interest among biologists than its size merited, being in a state of constant change, as plant life responded to fluctuations in animal life. A quarter of a century later, when bringing a party of Cardiff Naturalists to enjoy the scenery and wildlife of Anglesey, I was anxious to see more. Timing, weather and local help were of the essence, but all came together nicely.

Thus it was that on 28th July, 1975, twenty-two of us staying in student accommodation at Bangor University, crossed the Menai Bridge and made our way along the south Anglesey coast to Beaumaris, with its well preserved Norman castle. Built in 1295, this is a fine symmetrical example of medieval military architecture, standing guard at the narrowing of the strait separating Anglesey from the North Wales coast.

At low water the Lavan Sands extend two to three miles out from the mainland, pushing the navigable channel close against the shingle beach under the castle and making that a strategic site. The name is Norman, 'Beau Marais' or 'Lovely Flatland', which it still is, its low wooded backdrop contrasting with the spiky mountains of the Snowdonia National Park away to the south-west.

Our transport put us down at the toll gate leading to Black Point or Trwyn Du – the extreme eastern point of Anglesey. There had been monastic buildings here too, a thirteenth century priory coupled with the island one as 'Priestholme et Penmon', but most had disintegrated except for a Normanesque church containing a few relics of the original Celtic foundation. A Celtic cross was to be seen in the church and another a little way off in the park, while the font had been hollowed out from the intricately carved base of a third. Across the lane was a Tudor period dovecote.

We tramped down to the rocky, pool-dotted shore, towards the bell

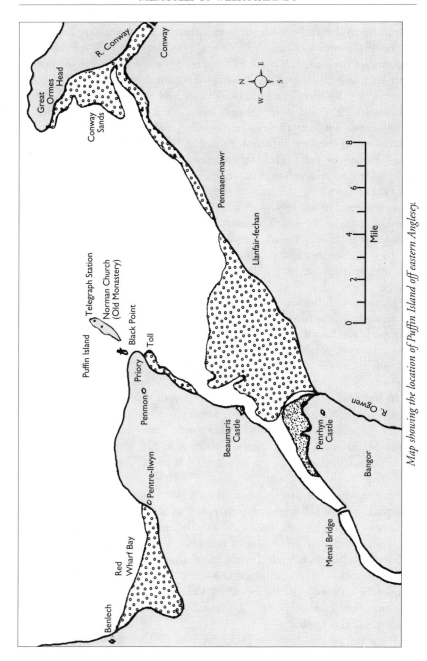

Map showing the location of Puffin Island off eastern Anglesey.

tower lighthouse, painted black and white and embellished with miniature battlements. This marked the end of the north-facing tidal spit that was non-aligned with the south facing one hanging off the opposing shore of Puffin Island towards Perch Rock, which had its own smaller warning for navigators. We were far enough out here to have pleasing views to the Great Orme along the north coast and down the Menai Strait to Caernarvon, with its fine castle and finer backdrop of mountains.

Silver flurries on the water to our right marked a shoal of mackerel, handsomely striped in iridescent humming-bird green. More on the left were skirmishing after a big shoal of sand eels – favourite food of the auks nesting on the other side of the narrows. These slender, sardine-sized fish are fair game for many of the sea's predators, just as rabbits are for those on land. They had allies here in the persons of the longshore fishermen casting their lines from seaweed covered rocks and hauling some of the handsome piscivores from their feast.

The twelve foot inflatable dinghy with twelve horse power motor that ferried us to the island landing beach at the base of the opposing spit could carry only five at a time, so we chugged across in relays, leaving ample time for beachcombing at one end or the other.

Not for nothing had one of the first biological stations in Britain been set up and manned from 1887 to 1891 on the island. The marine and shore life was incredibly rich. This was established in the old telegraph station, which we explored at the opposite end of the island. Functioning from 1841 to 1863, that was a vital link in the signalling system transmitting shipping messages between Holyhead and Liverpool seventy miles away, information able to be relayed in less than sixty seconds.

Stones on the shelving beach slid away noisily beneath our feet as we scrunched across to the zig-zag path leading to the summit. Some skin divers kitting themselves out for offshore exploration regarded us curiously. One removed his half fixed face mask and grimaced:

"You can't go up there. The island's filthy. Infested with rats!"

Another pointed at the feet of our local guide.

"Sandshoes too, it's alive with them."

They seemed to imagine a phalanx of warlike rats awaiting to attack feet and ankles as we breasted the cliff. Brown rats are common in many areas tenanted by today's throwaway society, but they always scamper off well ahead of visitors, like any other of our wild creatures. These proved to be no exception.

The effect of sea spray was minimal on this sheltered south-eastern face, the halberd-leaved orache of the beach soon giving way to coarse, scratchy inland style weeds and nettles, which were much more of a hazard than rats. The combination of the two discomforts, one imagined and one real, served to keep visitor numbers down.

Such few maritime plants as we found were all on the opposite face with the sea-birds. Choicest was the salt tolerant sea spleenwort fern, growing with scurvy grass, but none of the low herbs of more exposed islands. Sea beet extended further inland, but we looked in vain for typical limestone plants. Most others had been smothered by the tall weeds, which were able to withstand disturbance by the fauna and were not kept in decent check by salty winds, as on more typical sea-girt islands.

This ragamuffin flora clothed a veritable bird slum, the causative birds being gulls, that had spread across the plateau at an alarming rate during the last half century. Lesser black-backed gulls are the usual inhabitants of such terrain, but these were soon replaced here by herring gulls from more rugged marginal habitats.

Already, in 1895, Professor Newstead had estimated the population to be around 15,000 pairs of herring gulls, or 60,000 birds if we allow for an average of a couple of chicks in every nest. This, therefore, is not a recent influx concurrent with enlarged refuse tips on the mainland offering extra bounty. Forrest found both species to be numerous in 1907. By 1928 herring gulls greatly outnumbered lesser black-backs and were reckoned to be the biggest colony in North Wales.

They had spread right across to the north by 1960, when Mike Harris estimated an increase in herring gulls to 20,000 pairs with only 250 pairs of lesser black-backs. By 1971, great black backs, always scarcer, which is fortunate in view of the manner in which they prey on auks and others, had built up to 42 pairs.

Our impression four years later was of herring gulls distributed over most of the plateau apart from that occupied by the spreading elder wood. This seemed to be a case of birds moving in en masse to a habitat which was to their liking and changing it by their very presence so radically that they had finally to withdraw.

The initial 'des res' had been produced by a flock of goats which formerly grazed the plateau down to a pleasantly open grass sward. Scuffling and collection of nest material by the feathered host bared much of the ground, making way for the easily distributed seeds of thistles, burdock, nettles and docks to germinate and also, most particularly, two members of the carrot family.

At first it was mostly alexanders, as on Steepholm, very likely introduced originally as a pot herb by the monks. With this was hemlock, which is present to a smaller extent on that more southerly island. Alexanders was practically confined to the south-west at the end of the nineteenth century, but the robust black fruitlets that follow the attractive yellow-green flowers had spread apace, producing a chest high growth almost throughout by the 1970s.

Rabbits, which replaced the goats, preferred tender grasses to the coarse, the spiky and the stinging, and failed to keep the elders under control as the goats had done. These grew up, and coalesced, forcing nesting birds from beneath, although we saw a number perched on the upper branches – not a common sight in woodland, however low-growing. A decade later the elders were occupying thirty acres (12 hectares) and were thought to comprise the largest elder wood in Wales.

As we moved up the south-east side we stumbled on the ecclesiastical ruins quite unexpectedly, their masonry almost entirely enveloped by elders, ornamented with fleshy flanges of Jew's-ear fungus. Eleven years later, in 1986, they were cut back from around the buildings before the roots forced the foundations apart irretrievably. This was one of the few management tasks attempted during that decade.

Other ancient human artefacts encountered were stone corrals, apparently used for mustering sheep or goats. There is no evidence for crop growing, despite the abundance of ephemeral annual weeds – cresses, chickweeds, groundsels and the like. Seeds of these expectorated in crop pellets brought by gulls foraging on the mainland would have found plenty of bare soil on which to germinate, without the help of plough or harrow.

Rabbits served to open out grassy clearings in places but did little to curtail the rampant undergrowth. Two unusual plants which we found to be part of this undergrowth were henbane and stinking iris. These, like the others, are shunned by grazing rabbits and often thrive in the vicinity of their burrows as a consequence.

Henbane particularly, a member of the poisonous nightshade family, often marks rabbit warrens on closely nibbled Cotswold grassland, so that these can be located

Henbane.

Foetid Iris and Garden Tiger Moth.

from a long way off. A big patch of unpalatably prickly teasels had got away above the southern spit. Field mushrooms and one of the less scaly parasol mushrooms, *Lepiota excoriata*, had managed to survive.

Unlike that of Skokholm, the rabbit population was decimated by the outbreak of Myxomatosis in 1955. Already, by 1956, Bill Lacey noticed an increase in diversity among the plants, or perhaps the blossoming of species which had been constantly nibbled down before and were passed by un-noticed. He recorded 33 new species in a total of 102 that year. Many were grasses, which are notoriously difficult to identify when forming part of inch-high, non-flowering carpets. Rabbit favourites, like dandelions, sow thistles and clovers, present before, were much more abundant after the big kill.

Rabbit numbers began to build up in subsequent years, some thought to the benefit of the island puffins, which preferred short grazed turf and might also utilise their ready-made burrows. A hundred years ago a healthy rabbit population had produced the sort of sward beloved by red-legged choughs, which were breeding here at that time.

By 1960, however, Smith mapped three quarters of the island as still dominated by alexanders and nettles, while aerial photographs of 1969 showed about a quarter of the whole to be covered in elder scrub. Access to much was now increasingly difficult – a situation enjoyed by burrowing rats but not by puffins, which preferred open sites.

Our investigations in the mid seventies showed hemlock to be almost as rampant as alexanders in some parts. Marginally, where it cohabited with the elders, the shade drew the plants up to 3m high, so that their elegantly lacy umbels of flowers mingled with those of the elders. Those had taken over completely along the eastern clifftop, but the alexanders and hemlock were bordered on the west by rank cocksfoot, ryegrass and wall barley.

Bramble and a few raspberry canes were the only other woody plants that we saw, but these had a tenuous hold as yet. The principal herb under the trees was ground ivy, a species disliked by rabbits and often surviving round their burrows. Locally frequent on both Puffin Island and Steepholm was the usually rare small nettle, a frequent invader of bird colonies in the Antipodes, in lieu of our common stinging nettle.

Myxomatosis strikes most severely at rabbits crowded together in burrows and sufficient ground cover was supplied by the Puffin Island 'nasties' to accommodate surface-dwelling individuals. These may have escaped the disease, because the population was not completely exterminated.

Two colonies built up during the two years after the big kill, with twenty to thirty adults on the northern slopes and ten in the south. Smith thought these 1960 figures to be twice those of 1959 and forecast a similar rate of increase for the future.

Mike Harris came across variously coloured rabbits, quite small, and some so tame that they could be picked up. It seemed someone had been tampering by introducing domesticated stock. If formerly pampered and hand-fed, the change to this alien environment could have been quite a shock to their systems. Domestic rabbits are usually larger, not smaller, than wild ones. That such things happen emerged later on one of the Ynys Gwylan Islands in Aberdaran Bay, where white rabbits were introduced. Myxomatosis may have struck again, because numbers remained low. Peter Howlett saw very few on bird ringing expeditions in 1978 and 1979.

The tumble of displaced stones around the ruins offered plenty of niches and tunnels for rats as well as rabbits. We wondered if the walls had been built of rock quarried on the island or shipped in. There were

Brown Rat, Orache and Chickweed.

245

two nearby limestone quarries, an old one south of Black Point where we embarked and an active one north of the point, this currently shipping limestone to Liverpool.

Rats burrowed as prolifically among the walling stone as among the elder roots and seemed rather sluggish and in no hurry to move off. Were they, perhaps, suffering from thirst in the long drought? There was plenty of potential food about in the form of desiccated gull corpses but little juicy green plant life. That they were abroad at all in full daylight was not particularly surprising. The nocturnal habit is often adopted by animals just to keep out of our way – there are so many of us cluttering their landscape during the hours of daylight. With the help of scaremongers in the local press, these rats were doing a lot to deter human interlopers by their very presence, so were free to skip about in the sunshine.

The ground was pitted with their burrows, smaller than those of rabbit or puffin, the soil worn smooth around the entrances by their comings and goings. These were breeding burrows, lacking the 'doormat' of scuffled soil so usual outside rabbit burrows. Other smaller pits showed where they had dug down to gnaw at the tuberous roots of alexanders and hemlock. Were they immune to the toxins of the latter?

These would tide them over much of the winter, but many moved to the seashore then to forage along the driftline, having to run the gauntlet of other territory holders in their mini migration.

At sea level they might come in contact with the island's only other mammals, the Atlantic grey seals, which haul ashore in small numbers and probably leave welcome dollops of dung occasionally. Now and again a cow seal stays to give birth and suckle her pup here. These free spirits of the sea come and go as they please. The rats came ashore from a Polish grain ship in 1816 and seemed probably here to stay.

They were recorded as abundant in 1899, then dwindled according to an attempted count in 1960, but numbers rose again. A pest control officer visiting in 1971 estimated 500,000 rats and 250,000 burrows! Puffin eggs and chicks underground are sitting targets for voracious rats, which must have affected their numbers, driving the survivors back towards the less accessible western cliffs.

Inevitably the rat problem was much discussed by local conservationists during the seventies. An extermination programme using warfarin was suggested. This method had worked on Cardigan Island, which is much smaller than Ynys Seriol, but might be difficult to achieve here, with so

Elderberries and Jew's-ear Fungus.

much broken cliffland. It would in any case involve frequent repeat applications and had not been attempted up to the time of our visit, nor, it transpired, for almost another quarter of a century.

It was in 1934 that the rats had swum to Cardigan Island from the liner *Herefordshire*, which had severed her tow line when being taken to Glasgow to be broken up. She drifted onto the island where the rats, as well as the towage crew of four, had made it to the shore.

Cardigan Island puffins were referred to in the guide book of the 1890s as Welsh parrots and the individual who grazed his sheep there in the 1900s described the island as being "full of puffins". Numbers, however, were down to twenty-five or thirty pairs by 1924, so the remaining birds, unaccustomed to predation in the burrows, were doomed.

Ministry of Agriculture pest control officers managed to exterminate the rats in 1968-69. Efforts to decoy the puffins back to artificial burrows in 1984 attracted a few birds to scuffle round their entrances, but the deserted egg found belonged, not to a puffin, but to a shearwater – a species not known to nest here previously.

The Cardigan Island sward was suitably maintained for puffins by Soay sheep, estimated at ninety-five animals in 1975. It was decided that these should be culled for their own good, as grazing was insufficient during droughts, and this was achieved in June 1976. By a miracle of good organisation and a band of helpers, the entire flock was gathered from the forty acres and corralled within 350 manhandled hurdles. After inspection by a vet, from a total of ninety-nine sheep sixty-four were left on the island, tagged in age groups, and the rest exported to new owners, with nineteen rams slaughtered for human consumption. The rat problem on Puffin Island lay fallow for another twenty-three years. In 1998 whole wheat treated with 0.05% warfarin was transported to the island in readiness for an onslaught on the population. Customs and Excise officials landed the following night to investigate the nefarious goings on reported on the island – but found no hallucinogenic drugs so the operation was allowed to proceed!

The poison bait was placed inside the mouth of every burrow found, far enough in to be out of the way of grain-eating birds. Operators worked in lines across the island, finding more burrows than anticipated, so a second tonne of poisoned wheat was lifted in by an RAF Sea King helicopter.

Most rats died inside the burrows and subsequent visits produced no signs of them, dead or alive, although wooden spatulas soaked in lard were put out to tempt them, as chew sticks. Further bait was laid in January 1999, particularly on the cliffs, where complete coverage was more difficult, but no rats were found, nor in May 2001. Complete extermination on an island this size poses a big problem, but seems likely to have succeeded. This blitz on the population was reported by John Ratcliffe and Wil Sanderson in the first issue of the new Welsh Journal, *Natur Cymru*, Summer, 2001. Possible species which they hope may benefit, apart from puffins are Manx shearwaters, storm petrels and black guillemots.

Grey lag and Canada geese are breeding on the island now and the first record of a nesting eider duck in Wales was here in 1997, with two pairs in 2001. A peregrine falcon had a plucking post on the island. Removal of so many rats should have profound effects. Who knows what may turn up in the future and how the vegetation may change?

Peering over the south-eastern cliffs on Puffin Island we were able to spot the large and still expanding cormorant colony. Two hundred or so pairs were nesting here at that time, far more than in the similarly placed colony on the east cliffs of Steepholm, but far less than the seven hundred and fifty recorded in 2000. There were said to be eight thousand three hundred pairs in Great Britain in 1975, five hundred of these in Anglesey.

Looming large among the twigs and seaweed of their bulky nests were quantities of dry alexanders stems, these the most readily available building materials. Cormorants are regarded by some as direct competitors with man, but this applies mainly to those fishing rivers for trout and eels. Small flatfish were thought to be important in the diet of the sea-going population here.

Shags, always more oceanic and not breeding on the Bristol Channel Holms, were also present to the extent of two hundred pairs, but these were on the north-western cliffs with the other sea-birds. In 1975 very few of their eggs were hatching, this thought to be possibly due to mercury pollution from Merseyside, but they are prolific layers. RAF planes were no longer flying over and disturbing them and water skiers disrupting flocks on the sea were being discouraged. We heard that the number of nests had dropped to a hundred and ten by the mid 1980s.

Fulmar petrels started breeding on Puffin Island in 1947-48 and had built up to fifty-one pairs by the mid 1980s. It was interesting to note that the often prevalent tree mallow around the cliff nests of these 'tubenoses' on other islands had been replaced here by common mallow. With it were sea beet and scurvy grass.

The five hundred pairs of guillemots nesting on western ledges had unfortunately left the breeding sites by our visit in late July. This was an expanding population that had built up to nine hundred pairs by 1986.

There were no black guillemots or tysties and we were not expecting them, knowing them only on Scottish and Irish islands. We were surprised to learn, therefore, that some had started to breed on mainland Anglesey, as had equally northerly based common gulls, but both were rare.

Razorbills were present to the extent of a hundred and eighty to two hundred pairs, but their chicks, too, had leapt to freedom from their cramped infant quarters on the western cliffs. Plenty of the birds were still around on the calm sea lapping at their base and generous splashes of guano marked their breeding crevices, these nourishing pellitory-of-the-wall and more scurvy grass. Their numbers remained more or less static in subsequent decades.

Puffins, for which the island was named, had dwindled as seriously as on 'Lundy, Isle of Puffins' in the Bristol Channel. The popularity of these clownish little sea-birds has enabled them to creep into island titles where they may not thrive sufficiently well to justify this honour. Granted, Puffin Island sounds better than Rat Island or Gull Island, and we can scarcely blame the birds for their ill fortune. It is us who ferry rats ashore and provide bounteous rubbish to boost the gull populations.

It was Ray in his third itinerary as far back as 1662 who first mentions breeding puffins on Priestholm. Goldsmith in his *History of the Earth* in 1774 stated that the island puffins "might be likened to a swarm of bees". Thomas Pennant in his *Tours in Wales* at about the same time infers that they were present in considerable numbers.

John Price in 1883 reported that puffins had been exterminated by shipwrecked rats. Forrest, who reported this fact in 1907, also wrote: "the island was entirely deserted by puffins in the 1880s but was afterwards resorted to by the birds in considerable numbers, though, even now, they fluctuate in an unaccountable manner. Thus, in 1903, I reckoned there were less than fifty pairs. In 1905 I heard that they were again very numerous while, on revisiting the island again in May 1907, I found they numbered at least two thousand." The present tendency for bird-watchers to count everything they see is not just a modern fetish!

By the 1960s they were down to three to four hundred pairs seen by various workers on the land and up to four hundred and seventy on the offshore waters. Fluctuating numbers are to be expected, because puffins are notoriously difficult to count. Big crowds standing matily around on the clifftop may suddenly take it into their heads to swirl out en masse on a deep sea fishing expedition, leaving the cliff empty. Behaviour depends to some extent on what stage each group has reached in their nesting cycle and these do not tally. Half the population will be underground incubating eggs or brooding chicks anyway. Count the burrow entrances one might say, but some burrows have more than one entrance; some are empty and others are occupied by rabbits.

We, of course, made no such attempt, but were told that a count of four hundred and seventy birds had been made a few days before, these distributed on both the face and the top of the western cliffs. Burrows on the edge of the plateau were mostly among barley grass, Yorkshire fog and orache, but it seemed that more were now down in the safer cliff crevices. A 1987 count yielded only eighty-nine birds; a 1990s one just twenty pairs, but blame cannot be laid wholly on rats, gulls or rabbits because numbers were also falling on other islands where these vulnerable dumpling birds were not subject to competition with those.

1979 had been a bad year for sea-birds. The plankton bloom in the sea was late, affecting higher links in the food chain and causing the birds to go further afield for food for their chicks. Later in the year there were a lot of dead ones about, this not only on Puffin Island.

Herring Gulls among Mayweed on exposed cliffs.

Gull numbers were currently decreasing, from fifteen thousand five hundred pairs – the largest colony of herring gulls in North Wales in 1969 – to a mere one thousand in the mid 1980s and the other two plateau-nesting gulls were also fewer by then.

Deaths in many areas were found to be due to botulism caused by the bacteria *Clostridium botulinum*. The potentially pathogenic bacteria lie quiescent at the bottom of stagnant pools and are taken up by the small animals living there. During droughts such as those of 1975 and 1976, shrinkage of the pools causes the organisms to rise to lethal densities and brings the infected invertebrates within reach of the birds, which eat them and subsequently die.

The protein-rich toxins only reach pest level when nutrients collect in the pools, as guano or dead gulls, and belong to type C, which is harmless to humans. Gull mortality on Steepholm and Flatholm was blamed on the disintegrating chicken carcases and other edible debris brought by the gulls from airtight (anaerobic) black bags on the Cardiff rubbish tips, these providing a similarly benign breeding ground for the bacteria.

A few months earlier, in May 1975, we had spent time on the Farne Islands off Northumberland where shags were the chief victims, obviously from naturally stagnant waters rather than human leftovers. Either could have contributed to the death toll on Puffin Island.

Water fowl are not immune and there had been an outbreak among these on the Norfolk Broads that year. Two years before, in the hotter climate of the Coto Donana in Spain, thousands of coot had died of botulism when the causative bacteria, which are always present in soil, rose to lethal levels.

The thousand pairs of kittiwakes plastering their nests to the western cliffs came no further inland, swooping straight out over the waves in pursuit of their food, so they remained immune. Our seas are more polluted than we would wish, but are spacious enough to effect dilution of organic waste such as these products of decomposition. Nevertheless, only three hundred and ten kittiwake nests remained by the mid 1980s census.

We saw terns offshore, dipping daintily into the sea to harass the unfortunate sand eels. Common, arctic and sandwich terns fish around the island but do not come ashore. Little terns nest elsewhere on Anglesey, but on sandy beaches, where they are subject to human disturbance or may have their eggs or chicks washed away by extra high tides. Ringed plover are occasional delightful denizens of the island beaches, but there were only thirty-five to forty-five pairs left in the whole of Anglesey in the mid seventies.

The only passerines that we noted were starlings, the species which flocked into both Steepholm and Flatholm as elder became established on those islands. They come for the berries in autumn and also use the close-set, wind-trimmed branches as roosting cover. Peter Hope-Jones reported a large winter roost of starlings on Puffin Island in 1964 and a thick layer of bird droppings was reported under the trees in March 1966.

Small tortoiseshell butterflies flipped by as we moved past the nettle-beds that had nurtured their caterpillars, and there were a few large whites about. More exciting were the two fine specimens of garden tiger moths seen in the elder wood by the Norman church, their caterpillars feeding on a wide variety of herbs or shrubs.

Wild turnip plants were infected by the same grey aphids found on Steepholm turnips, along with the seven spot ladybirds that prey on them. Ragwort and burdock flowers had attracted greenbottles and also Syrphid hover flies hoping to fool predators with their black and yellow wasp disguise. With so great a preponderance of the small massed flowers of Umbellifers and daisies, there were few 'bee plants', but we noticed a few white-tailed bumble bees sharing nectar with the flies.

Back on the low boulder clay headland of Black Point we investigated the 'holiday haunt' of the overspill of gulls from the island. Crowds of immature and off duty birds jostled each other around the shores of a brackish pool sunk into a hayfield. A favourite preening place was an islet near the inlet stream, where ground and water were awash with feathers, whiffling in the breeze.

The pool waters were choked with beaked tassel pondweed (*Ruppia maritima*) with umbels of fruitlets and eel grass (*Zostera marina*) with fruitlets nestled in spathes clasped closely against the stems, these surrounded by the floating and tenuous varieties of bulbous rush (*Juncus bulbosus var. fluitans* and *var. tenuis*).

Eel Grass and Beaked Tassel Pondweed.

Sea sedge in the water graded up through sea rush and these to four different freshwater rushes, topped by the brackish water mud rush – all a real mix-up as salinity became concentrated in sunny weather and diluted in wet. Other, more showy, members of this half and half flora were celery-leaved buttercup, parsley water dropwort and various sea spurreys.

Nearer the sea was a small more normal wetland with reeds and meadowsweet, so it could be the throngs of bathing gulls, bringing in salt and guano that kept this most unusual pond the way it was. Very likely it was in a state of flux, swaying from one extreme to the other. Who were we to say, who only came across it this once?

During that delightful week around Anglesey we got to see a lot more. Alongside the splendid clumps of flowering sea kale and budding sea aster on Cemlyn's cobble beach were three to four hundred pairs of breeding common terns and several nests of red-breasted mergansers with tiny ducklings aboard. A whiskered tern hawked flies over the pool and a visiting avocet paddled along its edge.

Llandwyn Island was tidal, the sand-covered end of a narrow ridge of ancient pre-Cambrian rocks stretching across the famous National Nature Reserve of Newborough Warren. Crimson and black six-spot burnet moths swarmed over flowers of thyme and the birds-foot trefoil on which their caterpillars had fattened up in May.

From the RSPB's lookout post at Ellins Tower south of Holyhead we peered down at the thronging auks plastering the cliff, along to the South Stack lighthouse, with nesting peregrines and choughs for good measure. And we found the elusive spotted rockrose (*Tuberaria guttata ssp. breweri*) crouching among wind-pruned heather on the slopes behind. This was a new British site for that Mediterranean species at that time but is now well known.

Another rare plant was the spathulate fleawort (*Senecio spathulifolius*) on Holy Island. Special butterflies were marsh fritillaries and silver studded blues, flipping over kidney vetch, spring squill and Portland spurge.

The Skerries, two miles offshore, are out of bounds, but are famous for their colony of arctic terns, which numbered several thousand pairs during the late 1950s – the grassy summit of the stacks covered with them. Among the arctics were several hundred pairs of roseate terns, Britain's rarest member of the family.

By the 1960s this magnificent colony had been deserted, some thought because of the demise of the rabbits due to Myxomatosis. Terns need open ground and rabbits keep it that way. Rabbits were reintroduced and the arctic terns came back. In 1984 a hundred and seventy pairs bred on the island and the colony was on the up and up.

There are other birds breeding there, away from human disturbance: puffin, oyster-catcher, red-breasted merganser, raven and the three big gull species. These last three were unable to breed there when the tern colony was at its height but they moved in pronto when the terns left, building up to several hundred pairs of herring gulls and lesser black-backs alongside the expanding tern colony.

This is just another example of the changing face of these fascinating marginal habitats governed by moon-motivated tides, solar-motivated droughts and fluctuating bird and mammal populations.

14.

CALDEY: THE ISLAND OF SPRINGS, IN FAIR WEATHER AND FOUL

Moving back south from Anglesey down the coast of Wales, we pass the favoured islands of West Pembrokeshire and turn the corner to Caldey on the county's south-facing coast, beyond the sprawling ria of Milford Haven.

Each island has its own character but this one is different from the rest on a number of counts. It is an island for people, with wildlife pushed very much to the margins. On the others wildlife has priority. The people are few and are dedicated to the conservation and study of the animals and plants.

Many see Caldey first as I saw it on a blustery day of sunshine and showers at the end of April 2002, drowsing in the haze beyond the prancing white horses of the Sound. A powerful south-westerly was bowling crisped cotton wool cloudlets across the bluest of skies and whipping up platoons of those marine equines along the crests of parallel rollers. I was not to get to the island that day, but this was what I had always known as 'island weather'. April had come in like a lamb, to give us many days of blissful sunshine and was now going out like a lion.

We found the perfect spot out of the wind on a clifftop seat at the end of the great town wall. Chirrupy house sparrows were tearing narrow strips of bark from the adjacent sycamore and flying off with coiling tufts of this grass-substitute that put a temporary stop to their cheerful chirps. This was new and innovative sparrow behaviour to me, reminiscent of weaver birds stripping shreds of nesting material from palm fronds in warmer climes.

Caldey was spread, maplike, across the water, the three main features of the island aligned one behind the other when viewed from due north along the coast. The ebbing tide revealed the yellow sands of the landing beach separating the sunlit sea from the darkly wooded expanse of the north-east corner, with the tumbled grey face of North Quarry where

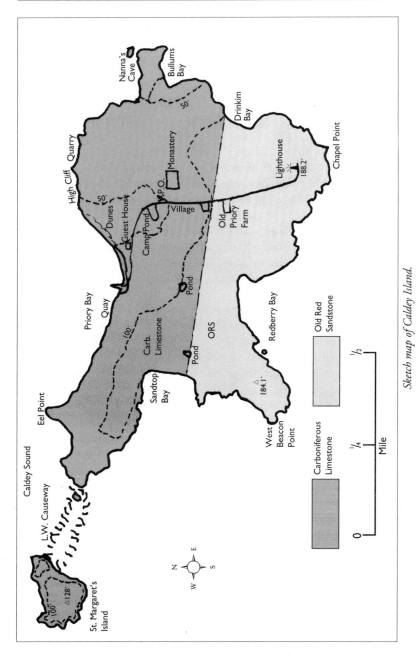

Sketch map of Caldey Island.

PUFFIN II

Fulmar Petrels.

Young Shag.

Razorbills.

Cormorants.

CALDEY I

Brother James outside his excavation cave.

Brother James on West Cliff, 1980.

Erratic Bluestone showing newly exposed and weathered surfaces.

Golden Samphire among limestone boulders.

Sieve for extracting artefacts.

CALDEY II

Priory and Medieval Church.

Cistercian Monastery.

Lady's Finger or Kidney Vetch.

Quay from the dunes.

BRISTOL CHANNEL ISLANDS

Yellow Horned Poppy.

Yellow Horned Poppies on Sully Island pebble beach.

Triassic Ripple Marks, Bendrick.

Three Dinosaur footprints, Bendrick Rocks.

Unconformity on seaward facing cliff of Sully Island.

the cliffs heightened to the east. Towards the top of the woodland was the red and white elegance of the monastery and in a direct line behind that the cluster of lighthouse buildings on South-east Point.

The slender spire of St. Illtud's church near the old priory lay away to the right where woodland passed into the green fields that occupied most of the area. Beyond that again, the rocky causeway that gives access to the satellite island of St. Margaret's was just appearing above water, with waves breaking white across the tidal isthmus, with its sea stacks at either end. Most of this lesser island was lost to sight behind Giltar Point, where the mainland coast turns from north-south to east-west to form the northern shore of Caldey Sound.

Just below our point of vantage the waves were beginning to recede from St. Catherine's Island, leaving a narrow rocky beach. A few hours later they had withdrawn completely, allowing me to cross the sands of Castle Beach under Castle Hill to the foot of the steps leading up to the blocky fort which topped the forbidding cliffs. This outlier is a great deal bigger than Goscar Rock rising from the centre of Tenby's North Beach.

Nestled against the north of Castle Hill were the lifeboat station and the harbour, with all the boats that might have plied to Caldey high and dry on the sand inside the quay. At this state of the tide the tourist boats, most of which are manned by members of the lifeboat crew, embark their passengers from portable landing ramps on Castle Beach around the headland. There were no boats on the sea today, however, only a lonely beacon bobbing on the turbulence.

It was Sunday, a day of no landing on the island, but it was the lively wind that was responsible for the lack of boats circumnavigating it. Tenby's South Beach, backed by scrub-covered dunes was nearer, but there were no embarkation facilities on that long stretch of sand for public traffic, which amounted to a boat every fifteen minutes at the height of the tourist season.

My mind pictures of the island that was proving so elusive today, were formulated in the sun-blessed early June of 1980 and the storm-ridden late August of 1985.

*   *   *

Although housing a resident population, both secular and ecclesiastical, and hosting far more day visitors than any of the other islands con-

Sand Dune Community.

sidered, Caldey has the edge on those both geologically and botanically. It is constructed of both limey and non limey rocks and possesses sandy beaches and even low sand dunes, which are approached in kind only by the sandy neck of Bardsey, which harbours few specific sand plants. Matching all but Bardsey is the impressive elevation of the cliffs, some of which are of Old Red Sandstone, as on Skokholm. St. Margaret's Island lying off the western headland offers haven for sea-birds and Atlantic seals and is a designated Nature Reserve, bringing this western outlier in line with the rest.

Although the centre of the main island is a bustle of human activity all summer, the wave-lashed headlands and quiet inlets remain much as they have always been. Few day visitors get to the potential holiday beaches other than that of the northern landing bay and few residents have cause to.

The interior, much loved and lived in, planted and tended, emanates a more placid charm than the windswept plateaux of the others. The long suffering inhabitants must relish the quiet of the summer evenings when the last boat has sailed back to Tenby and bless the days of autumn when the tourist rush is over.

Caldey lies three miles from Tenby town but only a kilometre from the contorted cliffscape of Giltar Point directly north of St. Margaret's, this easing the passage of plant and animal life across the strait. There have been so many people there for so long, however, that a goodly proportion of both have been artificially introduced.

The island is one and half miles long and three quarters of a mile broad, rising to a hundred and eighty-eight feet (fifty-six metres) at the southern lighthouse and only four feet less at West Beacon Point. The southern half lies above the hundred foot contour, this sheltering the lower inhabited north from the prevalent south-westerlies, as the island itself offers a modicum of protection to the tourist honeypot of Tenby.

Human history, both secular and religious, goes back a long way. Mesolithic man lived here twelve thousand years ago, before the island was separated from the mainland by the rising sea level of the Neolithic Submergence. Men of the Stone Age and Bronze Age who followed left traces in the form of knapped flints and primitive implements. Found with these in the limestone caves where they lived are the bones of the reindeer and Irish elk which they hunted and of the lions and hyenas which hunted them and competed with them for food.

The early Iron Age folk who came next were basically farmers. Romans were here too, leaving tell tale fragments of pottery – these not in the caves but turned up by the plough during modern husbandry in fields where they, too, might have been growing corn a couple of millennia ago.

Like the other islands, Caldey was the resort of monks from earliest times, the difference is that they are still here at the heart of the community. Celtic christians moved in fifteen hundred years ago. St. Pyro or Pirus was the first, in the sixth century, and the Welsh name for the island is Ynys Pyr. He was followed by Samson from St. Illtuds at Llantwit Major in the Vale of Glamorgan and it was St. Samson who became the patron saint of Caldey.

The English name of the island is attributed to the Vikings, who are thought to have ousted this monkish community by their raids in the tenth century. The monks' huts were clustered round a chapel well back from the coast. This was an obvious choice, right beside a reliable source of fresh water, among trees and hidden from the landing beach, to escape the attention of potential marauders – as was St. Samson's monastery at Llantwit Major.

Little escaped the attention of the Norse 'wolves of the sea', however.

They christened it the Island of Freshwater Springs. Spring is 'keld', island 'ey', so the spelling of 'Caldey' adopted by the new Ordnance Survey maps, is more appropriate than the 'Caldy' which appears on older ones.

The Celtic monks were succeeded by Benedictines in the twelfth century and it was they who set up the medieval priory whose ruins still enhance the island scene. The dissolution of the monasteries in 1536 ended this era.

The present Italianate style monastery was built in 1906 by Anglican Benedictines, who bought the island after many changes of ownership and occupation. Inadequate finance forced them to sell in 1925 and the present monks are the successors of Cistercians who moved in from Belgium in 1929.

Today's smart white-painted abbey on the hill overlooking the village started as a row of workmen's huts and was built piecemeal during the early decades of the twentieth century. Building was set back during a disastrous fire in 1940, but restoration and further building recommenced in 1951. Now it is as sprucely kept as any lighthouse and is a well known landmark.

Financial problems and the difficulty of farming on islands brought the monks' numbers low during the 1980s, but the day was saved by the burgeoning of the famous perfume industry and increasing tourism. Until recently there were around twenty monks attending seven services a day, but there is still time for shortbread to be baked in the monastery ovens and mouth-watering chocolate to be fabricated for sale in the village tea shop, post office and little museum.

The old settlement by the spring is currently occupied by the half ruined priory, which became a pig farm, and St. Illtuds church just south of the village green, Beyond is St. David's church and the clustered cottages of the lightkeepers and coastguards. The history of plant recording began with Ray in 1670.

*   *   *

A geological fault runs right across the island from east to west, separating the northern Carboniferous Limestone from the southern Devonian Old Red Sandstone. The strata of both rock types are vertically upended, although the angle diverges slightly at the fault. Sheer slabs of bedding plane are thus presented to the erosive force of the waves on the north and south coasts.

Junctions between individual beds obtrude on the east and west coasts, inviting infiltration of storm water along the lines of weakness between. The main cutting back has occurred along the fault itself, which is infilled with a softer layer of sands, clays and iron ores, accentuating the vulnerability of the rift. This has resulted in the eroding out of Sandtop Bay with its lovely golden beach in the west and Drinkim Bay in the east.

The more ancient Old Red Sandstone occupies the southern third of the island. It consists mainly of purple-red beds of shaly mudstone, with fewer of the coarser, greyer sandstone layers that occur in this formation on Skokholm. Springs arise along the junction of the two rock types, one feeding Sandtop Pond.

The northern two thirds of blocky limestone has a massive cleavage pattern and is veined with calcite. Rock is mainly silver-grey but the 'fossil cliff' set back from active marine erosion behind the north coast landing is stained a warm salmon pink – possibly by leachates from the red rendzina soil topping it. The low-lying land between this and the beach is covered by dune sand.

The limestone is fossiliferous, with sea lilies or Crinoids particularly frequent, but corals and lamp shells or Brachiopods also to be found. A steep-sided narrow syncline containing gash breccia, which stretches down the east-facing mainland coast from St. Catherine's Isle to Giltar Point, descends below sea level before reaching Caldey.

The Sound would seem to be floored by an eastern extension of the soft shaly beds that have worn back to form Lydstep Haven. These would have eroded out to form a valley which became flooded by the sea during the Post Glacial Transgression separating Caldey from the mainland. Once submerged, marine erosion would have taken over, deepening it further, aided by the strong tidal currents which sweep through.

Some fragments of Preseli Bluestone were transported here from further north as erratics by moving ice, their outer faces weathered the same grey as the limestone, but newly fractured surfaces as blue as the April sea. Pieces of this Pembrokeshire rock were built into Stonehenge, although all the larger stones of that formidable monument are of local origin. (These are grey wethers or sarsons – residual fragments of a siliceous sandstone bed thought to have overlain the chalk in this part of southern England.) Historians have wondered how the ancients managed to transport the Bluestone all the way to Salisbury Plain. Perhaps the moving ice had shortened the journey for them.

The two Caldey rock formations surface again on the mainland to the west, the Carboniferous Limestone at Lydstep Point and Skrinkle Haven, the Devonian Sandstone at Old Castle Head and Manorbier further to the south and west. The first forms the famous South Pembrokeshire coast with the Stack Rocks and Green Bridge of Wales, proceeding eastwards to the Gower Peninsula and Worm's Head.

We were fortunate to meet up with Brother James during our visit of early June in 1980. He was the community's geologist, naturalist, archaeologist and horticulturalist and became our self-appointed guide. He took us to Nanna's Cave on the east coast, where he had been patiently excavating fossil bones and discarded artefacts over the years. Sadly, many such remains had been destroyed during the quarrying of High Cliff a little further round the coast to the north-west early in the twentieth century.

Bee orchids have been found on the disturbed land here. 'Necklace' leaves of maidenhair spleenwort and the related sea spleenwort grew in the dim light inside Nanna's Cave and henbane had germinated on soil removed from the floor.

Inside the cave was the sieve elevated on a wooden frame through which every shovelful of soil was painstakingly sifted. 'Treasures' were extracted and the tailings replaced on the cave floor for ease of access. Brother James was craftsman as well as labourer, cutting and polishing stones and carving crosses, religious figures and animals in his dusty workshop, which was full of these intricate goodies.

*　　　*　　　*

Boats from Tenby drop their passengers off at a rather unusual quay composed of three large wartime landing craft aligned end to end in the shallows and filled with concrete. Laden though we were with gear, we lingered to savour the dune flora after stepping ashore. This was by no means typical, suffering invasion by all sorts of attractive garden escapes. The terrain was a single tall sand ridge, sloping more steeply on the seaward side and dissected by narrow paths of bare sand.

Marram grass, the expected sand binder, was here, but mostly overrun with wild Clematis or red valerian, whose pinky-red flowers produce neatly parachuted fruitlets, which waft everywhere. Leslie Thomas, who mentions few flowers in his book *Some Lovely Islands*, was impressed by this and refers to it as "A profuse raspberry-coloured weed, beautiful as a genuine flower, among what looks suspiciously like elephant grass."

Sand sedge rhizomes pierce the sand in straight lines sending up regimented shoots among the milkily poisonous sea spurge and Portland spurge and prickly sea holly. Thyme-leaved sandwort and the small mouse-ear chick-weeds were already dying off at the start of June, as the spring-time moisture evaporated from sand securely held by mats of rest harrow.

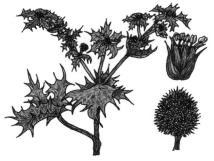

Sea Holly.

White-flowered gromwell, with its polished porcelain nutlets, more often in twos and threes instead of the fours that are characteristic of its borage family, is of special interest here, but is commoner along the woodland margins. By late August, wild carrot, hogweed and yellow pea were still at the height of flowering, but bird's-foot trefoil, tufted vetch and lady's bedstraw had passed their prime. Splendid patches of pink soapwort and orange montbretia nestled in the shelter of brambles on the hind dune, as part of a motley collection of aliens.

The backing limestone cliff, with its surface wash of 'Pembrokeshire pink' as used on so many of the cottages at this time, was the only place where wild wallflower was seen. Plants were large and woody, making a brave attempt at a second flowering in late August, seemingly unaware that summer had come and gone. This is characteristic of the limestone cliffs of Steepholm and Flatholm, along with alexanders, another Caldey species.

Curtains of ivy on the vertical face played host to parasitic ivy broom-rape and gave way to impenetrable blackthorn scrub with an explosion of Japanese knotweed, that ecological disaster that has taken over so much of the mainland. More acceptable is the bright-flowered *Escallonia macrantha*, which is such a successful plant in the windy Scillies. Others of this ilk here were *Fuchsia magellanica* and *Pittosporum ?crassifolium*. Ash, sycamore, elder and Buddleja have found a footing on the cliffs, away from disturbance.

The 5th June, 1980, was a perfect day, the sun at full midsummer strength and the sea a tranquil blue. Butterflies were out in force, the migrant red admirals and painted ladies in particular abundance. 1985 too (the occasion of our later visit) had promised to be a 'painted lady year' but the appalling weather had put a stop to that. We had seen hordes of the beautiful insects moving out across the north coast of Ibiza Island on a spring trip to the Mediterranean that year, and the flocks were drifting in across England's south coast as early as the beginning of April. Several were seen from the Pembrokeshire coast path in late August, progeny of some of the survivors, but most must have succumbed to the wind and rain of that long dreary summer, when nectar, if produced, was likely to have been washed from the flowers altogether.

Peacock butterflies were fewer on Caldey in 1980, but common blues thronged the trefoil flowers and shared the sweets of the valerian with hovering, zooming silver Y moths. Orange tips and green-veined whites frequented the watercress bed, where their larval phase was probably passed; large whites, speckled woods and small tortoiseshells flew among the crowds of people in the tree-girt village.

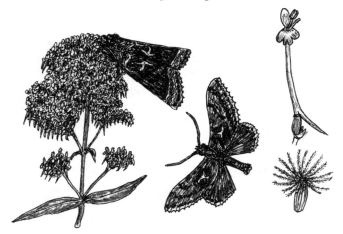

Red Valerian and Silver Y Moth.

Cockchafers or maybugs, prickly-footed when taken in the hand, lumbered ponderously around in the June sunshine and seven-spot ladybirds were doing a useful job among the aphids. Skipjacks or click beetles inhabited the gorse thickets, righting themselves with a spectacular leap when overturned. Hawthorn shield bugs pressed themselves to matching shrub leaves and powder-blue, broad-bodied Libellulid dragonflies droned over the village pool and off along the woodland edge.

Several slow worms were found basking under a discarded corrugated iron sheet, which exactly fitted their need for continuous, sun-warmed corridors, away from prying eyes.

Land slopes gently north from three high tumps in the south, the central valley opening out to the North Landing Beach. Elsewhere the cliffs are continuous, but there are seven other sandy beaches under nicks in these on the east and west coasts, the largest in the fault-created bays of Sandtop and Drinkim. Cobble beaches are not well developed. The fossil cliff backing the Priory dunes is as steep as the others but is well vegetated. Ivy is prevalent and none of the cliff plants have any special seaside affinity.

Three hundred and fifty acres are farmed, but woodland clusters round the valley settlement, this far from natural, with plenty of Eucalyptus and conifers. Even under the heavy shade of Monterey pine and Monterey cypress or macrocarpa, some plants are able to filter enough sunlight to persist and multiply. Most remarkable is the common scurvy grass – the old sailors' anti-scorbutic, gathered from cliff and foreshore when they reached land, riven with scurvy, in pre-refrigeration days. Although usually confined to the coast, a lax form of this creates a lacy white froth along many Pembrokeshire road verges, their flowers at peak in April and particularly fine in 2002.

To compensate for the deep gloom, this white-flowered cress on Caldey had increased the area of its shiny circular leaves to make enough food to carry on. In places it seemed to be practising synthesis without the photo, so deep was the shade, and one sturdy adventurer had given itself a boost towards the sun by rooting in a crotch of the tree trunk that had stolen most of its light.

Another round-leaved succulent cliff dweller able to compensate in this way was wall pennywort, this also perched on trees for a place in the sun. Polypody fern climbed them, not its usual oak, but craggy elders. The two light-excluding North American evergreens acted as a shelter belt, with the sycamore wood established to leeward.

"The flowers that bloom in the spring tra la" can complete the vital part of their life cycle before the sycamore leaves unfurl fully to block the sun. On our early June visit the primroses had faded and the leaves of lesser celandine were yellowing preparatory to rotting into the ground after passing their goodies into the smooth oval tubers.

The azure tide of bluebells had ebbed, the slack lapping anaemically around the unfurling croziers of hart's-tongue and male ferns. Triquetrous garlic, which has romped unhindered across the storm-wracked Isles of Scilly, had set its seed and flopped onto the leaf mould, its white flowers still more or less intact. The more widespread broad-leaved garlic or ramsons thrived on the limestone.

By late August the circular winter heliotrope leaves had expanded to form a complete ground cover under the trees and the next (January) crop of pink, perfumed flower spikes to which their manufacturing efforts were directed was nearer than the last.

Pleasingly numerous were the scarlet fruits of wild Arum, which had been invisible within the greenish cowls in June. Tiny midges trapped within had been ensuring their continued existence, shuffling foreign pollen grains onto expectant stigmas. Now the billious purple spadix and expended male flowers had passed into oblivion, the spathe had withered and the fertilised berries were flaunting a female supremacy positively indecent in this monkish land.

The mauve herb Robert competed but poorly in the clearings and the more rumbustious mauve of the marginal tree mallow had faded. Crowded trees imparted an autumnal aura of fecund fruitfulness and the first of the parasol mushrooms was pushing from the mush of fallen leaves among white poplar saplings, to provide the vegetarian monks with a more substantial meal than the button mushrooms in the fields beyond.

The lily pond at the village centre was excavated as a fish pond in the middle ages, its waters used to power a cornmill. In 1980 it was a glory

Parasol and Field Mushrooms.

White Water Lily.

of white water lilies and water crowfoot, fronted by Eleocharis spike-rush. Nevertheless, it was heavily silted, the amphibious bistort and watercress on the drying centre having ceased flowering and shrunken to clenched land forms to avoid desiccation.

At some time between our two visits the matter was taken in hand, the greater water plantain, woody nightshade and others rooted out, the silt removed and a smaller replica lined with black polythene installed to begin the cycle over again. The lower-lying reedmace swamp and osier bed behind remained unchanged. A splendid stand of Arum lilies with stranded duckweed fronds about their feet had gone; water lily and Iris were struggling through, but hemlock water-dropwort, greater willow-herb and fleabane had been relegated to damp wooded hollows.

The Priory Pool near the source of the spring and alongside the water-cress bed was as overgrown as ever. Its highlight was a fine show of greater spearwort, pushing between the reedmace culms, the golden orb flowers of June replaced by mounded fruitlets in August.

The spring show of milkmaids and wood bitter-cress in the water starwort patch had given way to aromatic mint and forget-me-not, the marginal cat's valerian to comfrey. Bordering crack willows and sallows, with their underlying brooklime, imparted a limpid humidy that belied the blustering gale beyond. This was a cosy world, fashioned by man from the barren islandscape bequeathed by his predecessors – and possibly closer to what the Creator intended before his land-hungry, fuel-hungry flock came to clear the woodland that had sprung up when the Ice Age passed.

Beyond the splaying tassels of pendulous sedge the priory still stands, a line of holes in the gatehouse welcoming a new generation of nesting doves among hoary stones festooned with ivy-leaved toadflax and pellitory-of-the-wall. On field boundaries were maidenhair spleenwort, wall rue and rusty-back ferns, white and yellow stonecrops, wall penny-wort, coltsfoot and sea-fern grass.

In the farmyard alongside was the piggery, where Caldey's famous large whites were fattened for pork and bacon. The animals seemed well fed and contented. Had the news filtered through that the monks, at least, were vegetarians?

A moorhen honked contentedly from among water speedwell and a cuckoo shouted his message – then, still, a familiar and now much missed harbinger of spring. Wood pigeons and collared doves cooed in the willows, seemingly uninterested in the ancient dovecote. Only the swallows had taken up residence in the buildings. Scattered through the wood were garden warblers, willow warblers and chiff chaffs, dunnocks and blackbirds, beyond were skylarks, meadow pipits and a pair of buzzards.

*   *   *

The monks cultivated salad crops, fruit and vegetables for home consumption and sale, as well as rearing prime Hereford beef cattle, sheep and large white pigs. We bought some of their big, shiny home-grown tomatoes, which must have ripened by the grace of God rather than the power of the sun in that ill-fated season.

Notwithstanding these activities and the production of shortbread and chocolate, the most famous product from the monastery is perfume. A wide range of scents and toiletries is on sale in the little shop –

Moorhen and Water Speedwell.

bath salts, bath essence, soap, shaving lotion, hand cream, pot pourri and, of course, phials of ladies' perfume. The abstemiously living monks evidently approved such vanity in others. Most who utilise flowers commercially produce honey and beeswax. This is rather more innovative.

The industry is said in various publications to have been based on gorse and lavender flowers growing in profusion on the island. Gorse yes, but lavender surely not. There is no shortage of gorse and it has a prodigiously long flowering season – through all the months when kissing is reckoned to be 'in season'. Much has now become overgrown by wild Clematis in a fine ecological tangle, the one being an indicator of acid soil, the other of limestone. God works in a mysterious way and is not responsible for the botanical textbooks.

The sharp reports of gorse pods cracking in the drying sun mingled with the chinking calls of stonechats and chatter of linnets. The spiny branches were traditionally burned in bread ovens because of the fierce heat produced. Does this help the shortbread towards

Linnet and Gorse.

its delectable crispness? Do the monks know that the yellow flower pigment was traditionally used for colouring Easter eggs or do their Easter celebrations embrace only home-made chocolate ones?

Lavender hails from the dusty, maquis-clad hills of the Mediterranean and does not normally grow wild in Britain except very locally as a garden escape. There is a little rock sea lavender (*Limonium binervosum*) around the cliffs, but this is unrelated and odourless, a member of the thrift and Statice family, having only the colour of the flowers in common with the other. The mauve calyces of the sea lavender are sometimes used in dry flower arrangements after the lemon-yellow corollas have fallen, as with the cultivated Statice – which thrives in the Abbey Gardens on Trescoe in the Scillies.

Crops of lavender proper grow well on the dry sandy soils of Norfolk, with similar aromatic mauve expanses in Northern Tasmania. Perhaps the monks brought some with them from Belgium, but I can find no record of its cultivation on Caldey. Nevertheless, the first manifestation of the new enterprise is recorded as 'lavender water extracted from home-grown plants'.

The industry has moved on from the days of laboriously hand-picked gorse flowers, whose prickly plucking must have been regarded as a penance by the monks detailed off to do it. Now the components are imported, these so compact as to pose even fewer freight problems than the export of the packaged end products.

It all started apparently, with Father Anthony, ex-Air Force officer and prisoner-of-war, who took the cloth after World War II and sought advice from experts. The crushing and distillation of essences from home-grown blossoms proved too costly and complicated, so flower essences were imported from France. These are highly concentrated and expensive. A phial containing one ounce of essence cost £40 way back in the 1960s. Musk, produced by male musk deer and used as a basis for perfumes cost a thousand pounds per pound weight.

The finest product, Caldey Number One Perfume, sold in those days at three guineas an ounce. Gorse scent was still highly rated and cost almost as much. Its perfume has been likened to vanilla, orange, pineapple or almond, but for me it is essentially that of coconut. Other subtle flavours are extracted from violets, carnations, lily-of-the-valley and unknowns contributing to 'Island Bouquet', 'Island Fern' and 'Brocade', based on patchouli from India.

Perfumes take six months to mature and the labels but not the containers are home-produced. Whatever flower the label indicates, it seems that all the best products contain attar of rose and jasmin.

*   *   *

When we sailed from Tenby in the late non-summer of 1985, the sky was heavy and the sea shrouded in mist. St. Catherine's Island fort lay grimly grey in drizzling rain and subdued gulls stood with shoulders hunched to a breeze which tempted few aloft. Butterflies and dragonflies were in hiding and woodland birds flitted only briefly from their dripping cover.

It was low water and we took off from a makeshift wooden jetty wheeled onto the sand of Castle Bay. On our return at flood tide, we nosed into the stone steps of the sturdy quay north of the dividing headland of Castle Hill. The sea was leaden and lumpy, slapping against the salt-rimed timbers of our open boat and sending lacy sheets of spray over the forrard passengers as we plunged through.

St. Margaret's Island lay stark and bleak off Caldey's western tip, a steep green slope breaking the formidable line of sheer cliffs, the old

270

Shags.

causeway connecting it with the larger island crumbled and passable only with difficulty.

Rising jaggedly from the summit, softened only slightly by the gently swirling cloud, were the roofless remains of the powder house and cottages used by the quarrymen who had extracted some of the blocky Carboniferous limestone. These were built in the nineteenth century on the remains of a monastic cell established in Norman times. In 1841 twenty-two people lived there in four cottages and ten of the total of twenty acres were cultivated.

As the boat swung in towards Caldey's northern landing, St. Margaret's Isle was lost to view and the jagged skyline became one of natural rock turrets, like home-grown skyscrapers. St. Margaret's is a West Wales Naturalists' Trust Nature Reserve, but is visited seldom, because of landing difficulties, and no comprehensive plant list existed at that time. Shags and cormorants, razorbills and guillemots, kittiwakes and other gulls nest there, but the puffins had been ousted from their burrows by immigrant brown rats. Rabbits, too, had died out, and Soay sheep intro-duced by the Naturalists' Trust, all succumbed to the 1959 drought.

We hove to in Caldey's Priory Bay, where concrete-filled sandbags, the bags long since rotted, had been added to the sunken barges lying in line astern for good measure. The section where we hopped ashore was under water for much of the tidal cycle – barnacle-crusted and support-ing tufts of spiral wrack with irregular inflations in the thalli, simulating the air bladders of the bladder wrack on the sand-girt boulders below.

These hollow compartments become inflated when the tide ebbs away and the slimy mucous coating hardens in the air to trap the gases that are given off from metabolic processes within. On an even wetter day than this they might not have formed, the hardening, automatic and obvious though it is, being a device to prevent undue moisture loss, and so needed only in a dry environment.

Photosynthesis needs water, but respiration continues, so the accu-mulated gas is carbon dioxide, retained along with the conserved water vapour. The hardness softens as the water seeps back, allowing free interchange with the outside again – and utilisation of the accumulated carbon dioxide for the resumption of carbohydrate manufacture.

We directed our hand lenses onto a four-plated Australian barnacle (*Elminius modestus*) which had settled itself fairly and squarely on one of the six plates of a British star barnacle (*Chthamalus stellatus*) with a view to engulfing it completely in due course – a takeover bid known to scientists as 'competitive exclusion'. This Australian invader had found none of its own kind and had homed in on a Pommie cousin as preferable to the cold iron of the underlying hulk. Perhaps a compatriot would seek it out as partner and all would not be lost.

When we returned at the end of the day the tide was full and all the barnacles had opened the flaps at the top of their tepees and were waving whiskered 'legs' aloft in a bid to waft in sufficient food particles to tide them over the next dry spell. The activity and dormancy of barnacles as well as seaweeds is programmed by the tides.

Like that American plant menace, the Spartina cord grass, the Austral-ian barnacles first turned up in Britain in Southampton Water – but as recently as 1935. It was assumed they had come on the bottom of ships until someone realised that organisms geared to temperate conditions would be unable to withstand the slow passage through the Tropics. The current thinking was that they travelled on the floats of Sunderland flying boats, the aerial passage, severe though conditions must have been, endured with all waterproof hatches closed. Evidently the change of planktonic diet on arrival had not upset them too much.

Elminius, although it has spread phenomenally fast around the British coasts, is still trying to find its proper niche. At present it is competing with star barnacles upshore and common barnacles (*Semibalanus balanoides*) downshore. The first is a southern species, at the northern limit of its geographical range in Britain and able to tolerate the long periods of exposure that an upshore site entails. The other is a northern species, at the southern limit of its range here, so has to remain downshore to keep cool. We could anticipate an upshore settlement of the interloper during the cold rainy 'summer' of 1985, but no doubt all will be evened out in the long term, guided by global warming.

August had a day or two yet to go and there was a riot of nectar-producing flowers in the damp shelter between cliff and dune, but few nectar feeders to profit from them. The purple spikes of Buddleja, pink heads of hemp agrimony and greater and lesser knapweeds should have been alive with butterflies – as they were along the mainland cliffs when the sun finally broke through the gloom a day or two later, but only the odd meadow brown and speckled wood ventured into the grey world of Caldey today.

The blue of borage and field cranesbill, pink of soapwort and bramble and yellow of corn sow thistle and ragwort tempted only hover flies, drone flies, green bottles and blow flies. Later, and on into November, the ivy flowers on the red-tinged cliff backing the path would be presenting sugary fluid for late wasps and flies, but this was in a bad way at present, a great slab of latticed branches ripped from the rock face by westerlies sweeping along Caldey Sound.

A brief respite would follow, while the few overwintering insects lay low, then the winter heliotrope would be shedding its sickly honey fragrance into the chill air of January and February. This species had made a big takeover through a range of Caldey habitats, the closely packed circular leaves a familiar sight from dune to woodland. Close on its heels would come dog's mercury, celandines and other spring flowers and the island would hum once more with life.

Furry bees are better protected against the cold and were out collecting the diluted nectar on this drear August day in fair numbers. A black cuckoo bee with orange tail (*Psithyrus rupestris*) lumbered across the path and suffered itself to be picked up and examined. It was dark and heavy, like a Mediterranean carpenter bee, yet uncannily close in appear-

Caldey Lighthouse and cattle pastures.

ance to the orange-tailed bumble bee (*Bombus lapidarius*) which it parasitises – just a little less plump in relation to length and with browner wings. Tiny fawn mites were tucked into the joints of its body and legs, but not the packed hordes that some bumble bees carry. Big fleas have lesser fleas . . . but its lethargy seemed more related to the general chill.

The chill of this particular dell was as nothing to the marrow-freezing, knife-edged gale that swept the southern cliffs. We edged around outside the lighthouse wall, the breath blown back into our throats, so that we had to turn our backs to push any words into that wintry summer air stream. At lunchtime we crept into the shelter of a low thicket of bramble and gorse, where nettle and hogweed, cocksfoot and tall oatgrass waxed lush in the secluded micro-climate. Life was tenable here, but the coffee cooled as it left the thermos flask.

Caldey's lighthouse was not regarded as a rock, like Skokholm's, so had been manned by two families rather than three single men. Now it was untended, its automated beam flashing alternately red and white through the hours of darkness and reaching mariners sixteen miles away when visibility was good. Today it was not good and the grey hump of Lundy was lost over the southern horizon and Gower quite invisible to the east.

We spent more time studying the plants that sheltered with us than

274

they merited. The blackberries were not quite ripe enough for the picking. Primrose-pale flowers of woodsage and purple whorls of the related betony, the wispy pink of red bartsia and starry white of lesser stitchwort, gave us excuse to linger. As appreciative of the shelter as we were, lady's bedstraw straggled up to two feet, vying with the rampant field Convolvulus.

Slabs of red mudstone thrust into the sea along the cliff base, but most of their height below the lighthouse was taken up by dangerously steep grassed slopes of soil and rubble. Their plants showed a curious mix of lime-loving wild carrot and creeping cinquefoil with lime-hating sheep's sorrel and sheepsbit – even mat grass (*Nardus stricta*). Most were middle of the road types, suggesting mixed soil pockets. Some were halophytes, sea campion and thrift, some grassland species, meadow vetchling and bird's-foot trefoil, others woodland understorey, ground ivy and vetches, but strangely none of the purple moor grass so prevalent on other islands.

Naked shoulders of wind-smoothed shale bore fleshy English stonecrop and fluffy hare's-foot clover: equally arid anthills were covered by buck's-horn plantain with tiny annual and silvery hair grasses. Rather less usual were the spherical, sometimes twinned heads of crow garlic bulbils and flower spikes of wood groundsel, which proliferated after gorse fires.

As we crested the cliffs again near the island's highest point, the straw-coloured panorama of uncut oats and barley gave an illusion of sunshine, stretching away down the smooth spine of the island to windward of the east central woodland. The plots were lightly flecked with the red, white and blue of

Hare's-foot Clover.

poppies, mayweed and speedwell, with white goosefoot and pineapple-weed in the gateways, but were mostly weed-free. When last seen in June 1980 there had seemed to be more grazing land with livestock hereabouts, though distant corn crops would have been too green then to recognise as such.

Exploration of the western cliffs seemed out of the question in this nose-dripping, eye-watering August gale, so we took the farm track to the limestone of the east, working our way around the coast from Drinkim, where the Old Red Sandstone and limestone meet, to Den Point, where passage was barred by a spiny blackthorn thicket. Even here, on Small Ord Point and Caldey Point, we had difficulty in standing against the wind, swaying drunkenly as we trained our binoculars on the spray-spattered purple sandpipers of the rocks below.

Little parties of curlew, of up to five birds, flapped determinedly into the rollicking wind, piping their complaints, and a tumbling lapwing answered from above the stoically grazing sheep. A raven honked from

Ravens.

the shore and there were other corvines – crows, jackdaws and magpies. Even now, so late in the season, the portly wood pigeons were noisy, with throaty cooings and clappering wings. A green woodpecker laughed from the seclusion of tall trees towards the monastery, secure in his own little patch of calm.

Out in the open small flocks of linnets were gathering for the winter's communal foraging. Social, even as breeders, these little finches become more gregarious during the hungry months, roaming the island in large parties, looking for seeds. On the morrow we saw upwards of two hundred gathered on wires near St. Justinian's, like swallows mustering for migration.

Down in the sandy bays there was more shelter, though we suspected that much or all of the sand might be scoured away by winter gales. Acorn barnacles are the hallmark of an exposed shore, brown wracks of a sheltered one, and here were more of the first than the second. Nevertheless, the plastering of slimy black lichen (*Verrucaria mucosa*) was more indicative of shelter and this coated the rocks below the usual black band of *Verrucaria maura* at the bottom of the splash zone.

A ginger-brown sandhopper, *Tallitris saltator*, had strayed up the cliffs to twenty-five to thirty feet above its natal beach habitat, to the inadequate feeding of a partially vegetated limestone face. Perhaps it had been blown there while executing a particularly vigorous hop. With it was a juicy green caterpillar, probably of the brightline browneye moth (*Laconobia oleracea*) nibbling at unusually succulent groundsel leaves, one of many common weeds which comprise its food plants. A prominent dark green and yellow lateral line bisected its grey-freckled, pea-green torso.

The silvery limestone slabs above the beaches were ablaze with golden samphire (*Inula crithmoides*) in a more muted purple haze of rock sea lavender – two species likely to be overlooked earlier in the summer when the rest of the cliff flora is at flowering peak. Golden samphire is quite local in Britain, although often abundant where it occurs and seems to be always a calcicole or lime-lover on cliffs, although occurring also on the gravels of Guernsey, the cobbles of Chesil Beach and the muds of the Neath Estuary.

On the adjacent Pembrokeshire mainland it is common on limestone faces just above the splash zone, but we found none on the Old Red Sandstone. Further east in Glamorgan it is a feature of the ancient Carboniferous Limestone of Gower and the newer Southerndown beds of Liassic Limestone up-channel from Ogmore-by-Sea. In Dorset it inhabits both the Jurassic Limestone and the newer chalk. Its habitual companion, the rock sea lavender, is much more widespread.

Rock samphire, after which the golden one is named, is common, as always, with thrift and rock spurrey, Danish scurvy grass and sea campion. Corn sow thistle, brightest of all the imbibers of sunlight, is nearly as common as its two weedier brethren, being by no means confined to cornfields.

Chunky sea beet, floriferous sea mayweed and splaying cushions of kidney vetch graded upwards into an east-facing bracken fringe or south-facing grassland of soft brome and Yorkshire fog, with betony, bartsia and clovers.

Though at present overgrown with weeds, it was not difficult to appreciate that the headlands of Small Ord and Caldey Points and much of the sweep of bay between had been used as roosting and preening grounds by herring gulls from the breeding colony to the north. There must have been a respite of several weeks to allow such a growth as existed by the end of August, but much of the area would have been bared by bird activity earlier.

Pushing up through the litter of feathers and meal leftovers was a community of fleshy knot grass and common orache with more robust sea beet. Mallow and common sow

Sea Beet and Golden Samphire.

thistle still flowered, wall barley and slender thistle had completed their brief life cycle and died. As always in such bird-dominated sites, successive generations of common chickweed and annual meadow grass exploited the defecated debris brought from seashore and mainland to enrich the island soils.

Maybe the gulls were not just temporarily elsewhere but non-existent. A July 1985 press cutting headed "Thieves taking Gulls' Eggs by the Bucketful" reported massed night time thefts of eggs and stated that the breeding population of gulls had been reduced from two thousand pairs to five hundred pairs in recent years, so this newly grown plant community of annuals might lead on to longer lived ones, instead of reverting to trampled soil and a new set of seedlings in 1986.

The Caldey gulls had been counted a decade earlier (*West Wales Nats. Trust Bull*, 15, 1975) when herring gulls had increased to three thousand eight hundred and fifty-seven pairs from around three thousand five hundred in 1970 – this a ten per cent addition. Over one thousand two hundred of these were concentrated here on the eastern cliffs, with another two colonies of two hundred to five hundred in the south and five hundred scattered along the mile and a half of the north coast. This increase was reflected on St. Margaret's Island.

One bird was mated with a lesser black-back, this closely related species amounting to only thirty-six pairs then, with four pairs of great black-backs, which obviously preferred St. Margaret's where there were a hundred and twenty-seven pairs in 1975. Five pairs of shags bred on the western tip of Caldey nearest to the satellite island and there were a few stray razorbills and oyster-catchers. Adult colour-ringed gulls had been seen well away on Carmarthen rubbish tips, while young great black-backs were dispersing as far as Devon and Cornwall.

It is on the more remote cliffs of St. Margaret's that most of the sea-birds choose to nest. Kittiwakes fluctuated from a hundred and fifty-six through two hundred and forty to three hundred and seventeen pairs in the early 1970s, when there were a hundred and eleven to a hundred and sixty pairs of guillemots and fifty-six plus of razorbills, increasing from twenty-six to ninety-five in this period, with a solitary pair of puffins still in 1973 rising to three pairs in 1975.

Razorbills and chick.

Thirty-three pairs of shags were nesting in 1973, but the main colony was of cormorants, with around three hundred and twenty-two nests, closely aggregated, with an overspill on outlying stacks and not necessarily in the same place each year.

This was deemed the largest colony in Wales and the second largest in the UK at that time. Birds have been ringed since 1967, recoveries including individuals wintering in the English Channel or along the west coast of France. Cormorants' plumage is insufficiently well-waterproofed for them to spend the winter at sea like the auks. Their need to dry widespread wings after fishing sorties is well known. (A Glamorgan individual regularly adopted this statuesque pose during the early years of the new millennium on the unlikely perch of a lamp standard on the central reservation of the M4 motorway at Baglan.)

Chicks are in the nest for around twelve weeks, with one parent in attendance during the early part of the fledgling period, so the immediate vicinity gets heavily fouled. Wood pigeons attempt to nest, both on the ground and on the ruined chimney stack in the absence of trees, but seldom manage to bring off chicks.

As often, tree mallow is associated with the sea-birds, being commoner on St. Margaret's than Caldey. It has persisted there for at least three hundred and thirty-three years, having been recorded by Ray in 1670 and again in 1805 and 1848. Common mallow is there too. Rock samphire was formerly gathered from these cliffs by Tenby folk for making pickles.

Brown rats persisted on St. Margaret's Island until at least 1976, these the only small mammals present. In the absence of predators they could presumably swim or scamper to Caldey, but would forego their pickings from the sea-bird colonies if they did, although possibly faring better during the winter food shortage. They may well have been exterminated by now, as on Ramsey and Puffin Islands.

As we moved north along the coast of the main island the blackthorn thickened, a few ashes and sycamores pushing up through the spiny mesh. Vertical faces were draped with curtains of ivy. Tall bracken, a probable precursor of the scrub, persisted along with taller herbs from a former grassland – yarrow, knapweed, carrot and hogweed. Salad burnet, a sure sign of limey soil, and creeping buttercup shared the limited clearings with cocksfoot and tall oat grass. Large white butterflies were on the wing, in no danger of being blown out to sea in this windless haven.

Hanging in the oscillating swell below the verdant cliff were some grey Atlantic seals, aware of us before we of them, and following our every movement with apparent interest. These were cows, with speckled heads, like wise Dalmations; relaxed, with all the time there was for weaving new knowledge into their uncomplicated lives.

Caldey's beaches are not among those most favoured by calving cows, few seasons yielding more than six pups. Nevertheless, Welsh beaches south of Aberystwyth can produce upwards of one thousand three hundred pups annually, while there are only eighty-two survivors from a hundred and two pups dropped in North Wales.

Figures published by the Countryside Council for Wales in the spring of 2002 reported that five thousand five hundred of Britain's hundred and twenty-five thousand grey seals live along this stretch of coast, and most of the rest in the Scottish Highlands – with an outlier on the Northumberland Farnes.

We threaded our way inland, through gaps in stone walls, over gates and along narrow woodland paths that we felt, too late, were not meant for public use. Alongside a tall privet hedge and a long row of diminutive telegraph poles bordering a lichen-festooned apple orchard, we found ourselves in an open-floored sycamore wood. The ground was flecked with scarlet fruits of Jack-in-the-pulpit, among the strawey remains of what must have been a splendid stand of bluebells. Red campion still flowered among looping honeysuckle and a warm zephyr wandered between noble tufts of broad buckler fern, beautifully spaced and shaped, with male fern increasing towards the sea.

The monastery was quite close now and we sensed we were intruding. (Ladies are not allowed inside.) Many centuries of prayer and worship seem to have pervaded the stilled air under the trees with an aura of tranquillity. St. David's church lay close against the monastery wall, alongside a grassy enclosure patterned with monkish graves marked by weathered wooden crosses. A stone shrine dignified a quiet clearing and we trod softly, veering towards a thicket of bamboo (all dead after a mass flowering) and over a mossy wall, beyond which we might rejoin the secular world.

There is an undoubted atmosphere about Caldey, but atmospheres dissolve in the face of crowds and no summer tourist can expect to appreciate it to the full. Only by violating the privacy that should belong to the residents can the true Caldey be savoured and that is obviously not for the masses.

15

OFFSHORE STACKS AND TIDAL ISLANDS EAST TO GOWER

ELEGUG STACKS, SOUTH PEMBROKESHIRE

The Elegug Stacks are one of the few places, along with Ellen's Tower at South Stack, Anglesey, where there is comfortable viewing of nesting auks and kittiwakes from mainland cliffs. The viewpoint is reached by a lane across the Castle Martin Tank Range, which occupies the delectable cliffscape stretching from Freshwater West, with its fine sandy beach and dunes, to Bosherston with its trio of extensive lily ponds reaching down three valleys to the sea at Broadhaven.

The military range is usually out of bounds on weekdays, but at most weekends it is possible to approach the sea-bird stacks and the Green Bridge of Wales – a natural wave-cut arch in the Carboniferous Limestone cliffs south of Warren. That is a stack in the making, but is still accessible to nimble terrestrial predators, so provides no nesting sites for sea fowl yet.

There is a scenic walk eastwards along the coast past Huntsman's Leap. This is a gut passing into the cliff and so narrow at the seaward end, that it is said to have been successfully crossed by a man on horseback. It broadens further in to form an unexpected and rather awesome natural chimney, plunging from clifftop to sea level, where the roof of the inner part of the slitlike cave has collapsed. At high tide in rough weather, waves roll in through the entrance tunnel and swoosh up the funnel at the head with a sonorous booming. Further along steps lead down to the tiny thirteenth century St. Govan's Chapel in an open cliff fissure not very much broader.

Elegug is said to be the Norse and Welsh name for guillemot and there is no shortage of these on the elevated inshore stacks. Around one thousand five hundred pairs, jostled each other on the top and spilled down the sides among two hundred or so pairs of razorbills and a thriving colony of kittiwakes. Puffins appear rarely and a few shags occupy spare niches, along with raven, jackdaw and great black-backed gulls.

Fulmars patrol the cliffs and the occasional curlew or cormorant flies past, low over the water, while turnstones dodge the waves on weedy rocks below. A black guillemot was seen here in 1972.

House martins collect mud for their cliff face nests from mainland puddles close by, standing in the water and scooping the malleable nesting material up in their beaks. Seldom do they alight on the ground except for this necessary chore.

Such Elegug vegetation as survives in odd corners is as lush as that of the Stack off Skokholm, dominated in some years by tree mallow. Orache and sea beet are fairly consistent, with odd patches of rock spurrey, curled dock, spear thistle and fescue.

Guillemot and chick.

Guillemots come ashore during the first week of May, just when the beleaguered plants might be limbering up for the summer's growth. The birds seek safety by crowding together and, while they can find respite from the noise and bustle by rafting on the sea, the plants' cause is a lost one from the start over most of the area.

The chicks pluck up courage to topple seaward while still quite small, but some fierce summer rainstorms must prevail before the site is sufficiently cleansed and the soil solution dilute enough to stimulate the average seed to germinate. Most here are not average. First comers are likely to be the aptly named chickweed and annual meadow grass.

Their rankness stands out sharply against the heavily trodden clifftop turf of bucks-horn plantain, spring squill, fescue, perennial ryegrass and rough clover (*Trifolium scabrum*), with wild carrot, green-winged orchid and the two knapweed species poking above the general level.

A rich butterfly fauna was present on a late July visit when most of the auks had gone off to sea and the fledged kittiwakes were flaunting striking black Ws as they flew. The air was unusually still and graylings were plentiful, settling with wings held obliquely to cast as little giveaway shadow as possible.

Meadow browns flipped restlessly from one grassy perch to another, seldom feeding. Small coppers favoured the thyme, common blues the various pea flowers, while the several Vanessids foraged indiscriminately. A rare humming bird hawk moth hovered motionless, to sip nectar from a greater knapweed head leaning out towards the stacks and there were cinnabar, burnet and small magpie moths on the wing.

We are well to the west of Caldey here, but on the same outcrop of Carboniferous Limestone, as is our next group of tidal islands clustered about the Gower Peninsula in West Glamorgan.

*   *   *

GOWER

Although far enough down the Severn Estuary not to experience the phenomenally high tidal rise and fall that culminates in the Severn Bore as the channel narrows towards Gloucester, Gower's tidal range is still considerable. It averages about half that experienced around Cardiff – this sufficient to isolate several tidal islands at high water.

Burry Holms at its north-western tip and Worm's Head reaching out from the south west are accessible for about two and half hours each side of low water, Mumbles Head off the south-eastern point for one and a half hours each side. In between is Sedgers Bank, which may be douched by waves during storms and is valued chiefly for its rich intertidal flora and fauna.

Tidal races are generated shoreward of the three main islands, making bathing dangerous, particularly at Blue Pool just around the corner to

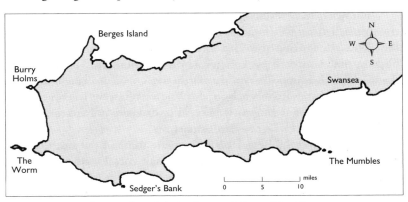

Map showing the Tidal Islands around Gower, West Glamorgan.

the north of Burry Holms, when the tide is careering out of the broad Burry Inlet. These currents and those around Worm's Head are good places for porpoises to show themselves.

The natural history of these tidal islands has been discussed more fully in Gillham, *The Natural History of Gower*, 1977. The first location in our passage east along the South Wales coast is Berges Island, the least spectacular, but a fine place for birds.

*   *   *

BERGES ISLAND

This scarcely qualifies as a true island. It is, perhaps, better described as a tied island, tied to the mainland by a ridge of vulnerable clay and sand. It lies within the mouth of the Burry Inlet or Loughor Estuary, which forms the northern coast of the twenty-one mile long Gower Peninsula. An island no longer, it retains the name on the maps and in the minds of the bird-watchers, who flock to it, summer and winter alike. Tidal swirl up and down the long sandy inlet has undercut the foredune ridge of the land behind to expose rounded cobbles in the run-off channels.

A wader and water fowl paradise, it started its independent existence as a mound on the old glacial moraine reaching out from Whiteford Burrows. Long ago it was levelled down and swallowed up by drifting sand to merge with the dune-covered spit of Whiteford Point. It has always been a magnet for ornithologists and has held a bird-watching hide for at least a quarter of a century.

Wildfowlers have revered the site from Victorian times for ducks and the British Trust for Ornithology's 'Estuaries Enquiry' launched back in the 1960s, designated this area as one of the top twenty for wading birds in the country. Most congregate on the southern, Gower, side of the inlet, but it is opposite, on the northern shore near Llanelli, that the extensive and innovative Penclacwydd Wildfowl Reserve has been established – an ambitious enterprise, second in diversity only to Slimbridge near the head of the larger Severn Estuary.

Feeding around the Berges Island hide are some of the vast flocks of oyster-catchers that compete with the human cockle gatherers on the North Gower sands, to be joined in winter by the big mobs of knot and dunlin that cannot fail to fascinate with their synchronised flights, wheeling and turning as a single entity. The evocative calls of curlew

Scoters and Sand Couch.

and redshank compensate for their smaller numbers, cutting through the sibilant whistling of winter flocks of wigeon, which may be several thousand strong.

Most eye-catching of the shoreline ducks are the glossy pied and chestnut shelducks. Most constant of the true sea ducks are the black plumaged scoters, which congregated on the sedgy pool to shoreward of the Berges sandspit before this finally sanded over in 1975. Mallard and teal gather more often in areas of open water on the grassed saltings, often in hundreds.

The ducks gaining the greatest notoriety, however, are the eiders, which should not strictly be here at all. Most reside on heather moors of Scotland, Iceland and Norway, where their eiderdown is still harvested in places – yet there are seventy or so birds here off North Gower, both summer and winter. None nest further south than Walney Island, a similarly sandy habitat off the Lancashire coast, but the Gower birds don summer plumage and go through the normal moults. The local Wildlife Trust chose the eider as their logo – scarcely typical and looking distinctly odd on the information boards of their mountain nature reserves, but no more atypical than the RSPB's avocet.

Then there are the migrating geese, brent and whitefront, and the vagrant divers, great northern and black-throated. Sanderlings patter along the tideline and statuesque cormorants pose on the derelict wrought iron lighthouse in the offshore shallows, Rustling flocks of starlings come winging across from the Pembrey Sands opposite, some resting briefly on the gaunt structure in passing. The old lighthouse stands only twenty feet above the water at high tide but forty feet above the sand at low. Built in 1854, it was superceded by the Burryholm light in 1933 – this automated well before most others.

One of the spectacles obtainable from Berges Island is of the Gower wild ponies – a herd that is as 'hefted' to its treacherous environment among the anastimosing tidal creeks as is the most habituated flock of mountain sheep to its crags and gullies. The older mares know on which islands of saltmarsh turf they can find refuge when the tide comes in, although an occasional foal can be drowned when they misjudge the depth of water they will be standing in when the flood is at peak. Sheep are pastured here too, these just as canny but staying on the more upshore saltings.

*   *   *

BURRY HOLMS

This is usually referred to in the plural, although there is but a single island. The epithet is Norse, as in the Holms up channel and islands of West Pembrokeshire. Like all the other tidal islands of Gower except Berges, it is of Carboniferous Limestone, deposited as soft calcareous mud in a warm shallow sea when the continental plate carrying Wales was in a southern hemisphere latitude equivalent to that currently occupied by Australia's Great Barrier Reef. Parts are rich in fossil corals, molluscs and other shell-bearers that flourish in warm water.

Traces of stone chipping sites have been located on Burry Holms, these left by contemporaries of the 'Red Lady of Paviland', actually a youth, whose bones were radio carbon dated back to 18,000 BC. These were the first people known to have penetrated as the early ice receded and great herds of game came to roam the open plains, later to be squeezed out by another Ice Age and then tree growth as the climate ameliorated. Diets changed from the flesh of herbivores to that of water fowl, fish and shellfish.

Neolithic people reached Gower around 3,000 BC and were responsible for the megalithic tombs. Like so many headlands along the Glamorgan coast, Burry Holms is the site of an Iron Age fort. This consists of a double bank and ditch delimiting five acres at the outer end. The early inhabitants did not exhaust the supply of shellfish. Mussels and oysters were being collected around this coast in the late fourteen hundreds and in the seventeenth century.

It was on the remaining ten acres or so of the island that monks settled, St. Cenydd, who was resident in the sixth century, being the best documented. The remaining medieval ruins may mark a centre of pilgrimage for those revering his memory in the fourteenth and fifteenth centuries. Cliffs reach a height of a hundred feet to seaward, sloping down to a quarter of this at the grassy inner end. A charter of 1195 refers to the site as an island, so the hundred yard wide channel that currently separates it from the mainland for five hours of each tidal cycle must have existed from at least medieval times.

Sheep grazing occurs, but not continuously. The hazards of losing some in the backing wilderness of sand dunes was avoided by driving them in along the great sandy beach to the south. Their grazing, coupled with that of rabbits, permits a wind-wisped 'waved heath' of fescue on the high cliffs and a woolly tangle of Yorkshire fog on the lower ground when the pressure lets up.

The yellow of early celandines and bulbous buttercups gives way to the pink and blue of thrift and sea squill in May and June and then back to the more vulgar yellows of ragwort and carline thistle. So much sand has wafted in from the backing dunes that the little valley at the landward end of the island is occupied by marram grass. The gully between the paired earth ramparts shelters lusher cocksfoot with salad burnet and lady's bedstraw.

Golden samphire, rock samphire and the rarer orpine produce succulent growths in gullies nearer the sea – the usual domain of thrift and sea campion. Only dwarf plants survive the pressure of feet on the paths, notably sea storksbill, doves-foot cranesbill and the inevitable buck's-horn plantain. Characteristic midsummer fungi, as on Ramsey, are fairy ring champignons and Bovista puffballs.

Twenty pairs of herring gulls nested here at the end of the 1950s and part has remained as a preening and feeding ground. The odd migratory tern may take a breather with purple sandpipers and turnstones on the rocks below, while oyster-catchers take their toll of the mussels clothing intertidal rocks and the dog whelks that prey on them. Among invertebrates on the grassy summit are green tiger beetles, gently spotted with lemon yellow, wolf spiders and pill bugs.

Alongside the fifteen feet deep Blue Pool gold moidores and doubloons came to light in the 1800s. The so-called 'Dollar Ship' was discovered in 1807 near the Spaniard Rocks, which lie just opposite Burry Holms. The treasure yielded since included silver and pieces of eight, canon and an astrolabe (a navigational aid used for assessing the position of the pole star). Spanish dollars which came to light were dated 1625.

The Rhossili Sands between here and Worm's Head are on a lee shore when the westerlies blow. The stark timber ribs of the *Helvetia*, cast ashore in 1887, still rise from the tide-smoothed sands. I played among them as a child on holiday from London in the early 1930s – between a dip in the briny and sausages cooked on a driftwood camp fire – long before the words banger and barbecue came into common parlance.

Many of the old farmhouses on the end of Gower are said to have wood from the various wrecks incorporated into their fabric. Subsequently the *City of Bristol* became a write-off here, iron plates from her hull still poking above the sands near Burry Holms at low tide.

*   *   *

THE WORM

Rhossili Down, the hill set back from this superb stretch of beach, and linking Burry Holms with Worm's Head, is composed of more ancient Old Red Sandstone with a superficial covering of Boulder Clay. On the three-partite Worm, from 'Wurm' meaning dragon, we are back on the limestone again after scrambling over the glacial drift at the approach.

The narrow tidal headland is a mile long, a third of this the seaweed draped causeway leading out and passable for about five hours at low water. Much of the thirty-seven acres remaining above tide level is taken up by the substantial block of the Inner Worm – the flat top representing an outlier of Gower's two hundred foot high sea-smoothed peneplain. The three smaller humps of the Middle and Outer Worm lie beyond the narrow causeway of the Middle Neck, which dips close to sea level.

The whole is a limb of an upfold in the blocky limestone strata – the Worm's Head Anticline – its highest point a hundred and fifty feet (46m). A cave opens out at the further end, this associated with an old raised beach, but this is no longer entered by the sea, which reaches only to within fifteen feet at high water. In it have been found bones of mammoth and rhinoceros from the Pleistocene period. Post Pleistocene relics unearthed have come from reindeer, bear, badger, wolf, dog and wild cat. The human bones and flint flakes are thought to be Neolithic. Another natural feature on the Outer Worm is the Blowhole on the vertical north face, from which may rise formidable boomings and hissings at high water when few are there to listen.

Foreshortened outline of the Worm.

Sheep, up to fifty at a time, were sometimes driven in across the bouldery causeway with its many permanent pools, to graze the Inner Worm, bringing the rabbited grassland there into line with that of the mainland. Few grazers pass across the Low Neck and the ultimate swards beyond take the form of a thick mattress of flopped red fescue grass building up on itself year by year.

This was first described by Professor McLean in the 1930s and suffered damage during a severe grass fire in 1957 but has recovered since, though not quite to the density of the fescue mattress on Grassholm that is being whittled inexorably away by the enlarging gannet colony. Only the more robust can compete – sea beet, sea mayweed and common mallow, with others squeezed back to pockets of soil among the rocks.

On the grazed Inner Head the taller growths are of gorse, bramble, hogweed and bracken. Among the crevice flora are again golden and rock samphires and rock sea lavender. Inaccessible parts harbour bluebells and cowslips, while bloody cranesbill and rock rose feature colourfully in the calcareous grassland.

I have a specially warm spot for Worm's Head, because it was here, at the tender age of twelve, that I had my first introduction to Britain's sea-birds, puffins, razorbills and guillemots. Later, when I came across Ronald Lockley's books on the

Salad Burnet and Bloody Cranesbill.

Pembrokeshire Islands, I was able to empathise, having a notion of the sort of world he was on about.

The tubby forms of puffins, seemingly much too ungainly for the frantically whirring wings which propelled them, were well established on the Outer Worm in the early nineteenth century, but had dwindled then by the 1930s, as on so many other islands. When I came again as a Glamorgan resident in the 1960s and 1970s, there were still a few about, with at least one pair nesting as late as 1976.

Chief spectacle in those years were the guillemots and razorbills huddled on the precipitous north cliff. These were in good numbers through the sixties and again in the seventies after a brief setback in 1970. Guillemots rose from seventy pairs in 1969 to around two hundred pairs by 1974. Razorbills decreased from thirty to forty breeding pairs to ten or a dozen during this period, but counts of up to eighty-five birds were made in 1976.

Members of our Cardiff natural history parties visiting annually during these two decades took turns to watch from a triangular declivity near the blowhole, where there was a fine view of the breeding birds on close by ledges. The auks had the sense to nest firmly out of reach of interfering humans but, as the number of people visiting increased over the years, the Outer Worm was placed out of bounds.

This is one of the many pleasures denied today's generation, now that population levels have got out of hand and mobility has increased. Such restrictions are inevitable – and praiseworthy – to save the relics of our once rich flora and fauna, but modern young naturalists can no longer expect to experience many of the joys that we oldies took for granted. Easier access to the wonders of far distant lands can now be gained by the fortunate few, but how long will those persist as the few once more become the many?

In those halcyon years some half dozen young shags might fledge on the Outer Worm and fulmar petrels were moving in as they spread down from the north. Sometimes an arctic skua, en route to or from its northern breeding ground, would linger to harry the locals. Sea watchers from this natural vantage point might spot a hundred or so gannets or upwards of a thousand Manx shearwaters fishing on the offshore waters in summer, or an idling flock of jet black scoters in winter, come to feed on the mussel beds, which are particularly rich here.

Then there was the nostalgic and insistent calling of the kittiwakes, which were first recorded breeding on the Worm in 1943. They were up to a hundred pairs by 1965, a hundred and fifty by 1966 and three hundred and ninety-three by 1974, with another hundred and forty-six pairs on mainland cliffs nearby. They nested on the north faces of all three sections of the Worm, not only the outermost.

The steepness of the breeding site means that they are best viewed from the sea, but nothing can detract from their evocative cries and circling black, white and pearly grey forms. The warm gleam in their dark eyes, so different from the pale hard stare of those of our larger gulls, is reassuring and their manners are altogether better. Broader views can be obtained of the mainland colony in Fall Bay near Mewslade.

The larger ragamuffin gulls are indestructible and are still very much with us. Great and lesser black-backs were present as twenty-five and thirty pairs respectively in the first part of the nineteenth century. Herring gulls retreated down the faces as human intrusion increased. From a thousand pairs at the start of World War II, these decreased to four hundred and sixty pairs by its end as a result of egg collecting to boost the meagre rations. After that numbers fluctuated around a hundred or two hundred pairs. The birds still use their old site as preening and meeting grounds, leaving crop pellets stuffed with cereal grain or weed seeds or a litter of banded wedge and tellin shells, crab or fish remains.

Curlews.

Passing species include curlew and whimbrel, common and arctic terns, great northern and red-throated divers. Passerines come through on migration – rock pipits, meadow pipits and pied wagtails, linnets, wheatears and various of the crow tribe.

When driven off the Worm by the incoming tide, there is a plethora of wildlife to be found on the tide-fields to landward, so long as a wary eye is kept on water levels. Interest varies from large hermit crabs in commodious whelk shells, free-living crabs and blennies, to pink starfish and more cryptic brittle stars. There are blue-rayed limpets on the oarweeds, which fade out as salinity decreases up channel – sponges, sea mats and dead men's fingers on sheltered rocks.

Among the pepper dulse and coralline weed is the attractive brown podweed (*Halydris siliquosa*). Another from southern waters, quite at home in Gower's mild climate is the peacock weed (*Cystoseira tamarisci-folia*), with spiky branches like a tamarisk tree and a pale blue-green sheen reminiscent of peacocks or opals. Molluscs are legion, from the humblest nut clam to the elusive common cuttlefish.

*   *   *

SEDGERS BANK

The sea-cut intertidal shelf around South-west Gower broadens off Porteynon as well as the Worm, and Sedgers Bank with Skysea's lichen-covered rocks protrudes above high tide level. Sedgers Bank, designated as a Glamorgan Wildlife Trust Nature Reserve in 1966, is the remaining fragment of a sand bar that once went right across the bay – as the sand bar at Oxwich, the next embayment to the east, still does.

Behind the curve of the bank, a foot or so beneath the sand, is a thick deposit of freshwater peat containing recognisable reed stems. Could the reeds have been mistaken for sedges when the site was named?

An iron age smelting hearth below the beach shows that the sea must have broken through subsequent to the ancient smelting, leaving the bank as a hazard to shipping using the busy little port which developed in its lee. The lifeboat station, later a youth hostel, was tucked in behind, the boat launched in the early days by a team of heavy horses, but the service was abandoned in 1916 after two capsizes and the loss of three of the crew. Its functions are now undertaken by larger boats based at Mumbles and Tenby.

The modern Sedgers Bank consists of hardwearing ridges of rock separated by gullies containing loose boulders and crushed mussel shells. Its seaward face was reinforced by a barricade of caulked timbers, which was broken through by the sea in the early nineteenth century, initiating a further phase of erosion. Strangers among the rocks arrived as ballast in the ships taking coal, lime and building materials along the coast and across the channel.

The largest of the several tidal islands comprising the nature reserve takes the form of a shingle spit of rounded cobbles and bluish shell fragments overlying rock and formerly overlain by sand, most of which washed away during the storms of 1974. Some of the former dune plants remain – sand sedge and sea Convolvulus, rest harrow and sea spurge with little thickets of dewberry. Fine shingle plays host to the

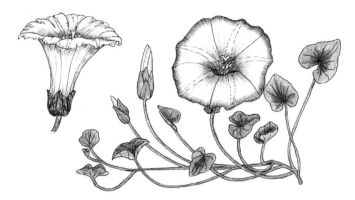

Sea Bindweed and Sea Convolvulus.

beautifully symmetrical shoots of sea sandwort, rocks to golden samphire.

Spray can waft right across the ridge in rough weather, but a closed fescue sward persists where sufficient fine substrate has accumulated – with thrift from the rock, sea couch from the sand and relics of former land vegetation, exemplified by field daisies, yarrow and lady's bedstraw.

Saltmarsh sea lavender abuts onto stands of the neater, tighter rock sea lavender while sea purslane climbs up from the saltings along crevices, emulating sea plantain in its versatility. Shells and seaweeds torn from

Two species of Sea Lavender.

their hold by the waves nurture a strand vegetation of tree mallow, sea beet and black mustard. This is alive with sand hoppers and kelp flies, an attraction for rock pipit, pied wagtail, turnstone and sandpiper.

An unexpected avian visitor on this scrap of sea-girt land is the green woodpecker, visiting for ants, which cohabit with beetles, woodlice and snails among mayweed and dock. Redshank, greenshank, curlew and dunlin frequent the shoreline in winter, sometimes with common gulls from the north. Adders may be found basking on the spit leading seaward from the old salthouse on the mainland when the sun tempts them from hiding

The sometimes fierce wave action can be a deterrent to the larger upshore wracks. It is thick beds of the smaller pepper dulse which separate and cushion the mussels of the mid tide zone. Laver grows on top of these, this red seaweed traditionally gathered and sold in Swansea and Llanelli markets as Welsh laverbread, to enhance the breakfast bacon before the modern habit of cereals and toast took over.

It is treated to repeated washings and long boiling to produce a gelatinous black mass which tastes a lot better than it looks. Fishmongers sell it rolled in oatmeal, ready for the frying pan and it can also be bought in tins. During Swansea's industrial heyday local sources became suspect because of pollution. Harvests are taken again now but most of that on sale comes from Anglesey or further north. Most algae have to run the gauntlet of voraciously grazing limpets when in the sporeling phase.

Bristol Channel oysters have been famous since Roman times and the Porteynon oyster fishery off Sedgers Bank was thriving in the eighteenth and nineteenth centuries. Few were taken after 1870, but the lines of poles which guided the boats were still in place until 1960. Collected mostly from the Bantum Oyster Bank in nets towed behind dredgers on steel hawsers, the oysters were stored alive in the shallows protected by Sedgers Bank. On ebb tides the low stone wall delimiting the storage area is still visible. At one time forty oyster boats were said to be fishing out of the little harbour. Of the great gluts which supplied the markets and fed the families of the fishermen, who were mostly quarrymen in winter, there now remain only empty shells, often riddled with little holes made by the boring sponge, *Cliona celata*.

Mussels are the predominant shellfish at present, their purple pigments said to be responsible for the dark humbug striping of the dog whelks which prey on them. Around the Mumbles, where dog whelks feed principally on white-shelled acorn barnacles, their own shells are white or yellow. All Bristol Channel dog whelks have longer narrower shells than average. Their clusters of flask-shaped egg capsules are firmly attached to rocks. The featherweight egg masses like desiccated frog-spawn which wash ashore are laid by the larger common whelks which live further out in deeper water.

The late Wynford Vaughan Thomas, war correspondent, broadcaster and author, tells in his book *Portrait of Gower*, 1976, of happy boyhood days collecting lobsters around Sedgers Bank and Skysea with a long hooked pole. There is much else of interest here, including crabs and shrimps. As well as the ubiquitous maroon jelly blobs of beadlet anemones, daisy anemones (*Cereus pedunculatus*) live half buried in fine shingle, mother of pearl fragments of shell linings clinging to their stems.

Grey sea slugs ooze across the rocks and transparent sea gooseberries pursue their pulsating course through the clear water. Bristle worms come in green as well as pink, appearing like ambulant seaweeds. A tiny carnivorous shoreline beetle specific to Gower in Glamorgan is *Aepopsis robinii*.

*   *   *

THE MUMBLES

The Mumbles are three rounded humps arising from a reef extending beyond Oystermouth Castle to form the western extremity of Swansea Bay. The innermost is firmly fixed to the mainland; only the Middle and Outer Mumbles are tidal islands. These protrude as two smoothly rounded humps from glistening tide or sheeny wracks like well stocked mammary glands, hence, it is thought, the corruption to Mumbles.

Buildings on the outermost overlie a lofty cavern – the lighthouse built in 1793 and a coastal defence fort from 1861. Other old walls, reduced almost to ground level, form an inhospitable but acceptable substrate for two members of the gentian family, centaury and yellow-wort. The original light was a fire in a beacon basket, this replaced by oil lanterns in the early nineteenth century and so to electricity and modern automation.

The Mumbles lifeboat, like that of Porteynon, has a proud history of heroic rescues and fatal disasters. When the lifeboat capsized off Aber-avon in 1903 the coxswain and five men were drowned. Going to the help of the *Santampa*, driven ashore on Sker Rocks off Porthcawl in

Cormorants over the silhouette of the Mumbles.

1947 with the loss of her entire crew of thirty-nine, the Mumbles lifeboat, too, was hurled ashore and her complete crew of eight was drowned. Yet there is no lack of new volunteers coming forward. Lifeboats, unlike lighthouses, cannot be automated and lifeboatmen will never be made redundant as lighthouse keepers have been.

Swansea's great fleet of oyster boats sailed into port round Mumbles Point as the Porteynon boats did around Sedgers Bank – this ably described in the famous Kilvert Diaries of 1874. Now these offshore waters are more often the haunt of common and arctic terns lingering on passage to dip into the kelp beds on their mighty eleven thousand mile journeys to the Antarctic. Unlike the gannets, which can be seen fishing further offshore, they can drop from heights of not much more than a metre above the water, emerging to juggle a fish held crosswise into a suitable position for swallowing. They cannot rest on the sea as gulls do, but join the purple sandpipers, oyster-catchers and turnstones on the weedy rocks when they need a break.

These islands tailing out into the sea provide rest and food for others. Swallows and martins, pipits and wagtails, finches and warblers, even butterflies, can all be seen here on passage. Porpoises and dolphins cruise past on occasion.

Porpoises.

Mobs of gulls gather on the islets when they are driven from Swansea Bay's sand and mudflats by the same incoming tides that drive the people from the Mumbles to make way for them. Sometimes they are tempted there when the tide is low, as when ants swarm on the middle tump on sultry summer days and they are the first in to reap the harvest of winged, would-be breeders.

The outermost tump is clothed in fescue grassland with cocksfoot and ribwort where untrampled, thrift, clover, bird's-foot trefoil and autumnal hawkbit where visitors gather. In the shelter of the lighthouse are ivy with wind-ravaged bramble and elder. In the closer shelter of limestone crannies are kidney vetch, sea beet and rock samphire, which last was formerly eaten in home made pickles.

Gilliflower Stock and Quaking Grass.

The most notable plants on the Outer Mumble are the rare and showy gilliflower stocks (*Mathiola incana*). These are firmly entrenched, despite the temptation afforded by their wine-red flowers to acquisitive humans. A species of South-east England's chalk cliffs, this grows at only one other site in Glamorgan, on the softer liassic limestone cliffs of

Nash Point near Llantwit Major. Glamorgan's other sea stock, *Mathiola sinuata*, with paler flowers, is equally rare, but is a sand plant, found occasionally on Gower dunes and Kenfig and Margam Burrows.

As would be expected, there are fewer plant species on the Outer Mumble, the ratio on the Outer, Middle and Inner Mumbles approximating to thirty-five, fifty-eight and eighty or 5:8:11. Guano and food remains from gulls gathering on the middle tump boost the plantains and chickweeds and add colour to the orange lichens. The gentle blue of spring squill mingles with thrift in early summer, to be followed by the similar hues of small scabious and harebells among shivery quaking grass and lacy burnet saxifrage.

Harebell and Small Scabious.

Golden samphire spreads up from spray-washed rocks to almost meet the more cosmopolitan member of its genus, the ploughman's spikenard (*Inula conyza*). Perforated St. John's wort and ragwort give late summer colour and bristly madder straggles up through wind-distorted sloe and bramble to produce its own little black berries in their shelter.

Two unusual plants in the sward of the Inner Mumble are knotted hedge parsley (*Torilus nodosa*) with twinned bur fruits and rough clover – these in ancient grassland with yellow hay rattle and knapweeds. Portland spurge is as happy on limestone rocks as on the shell sand dunes and co-habits here with thyme, rock-rose and salad burnet

One of Gower's unsolved mysteries is the presence of acid-loving Scottish and bell heathers living in association with these lime-lovers, often on bare rock unsoftened by boulder clay or soil creep.

16.

OUTLIERS IN THE BRISTOL CHANNEL

SWANSEA BAY

Moving on eastwards the Carboniferous limestone which has resisted marine erosion to form the tidal islands of Gower dips below sea level, leaving the softer Coal Measure rocks exposed to wave action. These have eroded away to form Swansea Bay, the old sea cliffs of Pennant rocks now well behind today's extensive sand flats which have subsequently built up to match the current sea level.

The Welsh hills beyond, while yielding the wherewithal, were unsuitable topographically for the development of large scale heavy industry, which came to cover much of the spacious coastal plain around Swansea, Briton Ferry, Baglan Bay and Port Talbot.

This is bounded by an ever-changing shoreline, moulded by those massive Bristol Channel tides and the winds which move the shifting sands. Today's golden beach can be tomorrow's chocolate-brown peat bed or a swathe of multi-coloured pebbles. Offshore are mobile sandbanks – a hazard to shipping, a source of profit for dredgers and currently the subject of exploration for installation of a wind turbine farm.

Further east are tiny outliers of the ancient limestone re-surfacing, and then the softer newer Triassic rocks, or an amalgam of both as on Sully Island. The only completely separate island entities on proceeding up channel are Flatholm and Steepholm, both several miles offshore, but Steepholm nearer to Somerset and not to be numbered among the Welsh Islands, although very much the twin of Flatholm which belongs to Cardiff.

Broad though the coastal plain is, with its still splendid sand dune systems and diverse wetland of Crymlin Bog, it has been broader (Gillham, *Swansea Bay's Green Mantle*, 1982). The sandy beaches which delight summer visitors are sometimes but a temporary cover over intertidal peat banks spawned around 4000 BC and remaining exposed for long enough periods to become greened over with growths of Enteromorpha.

Roots and branches of ancient trees shouldering out of the soggy but tenacious organic remains of a vast compressed reedswamp represent the most recent forest of several, which came and went as sea level fluctuated during the ice ages. These manifestations of 'bog oak' are separated by beds of slippery blue-grey estuarine clays, the trees principally swamp willows passing on to birch and then oak forest as the level built up.

The old Green Grounds Farm succumbed to submergence in Swansea Bay only some three hundred and thirty years ago, after which it was possible to walk out to the old pastures at low spring tides for a number of years.

During the 1970s we spent a lot of time fossicking to seaward of Margam Burrows, where there was more fossilised pine and less birch than further west, recognising the hoof prints of cattle herds in the estuarine clay and gathering fossil bones, some heavily impregnated with iron. These were of Caenozoic aurochs (*Bos primigenius*) with fine curving horns and smaller bones of the later Celtic cattle (*Bos taurus*). Other treasures coming to light were antlers of large red deer and remains of wild boar and Celtic horse.

Similar finds have turned up since on Aberafan and Kenfig beaches. Peat beds exposed west of Sker Point in February 2002 were impregnated with small fragments of fossil wood and imprinted by deer. The porous fossil hoof which I picked from the driftline above may have been ancient or modern. By June 2002 almost the whole had been sanded over again for the summer.

*　　　*　　　*

SCARWEATHER SANDS

John Blundell of Nottage Court, who sea watches with a telescope from the lifeboat station and exercises his horses over Kenfig Burrows, tells of tide-induced changes on land as well as seashore. In May 2002 a shingle bank which had been building up gradually suddenly moved north and blocked the mouth of the Kenfig River. Fresh water built up behind this and the bounding dune ridge, inundating the reedbed behind to form a twenty-five acre lake.

A drilling rig had been stationed some nine miles offshore for six weeks or so, its superstructure standing twenty feet above the sea on four legs. It had to be manoeuvred into position by tug and was manned on a temporary basis by three people at a time.

The Scarweather Sands where it was stationed stretch from east to west offshore beyond the shorter Hugo Bank and show as a golden sand bar four miles long and half a mile or more wide above water level on low spring tides. There is said to be a depth of a hundred and eighty feet (54 metres) of sand over the underlying bedrock, into which any wind turbines would need to be anchored, so it may have proved economically unviable in an engineering technology sense with such powerful tides and converging south-westerly swells to contend with. In fact wind turbines were in place and functional off Porthcawl by 2004.

Blundell recalls a two hundred foot high tower set up on those sandbanks three years earlier at the end of the 1990s. It was furnished with telemetering equipment to send wind data by radio to a shore station, with a flashing red light atop to warn aircraft and shipping. It lasted just five days before sinking from sight, complete with the red light.

The notice to mariners of May 2002 stated that the new rig would be around for a few weeks and transplanted at intervals to new sites along the thousands of acres of sandbanks left in place by the dredgers, in order to locate suitable anchorage for the mooted wind turbines. It was still there on the Kenfig National Nature Reserve Open Day on 29th June, 2002 – a sea mark on the land rover excursion for the public around the dunes and along the old haul road behind Sker Point, where limestone from Cornelly Quarry had been transported for the building of Port Talbot's deep water dock in the 1970s.

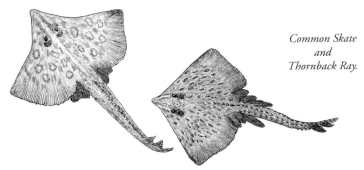

*Common Skate
and
Thornback Ray.*

Erstwhile inhabitants of these offshore sandbanks are skates and rays, which have shown a marked decline around the Welsh coast during the last decade or so. These detect their prey animals by recognising electric currents which those emit, and they are believed to navigate by using the Earth's magnetic field. Could cables from offshore electricity generators have a deleterious effect on these bizarre flatfish that were formerly an important component of coastal fisheries?

The Admiralty charts of 1975 and 1994 show three shoals breaking surface at low water of springs. The coastline here runs north to south from Briton Ferry through Porthcawl to Nash Point. Scarweather lies at right angles to it opposite Porthcawl, where the coast dips back to the mouth of the River Ogmore. The smaller Hugo Bank lies nearer the shore to the north and the Kenfig Patches, smaller still and nearer again, just outside Gwyl'r Misgl, which lies off the sculpted red rocks of Sker Point.

*   *   *

TUSKER ROCK

The next hazard to shipping is the Tusker Rock, a block of Carboniferous limestone rising from the sea bed opposite Ogmore Down south of Ogmore Mouth and the splendid stretch of Merthyr Mawr Warren, which was accorded full National Nature Reserve status at a ceremony on 3rd July, 2002.

This was a limestone hill during an era of lower sea level, when a modest River Severn wound its way down the wooded valley that is now the floor of the Bristol Channel. In crossing the woodland to join this, the River Ogmore passed round the northern flank of the hill.

Tusker Rock appears above water about two kilometres offshore on low tides, which occur around midday, giving good opportunity for viewing from Ogmore-by-Sea or mooring a boat alongside to explore on foot. Topographically it is a series of ridges slashed across by long narrow pools occupying fissures in the limestone. Thickly clad in seaweeds, it is now a marine biologists' paradise.

Back in the shadowy past Tusker was used by a local farmer for grazing his livestock. As the sea encroached and the animals were driven ashore, it became a source of seaweed fertiliser, this taken to land by horse and cart at low water.

The softer liassic shores of the Heritage Coast to the east form broad, wave-smoothed platforms of bare rock – not much richer in seaweed than the sand, peat and gravel to the west, so this organic fertiliser was much in demand.

Another source was that washed up in storms from the lower littoral zone and there are stone remains at the foot of Whitmore Stairs leading

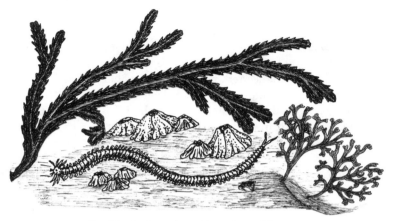

Saw Wrack, Carragheen, Barnacles and Ragworm.

down the cliff near Wick of what is believed to be a site for the burning of seaweed to ash. This reduced the labour of getting the product, known as wigmore, up the cliffs to the fields, while retaining the mineral nutrients if not the physical benefits.

Grosses Antiquities of 1775 tells of the two Vaughan boys from Dun-raven Castle who rowed their boat out to Swisker (Tusker) Rock and landed to explore. The incoming tide washed their boat away and they were drowned. This was said to be a partial judgement on the Vaughans, who practised wrecking, to profit by the salvage.

Tusker's presence as a shipping hazard was cited as one of the reasons why Ogmore Mouth was not developed as a port to export coal mined in Ogmore Vale during Glamorgan's industrial heyday. Instead, the coal produced up-river travelled by tortuous routes over the watersheds to the mouths of smaller rivers at Aberthaw, Porthcawl and, later, Barry.

A copper ingot ship bound from Bristol was lost on the southern ledges of Tusker Rock in 1806 – on a calm winter day, not driven on but just too close by an error of judgement. William Weston Young salvaged two thirds of the thirty-nine ton cargo. The rest, one might assume, must be still there.

The iron built ship *Malleny* bound from Cardiff to Rio with coal, was forced by weather to turn back for shelter and came to grief on Tusker Rock with the loss of twenty crew in the late nineteenth century.

*   *   *

NASH SANDS

Three months later the Nash Sands claimed another victim when the barque *Caterina* went down with all hands and the pilot. Small tankers delivering bulk liquid oil from Llandarcy Refinery in the 1960s, 70s and 80s, up channel to Gloucester and Worcester, would take the short cut inside the Scarweather and Nash Banks at high water – one suffering propellor failure and finishing up on the cliff under Nash Point lighthouse.

Although a hazard in winter, Nash Bank can act as a breakwater in summer, protecting quieter water under the cliff. Small fishing vessels and yachts sail over the top of the four mile long sand ridge at high water, when depth can be as much as two to three fathoms, but steer well clear when their skippers hear the noise of breakers filtering through darkness or fog.

Some of the many other wrecks on Nash Bank have been itemised in Gillham, *Sea Cliffs, Cwm Mawr to Gileston*, 1994, the fifth in the Heritage Coast Series. It was the loss of a general and other VIPs from the wooden steam packet *The Frolic* in 1831 that stimulated the building of the two lighthouses. These are now automated and the bank is marked by buoys. Mariners can line these up as sea marks to steer them through troubled waters when the sands are hidden. Dinghy fishermen linger alongside the bar at low water collecting turbot and other titbits from the depths.

Breaking waves on the falling tide may bring edible morsels to tempt gulls, which move in to rest and preen between explorations of the newly stocked larder. Terns and cormorants settle, nearer their profitable fishing grounds than is possible at high water.

Like the Scarweather, Nash Bank diverges from the mainland coast, being closest and minimally highest towards the taller lighthouse. The degree to which it shifts position is ably demonstrated on the Admiralty Chart published in 1994. Surveying for this was carried out over a span of several years and there is a marked non-alignment half way along, where the bulk of the sand had moved since the previous set of measurements were made.

*   *   *

BARRY ISLAND

Barry Island, like Berges, is another where the name has outlived the reality, its joining up with the mainland not a natural phenomenon as it was there. During the industrial era it was the eagerly anticipated

304

destination for annual Sunday school treats for children from the mining valleys. Eventually, as an industrial port, it became as built up as the ribbon development of the Valleys, but here was sea, sand and sun on a scale only dreamed of among the rainy confines of Merthyr, the Rhondda and the Cynon mines, pitheads and coal washeries.

Barry Island was separated from the mainland by a deep water channel. It embraces two of the three Carboniferous Limestone headlands stretching seaward from the newer Triassic rocks which form the basis for most of Barry town behind. These two, Friar's Point and Nell's Point, border the spreading sands and stepped promenade gardens of Whitemore Bay with the holiday complex and funfair behind: these still a visitor honeypot for South Walians.

The only part of the backing channel still subject to unrestricted entry of the great tides is the long sandy stretch of Barry Old Harbour in the west, behind its curved stone jetty. It is characterised by circular pioneering clumps of Spartina cord grass in the now quiet waters among the moored boats. Across its head is the combined road-rail link connecting the island with the steeply rising mainland.

Redshank and Spartina Grass.

The channel immediately behind was filled in and served for many years as a graveyard for clapped out steam-powered railway engines. In the rest were built the various docks, which became such a hub of activity, these extending obliquely inland towards the little River Cadoxton, canalised into a new course.

John Storie, writing in *The Western Mail*, 1896, under the title 'Excavations on Barry Island' states "The channel between Redbrink Point and Black Rocks on the Sully side, even quite recently, was fordable at every tide."

Some of the docks have since been filled in, as with so many along the coast from Porthcawl to Penarth and Cardiff. Those which remain share an exit to the sea with that of the natural harbour walled off from the holiday beach of Jackson's Bay on the island and used by the Yacht Club, the Lifeboat and the Flatholm Island Ferry. A sea wall leads east from here to the Bendricks and Sully Bay.

The Carboniferous Limestone of Friar's Point, famous for its cowslip meadow laced with crow garlic, and Nell's Point, once the site of a holiday camp, now demolished, surfaces at a few places on the main island. Mostly, however, this has been covered over by red marls of Triassic age, with fine nodules of crystalline pink gypsum and blue celestine.

Jurassic rocks above these have mostly eroded away – as had the upper surface of the tilted beds of Carboniferous Limestone below when the Trias was laid unconformably on top. Rocks are jumbled at the interface, with chunks of grey limestone embedded in a red matrix to form a breccia interleaved with narrow beds of the two parent rocks.

Ringed Plover and Alexanders seedlings.

Most typical plants at the junction must be the alexanders (*Smyrnium olusatrum*), which appears in the dead of winter as a rash of seedlings on the sand at the foot of the cliffs, to burgeon into early flowering yellow-green Umbellifers one to two metres high. The tall cliff of flaky red marl behind the Yacht Club becomes covered by a counterpane of non-matching mauvy-pink red valerian in summer and there are cryptic goodies like the little maidenhair fern at its most easterly site in Wales. Winter heliotrope floors some of the cliff woodlands with their well established input of evergreen holm oaks.

The remarkable botanical diversity around the docks and on the made land has been an irresistible lure for botanists over many decades. Incoming ships would jettison their ballast before loading up with coal and with it the disseminules of many strangers. Those coming from the West Indies with Geest's bananas had little chance in our climate, but many others liked what they found and infiltrated among the fairy tale glades of pink crown vetch and tuberous pea – blue bugloss species from home and abroad, yellow tansy, dark mullein, evening primrose and much much more.

This colourful diversity lives on only in the photographic archives now. Sadly those days of exciting discoveries have gone. Dock environs have been gardened into uniform lawns with a few buttercups and daisies and an occasional aniseed-scented fennel plant.

*   *   *

BENDRICK ROCK

East of Barry Pier and the lifeboat mooring is an old dock which was practically filled with rubble by 1979, leaving just room for a mallard and her family of ducklings. Immediately behind and across the newly walled course of the Cadoxton River are the Bendricks.

Here the red Triassic rocks have changed from flaky shales to smooth-textured Keuper marls (now going by another name). Geologists visit to admire the beautiful fossil ripple marks, set at right angles to the currents which shaped them, and the lines of current bedding, sloping slightly downwards in the direction of the current which deposited their narrow layers. On a seashore each new tide or wave would be likely to obliterate features left by the last, but these rocks were laid down in a shallow lake under desert conditions, when there was insufficient rain to wash the red ferric iron from the mineral grains, and sun cracks were nicely preserved.

It was not until 1974 that the Dinosaur footprints were found here. Some of the larger ones were identified as those of Anchisauripus, a set of these chiselled out on a flattened slab for an exhibit in the National Museum of Wales. This 'pavement', recent in geological terms, shows how the Bendricks appeared around two hundred and ten million years ago at the beginning of the Age of Dinosaurs, these being among the oldest known footprints from anywhere in the world at the time. Animals are believed to have ranged from four feet to twelve feet in height.

Subsequent field work has revealed more over a wider area and of different species (Steve Howe and Michael Bassett, *Nat. Mus. Wales Bull.*, 1990). The newly found footprints are larger than the others, with material squelched up alongside, suggesting that the animals were walking in soft mud, perhaps along the shore of a lake.

With them were non-Dinosaur prints, rectangular with four bent toes instead of triangular with three straight ones. These were identified as having been made by a Phytosaur – a large crocodile-like animal possibly new to science and of equivalent age.

One wonders what such sizable creatures could have been living on. Life in those shallow salt lakes must have been nigh impossible and there are no organic remains or fossils as clues. So many large creatures must have been just passing through – hence footprints and not bones.

It was 19th December, 1975, when I took my friends from New England to see the footprints (Arthur and Jennifer Gaines of the Woods Hole Oceanographic Institute, Massachussets, here on a teaching assignment in Atlantic College). They were thrilled.

"The same as ours in Connecticut, same rock, same age, same shape footprints, probably the same species. What if they were the same animals, passing nonchalantly from Europe to America during an afternoon stroll, before the Atlantic opened up?"

It was an intriguing thought, putting us firmly in our place as latecomers on this planet, arriving near midnight on the scale of the global twenty-four hour clock. These sliding continental plates have much to answer for!

During Triassic times Bendrick lay thirty degrees north of the Equator in Saharan Desert latitudes, under the influence of the North-East Trade Winds. As the land moved steadily northwards from the Southern Hemisphere coral seas and away from the equatorial rain forests which supply us with coal, the high mountains of Spain and Mauretania cut off wet sea winds from the south. Our red desert was in the middle of a continental land mass contiguous with what was to become north-east America.

By Jurassic times the white and blue Lias rocks of our South Wales cliffs were being deposited as a limey mud on the bed of a warm sea. This was the infant Atlantic Ocean, water flooding in through the Caribbean from the Pacific. As the plates drifted on, we moved northward into cooler air and the two halves – broken at Bendrick – slid inexorably apart -separating what we choose to call the New World from the Old – New England from Old South Wales.

Such gargantuan happenings are guaranteed sufficient to cause us to pause for thought. We should be appreciating how small a part the self-styled 'master race' has played in the evolution of our home planet and trying a little harder to conserve what still remains to us.

With my American friends I was gazing on a concordant series of raised footprints, alternating left and right and crossing some fifteen metres of a flat Triassic slab in the intertidal zone. Each track was elevated an inch or so from the surface, like a tea plate or a teapot stand, and very reminiscent of a line of raised footprints left in a snow-covered carpark when the melt sets in. Presumably the mechanism was the same, the Dinosaurs consolidating the mud underfoot as the man consolidated the snow, so that it remained after the rest had washed, blown or melted away. Some of the three-toed footprints on slabs at a higher level were infilled with fine grey breccia or conglomerate, some had lost their contents and appeared as imprints.

Today's fresh tracks on the rocks were ludicrous by comparison – these the smooth slime trails of intertidal periwinkles and the tight zig-zags of rasping limpets. Downshore, in the wet sand, were larger, three-toed ones, the smaller back-pointing toe leaving no impression, as with their supposed forebears, the feathered Dinosaurs – these the prints of splay-toed redshanks and web-footed gulls.

There are other geological excitements to be found at Bendrick Rocks near the ancient footprints. These are stromatolites – spherical concretions of blue-green algae which trap silt as they grow, much in this case consisting of the ossicles or stem segments of Crinoids or sea lilies from the underlying Carboniferous Limestone – which is as rich in fossils as the desert sandstones are poor. These segments, like vertebrae, put one in mind of the 'mint with the hole'.

The domes, when sawn in half, show concentric layers deposited during build-up, as sometimes demonstrated by more modern chunks of tufa concreting around successive surface layers of algae. I have had the good fortune to see an amazing mass of such stromatolites in situ on the desert shore of Shark Bay in Western Australia – after fraternising with friendly dolphins a little to the south.

Another phenomenon seen in the making – in South Australia this time – and found here fossilised at Bendrick, are the sand volcanoes or de-watering structures. About a handspan across, these are formed by water escaping from a sodden layer below, pushing up debris alongside which is consolidated by the next layer deposited on top pressing the water out.

A more liquid manifestation of such can fascinate the viewer in the bubbling mud cauldrons of moister climates in New Zealand and America's Yellowstone National Park. Barry's rounded pits evacuated by gypsum or alabaster nodules are similar, but with angular edges instead of raised rims, and often lined with a deposit of white minerals.

The Bendricks lie between the old and new courses of the little Cadoxton River and are approached through the land-based naval station of HMS *Cambria*, which moved here from Cardiff Docks in the 1980s. The island of isolated rock rises from the grey limestone of the older beach platform and is accessible across a minimal causeway from the shore through most of the tidal cycle. It is of the same red rock as the low mainland cliffs where slabs were chipped away to create an industrial tramway along the face, revealing some fine ripple beds.

Purple sandpipers gather on the lower rocks with turnstones and oyster-catchers now that the clanking trams no longer pass. Longshore fishermen cast their lines from the rock's extremity to catch pouting loitering over the sands that were formerly laced with lines of drifted coal dust. This is a summer pastime, winter fishermen concentrate on cod, mackerel and sea bass.

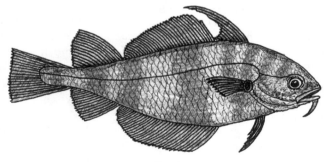

Pouting.

Plants in the Keuper crevices are mostly small – biting stonecrop, plantains, bird's-foot trefoil and kidney vetch. Growth is rank along the top, with attenuated rock samphire, wild carrot, sea beet and cocksfoot. Most characteristic from Bendrick to the Sully Island causeway is gladdon Iris, its mauve flowers producing splaying capsules of bright orange seeds, which persist throughout the winter, spurned by all seed-eaters.

17.

SULLY ISLAND

Sully Island is more substantial than the last few, occupying thirteen acres (about five hectares) and measuring four hundred and forty metres long by about a hundred and ten metres wide. Its long axis lies parallel to the mainland shore at Swanbridge and is linked to it by a rocky causeway four hundred metres from end to end.

Average tides here, six miles down channel from Cardiff, have a vertical rise and fall of thirty-three feet (ten metres) and the island is accessible on foot for about half the tidal cycle. When the tide turns the currents are strong and dangerous, whether the flood is surging in or out of the bottleneck, and lives are lost here almost every year when crossings have been left too late.

Longshore fishermen will maroon themselves at high water for some peaceful casting of their lines but others usually leave the island to the birds, particularly those which need it most when they are driven off their feeding grounds on the mud flats by the rising waters.

Triassic rocks overlie the Carboniferous Limestone here. They take the form of horizontal beds of Keuper Sandstone with pebbly conglomerates and flaky marls and contain cornstones, which dissolve out, liberating lime into the red soils.

It is the fine unconformity between the Trias and the limestone on the highest, south-eastern, corner, that merited the island's designation as an SSSI. The red rocks weather readily and crumbly exposures several feet in depth and interleaved with paler horizontal shale beds are exposed along the seaward south-facing cliffs which rise only about twenty-five feet (eight metres) from the wave-washed slabs of grey limestone below. This more durable foundation must account for Sully's survival as an island when all around was eroded away.

An old hill fort shows as a single and double earthwork cutting off this highest promontory, which is angled out to sea. Thought at one time to be Norse, it was called Dane's Fort, but is now known to be earlier, from the Iron Age, like the others along this coast, dating back to the pre-Roman period about five hundred BC. It is scheduled as an ancient monument but has not been excavated. A horde of Roman coins was unearthed in 1899 and a pirate called De Marisco is said to have used the island as a base during the thirteenth century.

Low cliffs bound the area except in the central part of the north, which is bordered by a storm beach of pebbles. Some of the land behind is low-lying – a reed swamp – usually furnished with fresh water but sometimes overrun by the sea. That this is a regular occurrence is shown by the salt-loving plants interspersed among the reeds, which are salt-tolerant but thrive better in its absence – the culms here less than half the height of those on Crymlin Bog referred to earlier.

During the twenty years that I knew the island best, during the 1970s and 1980s the vegetation altered considerably. The grassland, long and tufty in the west and closely rabbit-grazed in the east, was gradually giving way to scrub, spreading south from the cliffy parts at either end of the north coast.

Bramble was the pioneer, this becoming infiltrated by elder, hawthorn and wild privet. By the 1980s bracken was spreading and the thicket was being invaded by woodland understorey plants – broad buckler fern, dogs mercury, wild Arum and the inevitable nettles. Occasional fires caused temporary setbacks, both here and to the few gorse clumps, giving the grassland, which occupied rather more than half the whole, a sporting chance. In days when farming, even on islands, was viable the sward was grazed and there are records of oats being grown here in 1843.

The most spectacular flower, which occurs in profusion in some years, is the yellow horned poppy of the shingle beaches. Its big crinkly petals brighten the dullest days and lead on to a splaying sequence of narrow pods as much as a foot (thirty centimetres) long.

Rabbits and people are the main modifying influences on the grass-land. Professor Bellamy of the Cardiff University Zoology Department, was organising student surveys of rabbits on South Wales islands through the 1970s. He ranked his five locations in order of value as Skomer, Skokholm, Flatholm, Sully and Steepholm. The longest rabbit path he had ever seen was on Sully Island – a straight fifty-seven metres from the warren in the scrub to the heavily cropped grazing ground on the cliff edge, where the padmarks were lost on a turf as smooth as a billiard table and littered with the little brown marbles of rabbit pellets. That was in 1975.

Wood Mouse and Fairy Flax.

Peter Ferns of his department was supervising students on a small mammal study on Sully Island through the eight winters from 1972 to 1979. They were concerned mainly with rodents and shrews and he comments on aberrations in coat colour in the population of wood mice, with unusually dark and pale forms and one with shoulder patches of greyish-white.

Two hundred and eighty wood mice were trapped during the eight years, giving a fair sample of the variants, which tend to crop up more commonly in small island populations. The same variability occurs among the Sully rabbits, but this is known to stem from the introduction of domesticated breeds in the past.

Live-trapping between October and February in a representative selection of habitats, enabled animals to be weighed and marked by toe clipping, so that the percentage of re-traps and population numbers could be assessed. Wood mice were estimated at sixty-seven per hectare in winter, field voles at twenty-eight per hectare. Seven mammal species were identified, wood mouse and field vole (a hundred and ninety-two captured) the most abundant.

Field Voles and Mouse-ear Chickweed.

313

The single house mouse was discounted as an anomalous introduction, not found again. Brown rats do not fit conveniently into the standard Longworth live traps, so only young ones were caught. These are common scavengers along the local seashores and would have no problem in scampering across the causeway, although likely to be drifted off course if they attempted to swim. As omnivorous feeders, they would no doubt follow their noses from one sea-borne titbit to another at low water.

The weasel, which was less expected, would also have few transit problems – and plenty of potential prey on arrival. Traps were baited with whole oats, which are of no interest to the insectivorous common shrews, but fourteen of these entered to investigate.

Data on diet was sought by examining fecal pellets dropped in the entrance to the traps. Surprisingly for the mice, which we regard as nut and berry eaters, the winter diet was found to consist of 44% fungi, 22% Arthropods (woodlice and other small invertebrates) and 34% green plants.

Field voles were vegetarian, eating mainly grasses and of these mostly the finest and most important in the short turf which they frequented – the red fescue. Others, distinguishable by epidermal strips, were brown bent, perennial ryegrass and Yorkshire fog, with a certain input of broad-leaved plants, rushes and mosses.

Rabbits numbered fifty or so in the winter of 1973 according to night counts using an infra-red telescope, although the population had suffered from Myxomatosis as recently as 1971-72. Fifteen hundred epidermal fragments examined from rabbit pellets suggested that 88% of the food taken was again the needle-leaved red fescue grass, with 8% of other grasses and common sorrel and ribwort plantain favoured among the broad-leaved species.

Rabbits were domiciled in the scrub but fed on the short grassland, being particularly attracted to the high point of the hill fort. Field voles were found only in the grassland and the marsh and had smaller home ranges than the wood mice, which were more widely distributed throughout, but occurred at highest densities in the thicker cover of the scrub and the marsh. Shrews frequented grassland and the edges of the scrub and of isolated bramble patches. (Peter Ferns, 1981, *The Mammals of Sully Island*, Trans. *Cardiff Naturalists*, 99.)

Bank voles seemed to be absent, the wealth of suitable scrub habitat having developed only since grazing by farm animals ceased. The four hundred metres of rugged causeway separating the island from the mainland is largely covered by seaweed and pools – a formidably unfamiliar barrier to small furry creatures with so much less length of leg than rat or weasel. Maybe an intrepid individual will make the crossing one day or be caught short and washed ashore, but not, apparently, by the time of the survey.

Mice are greater travellers (and much more likely to jump out of traps at inconvenient moments than voles). Some have been seen swimming, but a more likely mode of arrival for them could have been in hay or other livestock fodder.

*   *   *

There is no obvious reason why the grassland, which occupied rather more than half the island in the 1980s, should be so clearly divided into the main block of long tufty grass in the west and the tight, lawn-like sward in the east. That they are maintained in this state by the preference of the rabbits for the finer red fescue grass, which competes poorly among the coarser species, is obvious, but the often sharp demarcation between the two is remarkable, particularly as the long growths are criss-crossed by the well worn tracks of rabbits travelling from their warrens in tall vegetation to the dining areas.

Myxomatosis comes and goes and it is likely that the boundaries between the two communities fluctuate accordingly. Certainly there can be a large component of ground-ivy in ungrazed areas, a species spurned by rabbits and increasing at the expense of others where they abound. This suggests former heavy rabbit pressure, since when the prostrate growths of this herb are being progressively swallowed up by the taller growths, as were many old rabbit burrows in 1983. Gladdon Iris, agrimony, knapweed and weld compete well here.

Poking into the matted base of the tall grasses, it is not difficult to find field vole tunnels. When these are in use there are little piles of one inch lengths of chopped grass at intervals of eight inches or so along them. Voles are more diurnal than the wood or field mice, which seek the cover of darkness, but they are clever at outwitting predators such as the kestrel which uses the island notice board as his favourite perch.

Having burrowed up to a tasty smelling grass tuft, they saw through the base of the culm and haul the blades down into their labyrinth. Here the harvest is chopped into handy lengths. Unpalatable dry sheaths are discarded as little piles of dead grass. This mode of feeding occurs only in the long grass communities. Elsewhere the soil is hard-packed under the close sward and the surface-feeding rabbits leave little top growth to be hauled down.

These short grass swards are much the most interesting floristically, harbouring not only the tinies like fairy flax and eyebright which would be smothered in the other, but most of the special lime-lovers as well. Here are violets, including the hairy species, and cowslips among springtime field woodrush or Good Friday grass. Yellow-wort, centaury, salad burnet and lady's bedstraw follow, with wild thyme and biting stonecrop on the knolls and spreads of rock-rose and kidney vetch between. Golden oat grass is a sure sign of a good lime content, hound's tongue of a sandy soil, these growing here with burnet saxifrage.

On a day in late August 1983 there were migrant clouded yellow butterflies in profusion, feeding particularly on the flower heads of corn sow thistle, which were also favoured targets of the many bumble bees. Meadow browns and large whites were everywhere, with wall browns, common blues, small tortoiseshells and painted ladies.

Leap-frogging grasshoppers were spooking the silver Y moths as they hung suspended among the hover flies. Recently vacated yellow silk cocoons of drinker moths lay discarded among a scatter of small brown toadstools.

By November the fungi were at prime, with good potential feeds of field mushrooms to tempt visitors, but beware: these are yellow stainers. Some folk can eat them with impunity, others can suffer diarrhoea and vomiting, even coma, before recovery. It is good policy to leave them alone if the base of the stipe goes bright

Corn Sow Thistle.

yellow when cut. There are parasol mushrooms here, too, but not the queen of species that provided some of our gourmet feeds on Skokholm.

Others, relished by connoisseurs of fungi, are aromatic wood blewits (*Tricholoma* or *Lepista nuda*) with attractive lavender-mauve gills, and ordinary blewits (*Lepista saeva*) with less purple. These are twice as big, up to fifteen centimetres across, and in clumps, the clumps clumped. Fleshy tops have close-set white gills and stumpy stipes. The first exude

Blewit Mushrooms and Eyebright.

copious liquid when fried. This should be poured off. The old hill fort can be embroidered with fairy rings right through the season.

Reeds of the marshy area, which occupies about 5% of the island, are short and there is a summertime path through the middle. Emulating the dominant is a small stand of the unusual bush grass or wood small reed (*Calamagrostis epigejos*) which is rare in Wales and more or less restricted in England to the south-centre. It grows here with tall oat grass and cocksfoot. I first met it in Holland, where it hybridises with marram grass to produce Ammocalamagrostis, which is a valuable sand binder on the dune systems which play such a vital role in keeping the sea at bay.

Most of the rushes formerly accepted as soft rush proved to be sea rush. Other salt lovers are sea couch, sea sedge, mud rush and sea arrow grass. There is open water in winter, and during summer downpours. The sea breaks in fairly frequently and the presence of flat stones washed onto the grass behind in a litter of limpet shells and pebbles shows with what force.

In a normal summer there is less water, this wriggling with mosquito larvae and topped by their suspended pupae. A pair of common darter dragonflies (*Sympetrum striolatum*), which we had earlier watched coupling on the beach, whirred in to lay their eggs, the scarlet swain whipping his khaki partner's abdomen down indiscriminately onto both open water and soft mud.

At the edge of the reedbed a flowering patch of sea milkwort graded up through silverweed to a woolly stand of fleabane. Spearing up through straggles of bittersweet were tawny sedge and spike sedge (*Carex hostiana* and *Carex spicata*) with tall orache and sea beet established well back among the reeds.

317

Much of the interest lies inevitably around the coasts and there is plenty of successional change to delay botanists on the mainland facing beach. Turning west down channel after crossing the causeway sometimes reveals a short-lived mini salt marsh with sea arrow grass and sea milkwort. This builds up on top of the pebbles during periods of calm, but is liable to be swept away again in rough weather. Beneath is the current storm beach, which is still subject to movement by the waves.

Orache grows on the seaward face with yellow horned poppy along the crest. The poppy was sparse in the early 1960s but increased enormously, mature flowering and fruiting plants separated by first year rosettes of attractively dissected grey leaves, to give a fifty per cent ground cover on what is usually a much more open habitat. Corn sow thistle takes over on the crest towards the east, overwhelming the annual crop of orache seedlings. Others are curled dock, woody nightshade and ragwort.

This storm beach overlies an older one which surfaces a little further east again, where there is less wave action. The even-sized stones here are no longer shuffled around and their upper sides are dark with slow-growing lichens, which would inevitably die of light starvation

Yellow Horned Poppies.

if the stones were being overturned. Associated are slabby growths of dog's tooth lichen and the common moss, *Hypnum cupressiforme*.

Ivy from the low backing cliff has insinuated itself among the pebbles to seaward, with honeysuckle trailing from above. This peters out where the beach flattens against the low-lying part of the hinterland. Here the plant succession has advanced to produce a thin skin of turf over the pebbles, with red-stemmed herb Robert, biting stonecrop, carline thistle and other composites, pierced by spears of gladdon Iris.

At one point beach material has been driven inland to form an advancing tongue across the marsh, which lies at a lower level than the beach crest. This spit contains a higher proportion of fine shingle and broken shells than the main beach, heavier fragments dumped further back as the force of the waves diminishes. Early colonists are scarlet pimpernel, buck's-horn plantain and ragwort rosettes leading to a scant fescue turf.

Backing this acreting, sheltered shore to either side of the wetland is scrub. Elder had overwhelmed much of the bramble at the western end, growing two to three metres high, but stag-headed with wind-killed leaders rising gauntly another half metre. The associated wild privet presents a smoother profile, 'clipped' by and leaning away from the prevailing wind. There is still room for bracken in the general press and this grows tall in its quest for light above canopy level.

The eastern scrub is impenetrable, the spiky branches matted together with cleavers and other creepers. Seedlings of common, turkey and holm oak were appearing marginally by the mid 1980s, the acorns unlikely to have arrived without human aid unless perhaps brought by a jay.

Woodland edge plants included wood sage, tufted vetch, greater knap-weed, hedge bedstraw, bittersweet and common figwort. Rarities recorded in the 1970s were unfamiliar varieties of the last two – *Solanum dulcamara var. obovatum* and *Scrophularia nodosa var. bobartii.* Ten snail species were recorded by Peter Dance of the National Museum of Wales in 1969.

This complex of beach successions is not replicated on the seaward coast of the island. Here few land plants descend onto the rocky beach platform and those on the earthy cliff faces are mostly spilled from the grassland above, with rock samphire the only species able to tolerate a deal more sea spray than it was subjected to here.

*　　*　　*

Traditionally the broad spread of the landward facing beach has been prized by ornithologists as a haven for wading birds driven off the mud flats of the Taff-Ely Roads at high tide. More than five thousand dunlin can assemble here, along with knot, redshank, oyster-catchers, grey plover, ringed plover and turnstones. As their alternative high water roost on the Penarth Moors became overrun with humans and later by big machines pushing monstrous quantities of urban waste around, the Sully beach became more vital as a sanctuary.

Then, at the end of the twentieth century, the Cardiff-Ely Roads were cut off from the sea by the Cardiff Bay Barrage. The tidal mud flats, with their wealth of marine prey items were drowned. The shore birds were no longer catered for and left. Implications of this saga of fundamental habitat change have been discussed in Gillham, *The Natural History of Cardiff. Exploring along the River Taff*, 2002.

There are long ago records of breeding oyster-catchers, ringed plovers, lapwings, shelduck, ravens and even water rails in the Sully Island marsh before the area became so popular with visitors.

Of these dunlin are far and away the most abundant, with a record of six thousand two hundred and three in January 1974 and two hundred and seventy-six redshank on the same day. Early 1970s yielded winter counts of fifty-one oyster-catchers, forty-six grey plover, thirty ringed plover and twelve curlew. During more intensive ornithological surveys Peter Ferns and colleagues cannon-netted turnstones and others on the beach for ringing and monitoring, but the rugged jigsaw of stones caused complications and smoother-surfaced sites up channel were favoured in later years for this.

The three large gull species commute across the island between Flatholm and the city's rubbish tips and there are plenty of black-headed gulls around for much of the year. Buzzards visit to hunt the rabbits, as kestrels hunt the voles, and there is an intermittent passage of cormorants passing by, low over the waves.

The island scrub forms an important adjunct to the bush-clad nature reserve of Lavernock Point on the adjacent mainland, supplying food and shelter for small passerines migrating along the channel. The early years saw breeding of a few each of rock pipit, meadow pipit, skylark, stonechat, song thrush, blackbird and blue tit, with possibly also robin, dunnock, wren, linnet and greenfinch.

A few ringed plovers were still laying their cryptic eggs on the beach pebbles and shelduck their conspicuously plain ones in the seclusion of rabbit burrows during the mid 1980s. An August visit at that time saw ringed plovers building up to fifteen on the incoming tide and a shelduck eggshell was found in the rough sward bordering the swamp with a chick-sized hole in the end. Hopefully the inmate had got away safely to sea. There were a few sanderlings about all day, up to six turnstones, some oyster-catchers and a curlew sandpiper.

Two young wheatears with an adult were turning over dried seaweed on the north beach and two rock pipits foraged along the south cliffs. Yellow wagtails were doing likewise on an earlier visit in 1963. Carrion crows favoured the beach, magpies the bushes and a thirty strong party of young starlings the western scrub.

The sixteen linnets utilised all types of habitat, as did the smaller charm of goldfinches, with greenfinches favouring the wind-shorn elders. Willow warblers with them numbered between forty and fifty, most of them yellowish-tinged youngsters, with one more distinctively marked wood warbler and a handsome cock stonechat. A kestrel hovered aloft throughout our six hour stay – indefatigable in its pursuit of small furry prey or lesser invertebrates.

The only additions on a winter visit were pied wagtails, dunnocks, chaffinches and jackdaws, these last part of a big mob of mixed Corvids which converged nightly at a treetop roost by the Sully Road.

*   *   *

With an average tidal range of thirty to thirty-five feet, coupled with the intricacies of the slabby intertidal rocks and gravel beach and wide discrepancies in the degree of shelter from the often turbulent currents, Sully Island is a first class venue for viewing marine life. The chief interest arises not from the overlapping of organisms from warmer and colder waters but from differing salinities. Saltiness fluctuates seasonally, being less in winter when the big rivers on the Welsh side of the channel are in spate. This gives a fascinating mixture of creatures from the open sea and the narrowing estuary.

An interesting overlap is of two kinds of barnacles, which are seldom found together, the sea-living *Balanus crenatus* going no further up channel and the estuarine *Balanus improvisus* going no further down. This last penetrates right up to Newnham-on-Severn or almost to the bridge at Gloucester, where brave hearts riding the Severn Bore finally fall off their surf boards.

Cardiff naturalists have spent many happy days fossicking around Sully Island's shores in the cheery company of Christopher Mettam, the university's expert in marine animal life. It was wise for us to start on the outer coast, working back over the sheltered gravels and from the lower littoral to the shallows of the causeway as the incoming tide followed inexorably behind.

Even before splashing out from dry land, we encountered small seaside creatures like the wingless bristletail, *Petrobius maritimus*, that clung to its very edge. Here were sea slaters (*Ligea oceanica*) like overgrown woodlice. Other Isopods, such as Idotea and Bathyporeia sandhoppers, scuttled round on rocks above the splash zone, while *Gammarus locusta* sand hoppers fed among the kelp flies and their larvae in the weedy driftline – both prey and predators, as some fell to the foraging wagtails and starlings.

For the gardeners among us who harbour a loathing for slugs, it was good to hunt out some of the handsome sea slugs, with their colourful frilly gills. Most live in the sub-littoral zone but come into the shallows to lay their spiralised or fluted egg clusters. Anemones, sea mats and barnacles are among their favourite foods, their soft bodies taking no harm from the poison stinging cells of the first, even utilising these as a protection for themselves.

Sea Anemones, Chitons, Sea Gooseberries and Sun Star.

Big chunky Dahlia anemones (*Tealia felina*) thrive here, as well as the shiny jelly blobs of beadlets (*Actinia equina*). Gently squeeze a beadlet and young ones sheltering inside may be disgorged. Small sea spiders (Pycnogonids), which seem to be all arms and legs and no bodies, can be found nibbling at the Dahlias' red, pink and white striped tentacles.

Another decorated in pink and white was the common sun star (*Solaster* or *Crossaster papposus*). Chris Mettam had not seen this so far up channel before, but it was very much alive, not just an orphan of the storm. Sea mats, on the other hand, are often cast adrift, although four or five different species can sometimes be found living on a single stone.

Much more mobile are the rock pool fish. With the blennies of the mid-littoral zone are sand gobies and another more tolerant of low salinities (*Blennius pholis, Gobius minutus* and *Gobius microps*). Here too,

Blenny, Sprat and Goby.

322

were fingerling grey mullet and other pelagic fish fry, with elvers in season and *Leander serratus* prawns.

The muddy gravels where wading birds gather to roost and feed can be blackened by anaerobic activity among the finer particles. Lack of oxygen does not worry most marine worms as these poke their breathing tubes above the surface. It is here that fishermen come to dig for bait, a favourite with them being the king ragworm (*Nereis virens*), which can reach more than 50cm long and is green above and pink below.

Baltic tellins and sting winkles or dwarf triton shells (*Macoma baltica* and *Ocinebra erinacea*) living in these beaches are relished by the waders, and the little laver spire shells (*Hydrobia ulvae*) tempt in a few shelduck.

Sand reefs built on the rocks by honeycomb worms (*Sabellaria alveolata*) come and go. Sometimes the fragile sand tubes build up to a mass fifty centimetres or more deep, then erosion can set in and the system becomes moribund, particularly if the worms that keep them in repair are killed by frost. A dying reef may become muddied over although still crunchy underfoot; then the sediment washes away and the whole edifice builds up again, supplying hidey-holes for more than the sand worms which build them.

These reefs occur in fully salt water down channel, but also extend well up, past Cardiff. Where strong currents scour the rock free of sand and mud, the worms can capture sand grains as they pass, to continue building, but they select only a certain size of grain. Old reefs on the Sully Island shore can erode so fast that the usual green algae are unable to take a hold, leaving the honeycomb mass as clean as when in use.

Most familiar to shore fossickers are the shellfish, the sea snails which live on rock rather than the bivalves which, apart from mussels, tend to bury themselves in the sand. Black-shelled edible periwinkles of the fishmongers' slabs live mainly downshore. Smooth or flat periwinkles come in bright orange or yellow at Barry but have shells of a more muted olive-green or with netted markings around Sully Island. Rough periwinkles, too, can vary widely in shell colour.

Purple top shells moved further up channel after the hot summers of 1975 and 1976, having been found only below Barry before then. There were no good mussel beds at Sully Island and dog whelks were sparse, with white or yellow shells and feeding on barnacles.

Chiton or coat-of-mail shells clamped to the Sully rocks have eight shell plates, which separate when the animal dies, sometimes causing an identification problem. These are multivalves, not falling within the usual categories of univalves and bivalves.

And then, of course, there are the crabs. It is not unusual to find a male shore crab clasping a female possessively, waiting for her to shed her carapace in the normal course of growth, the moult or ecdesis, so that he can mate with her before her new armour hardens up. While this species can be found up channel well beyond Cardiff, it is unable to breed in the less saline part of its range.

Others are fussier. Sully Island is about as far up the estuary as edible crabs go, but they can breed here, as do hermit crabs and squat lobsters (*Galathea squamifera*). A rare relative like a small lobster is *Axius stirhynchus*, which is usually found in deep water, but lives here in muddy gravel upstream of the causeway.

Highest in evolutionary terms, but in the lower part of the littoral zone are gooseberry sea squirts (*Dendrodoa grossularia*). These are chordates, the first step on the ladder from invertebrates to vertebrates, and have a tadpole-like larval phase. Ours are small, gooseberry-sized, unlike the noble six inch high squirters or cunjevois (*Pyura stolonifera*), which amuse children and adults alike on Australian holiday beaches. Fixed to the rocks, they resemble sponges with two openings, an inhalant and an exhalant. More familiar true sponges are the Haliclona mermaids' gloves.

Common piddocks (*Pholas dactylus*), which bore only into the softer shale layers and not the dominant Liassic limestone along the Glamorgan Heritage Coast, are well able to tackle the red rocks of Sully Island. They burrow out holes up to an inch across, mechanically by rotating the apparently brittle but surprisingly strong spiky shells. Other species are 'solution borers', dissolving their way into the limestones.

In fact these Triassic rocks, which crumble to a red loam on the low cliffs, can just as easily work down to a red clay under water, into which a spade can be thrust with no difficulty. Smaller white piddocks and rosy-nosed rock-borers (*Barnea candida* and *Hiatella arctica*) are other boring molluscs here.

The red rock worm (*Marphysia sanguinea*) reaches to only five inches of its potential twenty-four on Sully Island and lives in ready made crevices. Scale worms can be most unwormlike, an attractive example being the iridescent Aphrodyte sea-mouse, which is more like a mini 'Dougall' of children's TV fame, with scales so fine that they seem fit to clothe a shaggy dog.

Other worms build on rather than bore into rocks. Those secreting limey tubes about their bodies include irregularly shaped Pomatoceros keel worms and the little coils of Spirorbis, which are glued also to seaweeds.

Sully Island was threatened with various plans for inappropriate developments during the 1970s and 80s. Had developers had their way there would have been a partially underground health-hydro-complex here, entailing a helipad and excavation of the south-west half of the island, with no provision for the disposal of excavated rock.

As a geological SSSI, it has fine examples of sand volcanos or de-watering structures as well as the classic unconformity and – who knows – possibly more Dinosaur footprints. The hazards of the causeway crossing, potential rising sea level, the current amenity use of the natural features and conservation of the rich plant and animal life won out and planning permission was refused. Sully Island lives on, giving pleasure and knowledge to the many instead of the pampered, moneyed few.

18.

FLATHOLM: THE BACKGROUND

Most Cardiff residents and visitors to the Penarth seafront will be familiar with the distinctive outlines of Flatholm and Steepholm Islands, dropped into the Bristol Channel between the limestone headlands of Barry and Brean Down. Walking the clifftop path to Lavernock Point the pair seem to slide around in relation to each other, jockeying for position. From being well to the left of its loftier twin, Flatholm sidles across in front of the other, which is politically English, and so further away, to be lost against its larger bulk, and then reappears on the right.

Flatholm is the one with the lighthouse and a gentle gradient from not quite a hundred feet in the east to almost nothing in the west. Steepholm is big, blocky and flat-topped, rising to two hundred and fifty-six feet. As Glamorgan's only true island, six hundred by five hundred yards or some five hundred metres in diameter and occupying fifty-seven acres or twenty-four hectares, it is a surprise to find how many locals have never set foot on Flatholm. That was not always as easy, however, as it is today.

The indomitable pioneers of the Cardiff Naturalists' Society had launched expeditions to the more accessible Steepholm as long ago as 1877 and 1883, and in 1890 they made it to Flatholm. This was no summertime picnic. With noses to the ground and notebooks at the ready, they produced a preliminary list of a hundred and seven different plant species and the first authenticated records of the fauna – published in *Trans. Cardiff Nats. Soc, XXII, Part II.*

A gull research station was operating on Steepholm from the 1960s and negotiations were afoot to purchase that island as a nature reserve in memory of the writer and naturalist, Kenneth Allsop. Flatholm lagged behind.

When gulls started moving in there in 1954, wheels were set in motion to monitor their spread and Cardiff Naturalists' parties went across regularly to attempt nest counts – not an easy task, with few landmarks and a whirling mob overhead scattering 'whitewash' and screaming invective.

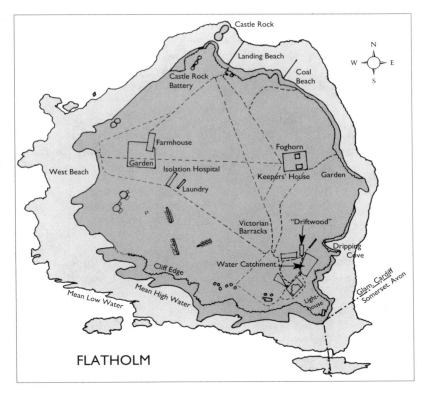

FLATHOLM

We battled on, and by the end of the 1960s had recorded over two thousand pairs breeding across the flat grassy plateau.

Colonel Morrey-Salmon, ornithologist and photographer extraordinaire, writing in support of reserve status for Flatholm in 1974, commented in exasperation:

> "From 1970 onwards it has not been possible to organise regular counts, due to greatly increased costs and, indeed, the great difficulty of hiring any boat at all."

He could have added that counting what was eventually over ten thousand nests scattered higgledy-piggledy hither and thence, was a formidable task, not lightly embarked upon.

A bird migration station had been operating at Lavernock Point on the adjacent Glamorgan mainland for fifteen years at that time, manned by the Ornithological Section of the Cardiff Naturalists, and it was desirable that recording should be extended to this obvious stopping off place for weary travellers, away from human disturbance.

The Rev. Peter Leonard, writing on the same theme in the *Bulletin of the Glamorgan Wildlife Trust*, around that time says:

> "Getting to Flatholm is not particularly easy. There is no regular boat service and the usual way for naturalists is to make up a party and charter a local boat for a day visit. Landing conditions can be difficult and the boatman will not guarantee to land the party."

And then along came *Naomi*, but not until 2nd February, 1983, when I was able to attend her launching ceremony at Barry Graving Dock. Eight years before, in 1975, the island lease had become available and the South Glamorgan County Council had taken it up for the next ninety-nine years, leaving the lighthouse, foghorn and Keepers' Cottage in the hands of Trinity House. Under the conditions of the lease the island was designated as a Local Nature Reserve run by the local authority. Earlier, in 1972, the Nature Conservancy Council had declared it an SSSI, as an area of Earth Science Interest. This was confirmed in 1993.

Today's boat, the *Lewis Alexander* was purpose-built for the county council to service the island. She carries forty-seven passengers (thirty between first October and thirty-first of March) and is furnished with life jackets, life rafts, two VHF radios, a navigation radar and radio telephone (this before the invasion of mobile phones). Leaflets advertised her as "Making regular crossings seven days a week, summer and winter, from Barry Harbour." The advert continues: "Comfortable self-catering accommodation is available on the island in the renovated farmhouse. Fully equipped with modern conveniences." So there is now no excuse for not visiting.

*   *   *

St. Cadoc is the first visitor we know about – in the late sixth century – and crossings by holy men were not without their hazards. Two monks were drowned when returning from the island, the body of one taken back for burial. A priory is marked on early Ordnance Survey maps but no tangible remains have been found. Excavation of suspicious looking mounds on the plateau turned out to be spoil heaps from trial borings for lead and not ancient burial sites.

The island then was known as Echni – the 'Holm' or 'River Island' originating with the Vikings, who may not have stayed long but used the islands as navigation aids. Some say they took refuge here after defeat by the Saxons at Watchet in AD 917. Habitation is thought to have been continuous since the twelfth century

Two ancient gravestones near the farmhouse were a conspicuous feature at the beginning of the 1960s, one of mountain limestone and one of Purbeck marble. Legend has it that they cover the remains of the two knights who murdered St. Thomas-a-Beckett. Through the sixties they were in use as anvils on which the local thrushes smashed their snail shells!

Song Thrush and Snail anvil.

The stones are said to be identical with those at Blackfriars in Cardiff and it is suggested that Blackfriars monks may have fled from Bute Park to Flatholm during Henry VIII's persecution of the monasteries. The island was allocated to the parish of St. Mary's in Cardiff in 1066 and the vicar of St. Mary's visited annually thereafter to collect his tithe.

Medieval potsherds from the twelfth and thirteenth centuries were found under the floor of the seven hundred year old house which preceded the present farmhouse, built in the eighteenth century and renovated during the past few decades.

Records from 1550 refer to "The farm and profits of conies of fflat-holmes" the farm then consisting of sixty-one acres of pasture and arable. Smugglers made use of the island from the seventeenth to nineteenth centuries – little hindered by authority, according to a contemporary record of the Customs and Excise Department, after their purchase of a telescope, which expense they vindicated with:

> "Very necessary, as we can see every vessel that goes to Flatholm – an island where smugglers at present run a great deal of goods and cannot just now be prevented by us as our boat is too old to go to sea."

The same old story of lack of public finance! In the later years contraband was stored in an old lead mine opening out on the cliff northeast of the foghorn.

Farming continued for around seven hundred years and a visitor in 1815 counted seven cows, two bulls, three calves, one horse, two pigs, five sheep, two dogs, one cat and an unknown number of rabbits and rats.

The rats, unlike most in the UK, were not the brown *Rattus norvegicus* but the black or ship rat, *Rattus rattus*. Barbara Jones, *'Distribution of Mammals in the Bristol Channel Area'. Trans. Cardiff Nats., XXXI, III,* 1967, states: "Ship rat was known to be present in the Bristol/Avonmouth area and a record from Bristol is received each year," but she was not easily persuaded about their presence on Flatholm.

Rae Vernon, a CNS ornithologist, recalls watching four feeding on blackberries near the lighthouse in 1962. He and his companions caught one in a live trap and took it to Bristol for confirmation of the species.

Black Rat and Blackberries.

Perhaps the 1815 record referred to ship rats, seeking quarantine on the island before venturing ashore, like some of the sickly sailors.

The species has long since been exterminated and Flatholm's fifty-seven acres were strategically placed, with its sister island, for a navigational aid and defence stronghold. The lighthouse came first, in private hands as Trinity House refused to take it over until 1823. The first petition for a light, in the main shipping channel to Cardiff, Newport and Bristol, was in 1733. Nothing came of this until a vessel was wrecked near the Holms in 1736 with the loss of sixty soldiers.

A year later a coal-fired beacon was kindled, at the expense of the owner and the Society of Merchant Venturers in Bristol, who hoped to be reimbursed by tolls from the shipping fraternity which benefited. Twenty-five tons of coal had to be brought to the island each month and carried to the top of the tower by the keepers. The light was dim and ship owners often defaulted with their tolls, so those responsible went broke. Eventually, in 1823, Trinity House installed an oil burner and strengthened the tower in 1890. 1923 saw the installation of a Hood petroleum vapour burner.

In the early years lighthouse keepers had their families with them, their homes clustered round the base of the light. Later Flatholm was classed as a 'Rock' and there were just the keepers, three at a time, serving six weeks on duty and four weeks off, and their quarters were moved to the neighbourhood of the foghorn.

This last, installed in 1903, depended on a compressed air system which issued a blast every thirty seconds. I had a good friend living in Penarth in the sixties, who offered me overnight accommodation when the frequent Bristol Channel fogs were too thick for me to drive home after my weekly evening lectures. I was a lot further from the blast than the unfortunate keepers and my heart went out to them.

Before and around that time, instead of slipping up from their cottage to tend the light in the night, a keeper had to trek there from the foghorn at two hourly intervals throughout, to wind the clockwork mechanism that kept it operational. The small paraffin lamp that lighted them up the tower was swapped in the war years for a small battery-powered torch for the spooky return in dark, wind or rain. At least there were no banshee shearwater calls.

During the 1960s and 70s friendly keepers would allow us up the lighthouse tower, both before and after the lantern was converted to electricity in 1969. It has a characteristic pattern of red and white lights flashing three times every ten seconds and a range of twenty-one miles in clear weather.

Views from the summit were all-embracing, a fine site for photography. Only from so far aloft could the extent of the purple spread of thistles or golden sheet of ragwort be appreciated in late summer. Both are 'noxious weeds', not usually allowed to get away to such an extent on the mainland.

These little exploits ceased with automation and the works are now controlled by computer installed in Nash Point lighthouse. The monthly arrival of the Trinity House boat with victuals and fuel and the exchange of bonhomie with other mortals, was superceded by a helipad outside the foghorn garden and the occasional dropping in of a maintenance engineer.

*   *   *

The island was fortified twice, both times at great expense and both times in vain, with no gun fired in anger. Napolean III was enemy number one, but he failed to get around to bringing his war fleet up the Bristol Channel, so the nine guns in four fortified batteries on Flatholm became known as 'The Palmerston Follies'. The idea was born with Prince Albert in the 1830s, but Lord Palmerston was in charge of their installation and carried the can.

Flatholm was one of four local sites thus armed, the others being Lavernock Point, Steepholm and Brean Down on the Somerset side. It was as well the guns were fired only in tests, as those in the know say they would have had little effect on the French navy's new ironclad warships.

They were muzzle-loaded and mounted on new Moncrieff Disappearing Gun Carriages in circular stone-walled pits eighteen feet across and ten feet deep, these indestructible. The gun was forced down into the gun pit after firing and raised by the use of a large counterweight after reloading. This protected the crews and rendered the gun sites invisible on Flatholm's open terrain. The Moncrieff Carriages were dismantled and removed but most of the heavy iron cannon and shell stores at the Lighthouse, Well and Castle Batteries are still present.

The Victorian Barracks, built in 1869 to accommodate the fifty soldiers needed to man the guns, fell into disrepair – after only a master gunner and five gunners were ever stationed there. They have now been re-roofed

Gun and Gun Pit, Steepholm beyond.

and refurbished as lecture rooms, laboratories and common rooms for the many school and college parties which enjoy educational courses on the island.

The fine tiled water catchment area leading water to an underground tank in the north-east corner is a useful legacy from those times: also the toilet block and the building known as 'Driftwood', where we used to doss down on bunk beds or worse in the early days. 'Driftwood's' sleeping accommodation is now as palatial as the dormitories and teachers' bedrooms in the renovated farmhouse – and furnished with modern toilets instead of an Elsan in the corner of a ruined outhouse behind a screen of brambles.

The whole complex around the lighthouse and gunners' quarters is surrounded by a defensive dyke and bank, constructed to repel invaders approaching overland. The deep ditch followed the line of a natural north-to-south fault through the limestone for much of its length – rocks quarried to form the rest being used in the buildings. The broad gully is now so densely filled with trees that it would be easy to cross by flinging a few planks over their tops, which are trimmed off by the wind flush with the ground on either side

The idea of an isolation hospital to serve as quarantine for seamen coming in with infectious diseases was inaugurated in 1884, when three cholera patients from Marseilles were accommodated in tents. In 1886 a farm building was converted to a makeshift hospital and in 1896 quarry-men were deployed to construct a purpose-built hospital. In 1898 a patient died from bubonic plague, but there were few other inmates to utilise the two six-bed wards. The whole concept was unpopular with the farm workers and artillery men stationed on the island, while folk on the mainland stopped buying the farm produce and rabbits.

In 1935 the hospital was condemned, by 1946 it was abandoned and all attempts to save this handsome, pavilion-type building came to nought. By the turn of the century all the roof slates had gone, most of the rafters were adrift from the slits in the stone walls where they had been lodged and many were missing altogether. Elder bushes were encroaching over the eaves and rank bracken and ragwort snuggled up against its base. Nevertheless CADW, the Welsh equivalent of 'English Heritage', had it on record as a listed building. Now only gulls and pigeons are in residence.

The next notable historic occurrence was the visit of Guglielmo Marconi. Failing to raise interest with the Italian authorities, he brought his new telegraph system to Britain in 1897 to file its patent. After erecting masts a hundred and ten feet high on Flatholm and Lavernock Point, he sent his first wireless message over sea water between the two in May of that year. In morse code, it read: "Are you ready?"

Later he achieved a new communication record of nine miles across the Bristol Channel. It was not until 1974 that a Marconi Memorial was placed on the island in memory of the day that led us all one step nearer to stoical peering at television screens.

The second military occupation of the island was during World War II. By the end of 1940, after a spell of heavy air raids on Cardiff, it was decided to refortify the Bristol Channel approaches from invaders. Mr. Harris's tenure as long term farmer and short term hotelier came to an end and the sheep were removed. The farmhouse, when functioning as a pub, had elastic opening hours to suit the needs of the boating fraternity which used it.

During the war it served as the officers' mess, the tradition of im-bibing stimulants no doubt continuing. The two wards of the cholera hospital served as NAAFI and cinema-cum-concert hall. An astonishing total of three hundred and fifty soldiers were stationed on Flatholm to man the anti-aircraft guns and two back-up searchlights. The proud claim of the hundred and fifty men needed to work them was that they were at their posts three minutes after the warning siren sounded.

Lesser Burdock.

The 'Benger Goalpost' erected in front of the gun housed in the Lighthouse Battery was an arch of two inch diameter steel piping, forcing the gun barrel to be raised high enough to avoid blowing the top off the lighthouse during the excitement of action.

Nissen huts on concrete and brick bases were erected all over, to supplement existing buildings – the foundations and steps leading up to them in position during the 1960s and 70s. The 'doorstep flora', where the men preened burs, prickles and fluffy seeds from their lower garments before entering, included burdock, houndstongue, cleavers and the thistle fraternity.

There were sandbags everywhere, these presumably filled on Glamorgan dunes and an undoubted source of sand vegetation such as viper's bugloss which had not been recorded before. These were just the right sort of plant to spread through the open habitats produced by the post war gull invasion – which had a more fundamental effect on the island ecology than the anticipated German one.

Soldiers cultivated the garden and kept chickens and pigs to supplement the rations arriving daily by boat from Barry, along with water, fuel, cement, mail and men. Aboard were the inevitable plant introductions, from selected garden shrubs to unitemised weeds. Boats had only four hours with water of sufficient depth for unloading – with the help of a diesel-powered crane and winch hauling goods to the top of the cliff. From there they were transported on the four wagons of the narrow gauge railway.

Operations ceased in 1944, the equipment dismantled by German prisoners of war, who cooperated well with the lighthouse keepers, helping to hump stores around and baking them fresh bread. Des Sythes, an eighteen-year-old trainee light-keeper in 1947, writing in the *Flatholm Society Newsletter*, Spring 2002, recalls how the keepers looked forward to the German's supply boat which called every second day with mail and extras. The prisoners kept fit by jogging round the island and occupied with handicrafts involving driftwood, until taken ashore by tug-drawn barge in early 1947.

The Nissen huts were lifted from their foundations which remained, along with part of the radar station and searchlight bases, all soon to be overrun by rampant plants.

For historical information I am grateful to David Worrell and P. R. Surtees, *South Glam. County Council booklet*, 1984.

*   *   *

Flatholm and Steepholm were humps of Carboniferous Limestone protruding from a red desert plain or shallow lake when the newer red sandstone was being deposited around and above them in Triassic times. The continuous land bridges of the pre-Neolithic era were not to last. Cutting of the cliffs post dates the Neolithic, as the new coral sea flooded the wooded Bristol Channel, converting the hills to islands, with the course of the old River Severn flowing past Flatholm's southern flank.

There are said to be no beds of comparable geological interest on the South Wales coast this side of Gower and it was principally for its geomorphology that Flatholm was designated as an SSSI.

The rocks are a continuation of those forming the Mendip Hills of Somerset and cropping out at Barry on the northern side of the channel. Strata of limey mudstone are interleaved in places with oolites (rocks composed of egg-shaped granules), their juxtaposition resulting in differential erosion. This is well seen in a thrust fault where the beds are steeply tilted on cliffs west of the lighthouse. Sea campion dominates the smooth stable rock face here, but is unable to gain purchase on the more mobile shatter face jutting out from it.

An interesting rock formation on level surfaces appears like crazy paving, patterned on old sun cracks in the clay, with walnut-sized pits over the surface, where nodules of more soluble material have dissolved out.

The dip of the folded rocks varies from near vertical in the south to the gently folded crest of the east to west anticline which emerges in cross section on the east and west cliffs. The southern portion of the rock platform extending from the base of the low cliff where it appears on the western shore consists of a series of parallel ridges and furrows running down towards the sea.

These are mega-ripples formed in Carboniferous times, before the limey mud solidified into rock. They are on a much larger scale than those formed in the newer Liassic limestone of adjacent mainland beaches at Penarth and Lavernock. Resembling wrinkle folds formed by lateral pressure on existing rock beds, they were described as such by earlier geologists.

In a few places the undulating bedding planes can be seen as wavy lines on the backing clifflet. Waves swilling into the lower ends of the gullies sometimes brought wads of driftweed, which stranded to form cosy nest sites above, and herring gulls were not slow in taking advantage of these.

Strata which formerly curved over the top of the anticline remain on either flank of the West Beach, running out to sea as low reefs, their broken edges facing inwards and their more gentle dip slopes outwards. Seaweed covered reefs south of the lighthouse follow the same east to west trend, following the line of the tall cliffs there.

An associated feature on the low western cliff is the differential weathering of rocks of varying hardness, resulting in soil formation both above and below solid beds of rock. The ever changing face examined in 1983 yielded from the top down: a few inches of normal topsoil between the buck's-horn plantain sward and a thin layer of pebbles and shells drifted on top of a four foot deep layer of sticky red rendzina soil overlying several narrow beds of limestone. Below this rock was another four foot depth of red clay with a few shaly fragments which washed out to form cavities roofed and floored by limestone beds.

The floors were part of the ripple-marked beach platform – the width of which is evidence of the large amount of cutting back that has occurred. Unsupported sections of the limestone collapsed to form angular beach boulders. The overlying Mesozoic strata have largely disappeared, but red clay seeping down joints and lying above the grey bedrock is thought to have been derived from Triassic marl.

The eastern end of the island's anticline can only be easily seen from the sea. As we approached on the *Lewis Alexander* after a tour of the island on 21st June, 2003, I was surprised to see what appeared to be a pale seal a few feet above sea level, framed by the symmetrical arch of grey rock demarcated on the cliff behind. The animal lay on the crest of a low ridge of rock projecting seaward from beneath the arch due to differential erosion.

A fine spread of horns materialised on the head gazing out at us as we came nearer and the fluffy seal was transformed into a silky Kashmir couchant. There was no way he could vacate his perch at this state of the tide without swimming and I wondered if he was stranded. Not so. Apparently he often chose to rest here away from the madding crowd, despite the precipitous scramble via the beach, which would be exposed at low water.

He was the last of his tribe on Flatholm. When the herd was removed for eating too many of the plants that were taboo, he was one of the two that got away. The blind billy had also been left, as he knew his way around here and it would have been foolish to deport him, but he subsequently died. One of the other two later washed up as a corpse, so the sole survivor was not trying to escape from his own kind, only from too many people or the dark Soay and white lowland sheep.

The stacks forming Castle Rocks near the landing place are a fine sight on an island with so few surface features. They show tension gashes, a manifestation of structural contortions. These are infilled with sparkling calcite, some of deep red grading to white and some having markedly radiating crystal structure – the same white mineral that infills some of the Goniatite fossils.

These last were large snail-like animals, differing from the Ammonites found in Liassic Limestones of the mainland in that their coil gets broader towards the mouth of the shell instead of remaining more or less the same width. Other fossils from the limey muds are Gastropods, Belleropha and Euomphalus, and there are Syringopora corals. A raised beach formed during a period of higher sea level can be recognised in places.

Seams of sparkling galena or lead ore were mined from the seventeenth century, one of the old partially blocked tunnels opening out on the cliff north-east of the foghorn for the later convenience of smugglers.

Porosity of the limestone prevents surface water from accumulating although a pool to supply the farmhouse was referred to in Wootton's account of 1890, along with a list of freshwater molluscs – these profiting from the high lime content for their shell building. There was no open water in the sixties, seventies and eighties, but a duckpond was constructed by Gwent Young Farmers' Club members – also a new tractor shed, in 1990.

Telegraph poles were used in the foundations and a 'landing stage' put in place for pond dipping. Sadly the mallard that elected to nest alongside in 1992 lost all six of her ducklings to marauding gulls – as did others in subsequent years – but an optimistic mother duck was still producing ducklings in 2003. Rushes, so common throughout South Wales, are virtually absent from the Flatholm sward.

Catchment wells have been constructed in the past for farm, lighthouse and hospital. The old Dripping Well in a high cavern has been walled around. Bottles Well in the south-east fills and empties in synchrony with the tides, and is an old mine shaft with bricked tunnels radiating from the bottom. Currently this is covered with undergrowth and fenced around for safety.

19.

FLATHOLM:
WITH AND WITHOUT GULLS

Insularity inevitably adds intrigue to the composition of island plant cover. What species were installed before the land bridges were severed, which came on their own accord and which with the human inhabitants? To how great an extent have man and his followers affected competition between the incomers, 'followers' here implying the conies that were formerly farmed and the gulls, which we have supplied so liberally with victuals in our mainland rubbish tips and sewage outfalls?

The threat of a Severn Barrage hung like the sword of Damocles over both the Holms for a couple of decades, when the favoured route would have used them as stepping stones between Lavernock Point and Brean Down, leaving Steepholm on the seaward side and Flatholm on the upstream, freshwater side. Fortunately this never happened: we got the Cardiff Bay Barrage instead – but not as a source of electrical power.

Maritime influence is greater on Flatholm than the loftier Steepholm, which supports mature sycamore woodland in part. Flatholm's summit plateau lies only a few feet above high water mark on its westerly side, which is open to the prevailing winds bowling storm waves into the bottleneck of the Severn Estuary. Land slopes gently upwards from there to ninety-six feet on the eastern side, with no obstacles to the wafting of spray right across the formerly treeless landscape.

My panoramic colour photos of the island centre show an unbroken expanse of pink thrift on the level ground around the foghorn buildings during the first half of the 1960s, when the vegetation was in equilibrium with rabbits but had not yet come to terms with the gulls.

Rabbit pellets, which are twice defecated, return to the soil only a fraction of what the little munchers have taken from it. Gull guano, spiced with all those goodies so avidly collected from the garbage dumps, with little or no input from the island ecosystem, is an entirely different matter. The cumulative fertility passed on to the soil has an inevitable effect.

The tumps of thrift, truly the thriftiest of plants and overwhelmed by the new riches, started disintegrating from their central sites in the mid 1960s, contemporary with and followed by an overall red haze of common sorrel, visible from far out to sea. This peaked during 1963 and 64 but lingered on, as it had done in similar circumstances on both Gower and Skokholm. By 1971 the red coverlet was fading and then came the 'nasties', the nettles, thistles and ragwort – a rank multitude imbibing the superfluity of nutrients and swamping most else where gulls congregated to build their nests.

With water salinity down to four-fifths sea strength at twenty-eight parts per thousand of chlorides as against thirty-five ppt in the open

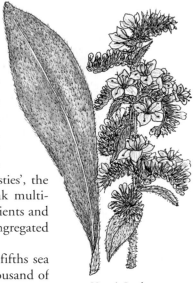

Viper's Bugloss.

sea, it is unlikely that the change would have been quite so spectacular on Steepholm, where gulls had nested over most of the island summit since the 1850s, so that early records of the vegetation changes promoted there are not available.

It was a century later, in 1954, that the gulls spilled over onto Flatholm, where the early stages of change could be better observed. With most of Steepholm rising abruptly to two hundred and fifty-six feet (seventy-nine metres), the vegetation first affected would have been a lot less maritime, with thrift and its fellow halophytes confined to rocky shores, as now.

The prevalence of Bristol Channel mists tends to mitigate against the scorching effect of salt and the drying effect of wind, both of which are aggravated by drought and rabbit grazing. Nevertheless, Flatholm's cliff flora shows a greater affinity for salt than any other this far up channel, where coasts are backed by sheltered woodland, scrub or grassland filtering shorewards.

The only sign of woodland on Flatholm outside the deep-cut dyke around the lighthouse when I first visited in 1962, was a group of twelve, partially dead, wind-scourged hawthorns, six to eight feet high on the eastern slopes, one with a crow's nest in its bared top. Crows, like sailors, prefer their crows' nests to be as high up as possible for all-embracing views, but this pair had had to do with something much less ambitious than the optimum.

With the added fertility, certain trees had no problem in growing. By the twenty-first century much of the island centre was occupied by a grove of elder bushes, as healthy as those which had covered most of Steepholm (and much of Puffin Island off Anglesey) half a century before.

Northward and eastward of the central thrift community, Flatholm was clad in classic limestone grassland. Little of this remains, although gulls have not affected this area as much as the south, centre and west.

Climbing up past the tattered elders plastered to the cliff face above Coal Bay in the north during the 1960s, the May-time visitor was confronted with a fine sward of bluebells rising from splayed rosettes of succulent leaves almost as robust as those of garden hyacinths. Each year we found a few handsome clumps of cowslips, now no more, and the big hairy leaved violets among lime-loving golden oat grass and crested hair grass (*Trisetum flavescens* and *Koeleria cristata*).

Here were yellow-wort, which still grows in the rich sward between the lighthouse and Victorian Barracks, with perforated St. John's wort, centaury, salad burnet and various legumes. Eastern cliff slopes became completely white with sheets of scurvy-grass in early spring, just as they do on Skokholm. In the sixties this plant was spreading, with circular blobs of white advancing through the deep sward of rich green red fescue with bluebells and wild Arum – which last is widely scattered throughout the island still, despite its affinity with woodland elsewhere.

On tall cliff faces the scurvy grass shares supremacy with wild wall-flowers, mostly yellow but some with chocolate-brown petals. True to their name, these had colonised walls and roofs of ruined buildings before those were renovated. Here too, were pellitory-of-the-wall, sea spleenwort and a little rusty-back fern. Wall pennywort and yellow stonecrop were an essential part of this community, as on old stone walls and masonry elsewhere on the island. Taller lime-lovers were plough-man's spikenard, foetid Iris and low tangles of the uncommon sweet briar (*Rosa rubiginosa*).

Rarities to be found in these early years were star-of-Bethlehem, slender St. John's wort and the uncommon, southerly prickly sedge (*Ornithogalum umbellatum, Hypericum pulchrum* and *Carex pairei*).

The champion rarity, the wild leek (*Allium ampeloprasum*) is still very much with us. This is fitting as it is the native version of Wales's national

Wild Wallflowers.

emblem, yet its only other sites are Guernsey, Cornwall, Pembroke and the two Holms. Its natural home is in the Mediterranean.

Less eye-catching are fenugreek and small-flowered buttercup (*Trifolium ornithopodioides* and *Ranunculus parviflorus*). Others have turned up over the years, many certainly carried in from the tips by scavenging gulls, with all the other debris. Among them are small-flowered mallow, spotted medick, white horehound and white goosefoot, with others making little significant impression on the overall flora.

Small-flowered Buttercup and Fenugreek.

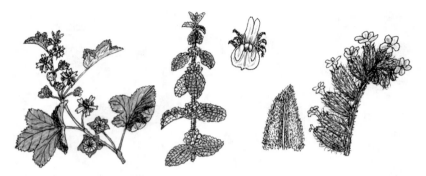

Small-flowered Mallow, White Horehound and Fiddleneck.

The bristly, well-named Californian fiddleneck (*Amsinckia retrorsa*) which unleashes coils of the forget-me-not-style flowers of its borage family, but with orange petals, is an obvious alien. Can it be significant that the only other place I have come across it in Britain is in the tern colony of the Inner Farne Island off Northumbria?

Another unusual plant, which is well entrenched on the rugged paving around 'Driftwood', is annual mercury, like a lusher, short-lived version of the dog's mercury of our woodlands. Henbane, familiar on Steepholm, has appeared and proliferated during the past few decades but, surprisingly, alexanders, which has complete coverage over the higher island, keeps a very low profile on the lower one if, indeed, it has arrived at all.

The peony, gem of the Steepholm flora, has been introduced to Flatholm and is thriving in its wire netting enclosure, spawning a rash of seedlings each year. This is a beauty, whether judged on its large pink flowers, its striking scarlet fruit capsules or its splaying palmate leaves.

Not unexpectedly, the plant life of the low western rocks has most in common with that of the true sea-bird islands of West Wales. Vying with the thrift as chief colour giver are the yellow tapestries of biting stonecrop, which need the lime that those cannot supply. Here they migrate over masonry put in place in defiance of Napoleon. Gulls nesting among the stonecrop may sometimes tweak off green shoots to incorporate in the matrix. Sheltered cliffs are white with scurvy grass, those suffering intermediate exposure with sea campion. Wallflowers grow better on these near vertical rock faces than in the seemingly more hospitable flower beds of my garden.

The coastal red fescue is again represented by the varieties pruinosa and glaucescens, the neat, waxy, blue-green tufts of the latter having commended it to gardeners, now that grasses have become so popular as ornamentals. Chunky coastal versions of cocksfoot, soft brome and meadow grass occur, these *Dactylis glomerata var. collina, Bromus ferronii* and *Poa subcaerulea*. All are dwarf and with densely compact flower spikes, the brome hairy, the meadow grass with bluish foliage. Here, too, are both of the hard little darnel or fern grasses (*Desmazeria marinum* and *Desmzeria rigidum*).

Difficult though it has been to appreciate during the dominance of the coarse weed flora of the last three decades, these two types of grassland covered the bulk of the island in the 1960s. Baring of the soil by the impress of webbed and furry feet left the ground open to opportunist incomers. Their spread was no problem. Two of the three current dominants, thistles and ragwort, having parachuted seeds which waft everywhere.

Photos taken from the top of the lighthouse at any time between late July and the start of the new spring growth in April, shows as good an example of a sea bird slum as could be found anywhere. Nettles,

Common Ragwort.

the third overall victor, are greener when seasonally dominant in mid-summer but no more endearing, and equally ugly and straggly through the winter.

Land management has been aimed at getting back as much of the original limestone grassland as possible. With this in mind, mowing of the rank plant cover after gulls have finished nesting and before the seeds are shed has been practised in various ways. Nesting sites have been restricted by removal of the first laid eggs and general discourage-ment, this helped by the dwindling of gull numbers from other causes.

Four-footed helpers were brought in and electric fences erected to confine their clearance efforts to defined areas – grazers on one side and gulls on the other. Such precautions may not have been necessary, the small herd of goats present from 1963 on suffering constant dive-bombing attacks during the nesting season and cantering away from their persecutors with complete loss of dignity.

The half dozen or so white nannies were more easily cowed when their male consort died so Michael, brown, shaggy and as male as they come, was introduced in 1971. He took an instant dislike to a particular nanny – was she, perhaps, disputing his dominance? – and pushed her over the cliff to her death. Two new concubines were introduced for his pleasure and matters settled down, but the herd remained wild, with none of the cosy milking sessions that we enjoyed on Skokholm. Animal husbandry needed to be kept to a minimum with the frequently changing island personnel and the mid winter gap in manning, so Soays were the obvious choice of sheep. They came and they thrived, as a nostalgic reminder of those other islands to the west.

In 1990 a small herd of Angora or Kashmir goats from the Great Orme in North Wales was brought in to help them with the good work. The nine at the start were billies. Some nannies were added and by 2001 there were ten of these and Soays had dropped to thirty, but numbers were boosted in 2002 by the addition of common or garden sheep; mountain X lowland cross.

The wardens are gradually winning, but the vegetation still consists largely of aggressive species which have less appeal to the grazing livestock than the more tender limestone down species that have gone under and are unlikely to return until more of the excess phosphates and nitrates have been washed from the soil.

Plant colonisation on the water catchment area has been of continuing interest, because this has been cleared every few years, and more regularly now that water is needed for a much bigger population.

The square pink tiles still fit neatly together after all the years since laying, but it is in the narrow joints between that seeds lodge and colonisation begins. Lumping the various analyses over the years together the average sequence appears as follows, with no mosses and the lichens only of the crustose variety on the tile surfaces where they do not get scraped away periodically.

Lines of yellow stonecrop follow the cracks initially, their sideways bulges hosting buck's-horn plantain and sea storksbill with occasional scarlet pimpernel. Sea campion moves in, spreading laterally, trapping debris and run-off and forming low cushions in which ground ivy and wood sage can establish.

Next come the more formidable teasels, with the tremendous seed output that can make them such a menace in gardens, and bramble with common and slender thistles. Finally there are the nettles and wild

Arum, building up against the margins and trapping gull feathers and rabbit pellets. At this stage an island work party generally moved in to scoop everything off and give more space for the painted ladies, meadow browns and grayling butterflies, which flocked to the sun-warmed tiles to bask in good weather.

*   *   *

The ever richer pickings offered to the gulls on refuse dumps coincided with the contraction of nesting sites in the face of increasing people pressure on mainland cliffs. Populations are normally governed by the availability of food, so the surplus young from successful breeding seasons were looking for new areas to bring up their own young in the mid twentieth century. Flatholm was seldom visited at the time because of boating difficulties, so was a 'natural'.

The first birds moving in during 1954 were believed to be from the century-old gull colony on Steepholm, which was then regarded as the most important herring gull colony in Britain, with 3,500 nests of that species alone in the 1956 census. By the 1960s Steepholm had reached saturation point, with some of the normally ground nesting lesser black backed gulls pushed up to build on the top of elder or privet bushes, which the herring gulls used as perches. These birds have started using buildings in a big way since, but how often do we see gulls perching in leafy trees?

The steady increase on Flatholm suf-fered a twenty per cent decline in the freezing winters of the early 1960s, but this was made good by 1964, when six hundred and sixteen lesser black backs and three hundred and eighty-one her-ring gull nests were occupied. From the rise to a thousand in a decade, the increase continued apace, making nest counts im-practical.

Herring Gull.

Herring gulls had formed the majority on the clifftop island of Steepholm but the main invasion to the vegetated flats of Flatholm was by lesser black-backs. Some of the herring gulls adopted sites on the roofs of army buildings or against brick chimneys quite early on. By the 1970s they were nesting on floors and window sills inside the dugouts, often in subdued light far from the entrances, and they continued to increase more rapidly than the others to four thousand and fifty-five pairs of each species (Mudge and Ferns) when they peaked in 1974.

The rate of population growth of over fifty per cent per annum was far greater than the thirteen per cent or so that could be achieved by the natural increment of young, this implying immigration from elsewhere. That at least some of the incomers were from Steepholm was substantiated by recoveries of birds ringed there as chicks.

The island is occupied throughout the year, but can seem empty in winter as the mob surges out to the mainland each morning for a day's scavenging – often at considerable distance, as shown by the daily commuting of flocks along the Taff Valley to Merthyr Tydfil.

During their first thirty years on Flatholm the gulls changed most of the vegetation from the high diversity limestone grassland resulting from centuries of farming and grazing by cattle, sheep and rabbits, to something much less desirable. From the mid seventies their numbers dwindled, but there was little redress in the vegetation. Some consisted of rampant weeds, some of almost bare soil. All was littered with chicken bones and the plastic bags containing chicken entrails, which are no longer included in supermarket chickens for householders to pass on to the carrion feeders.

Rank vegetation excluded human access to parts of the old farmland. The bare patches cracked during dry summers, resulting in loss of humus and impoverishment of physical soil structure. While much of the nitrates would leach out during winter rains, phosphates built up – to nurture quantity rather than quality.

Although the island was first leased from Trinity House as a nature reserve in 1975, when the gulls had already peaked, little management was attempted during the early years because of disagreement as to whether or not to reduce gull numbers by culling. Should plants or birds get conservation priority? Finally, it was decided to maintain numbers at half the current level in the mid eighties, when the population had decreased by natural means to two thousand nesting pairs of lesser black backs and six hundred and twenty-four pairs of herring gulls, in the hope of getting at least part of the island back to the attractive swards of the earlier years.

This might be achieved by mowing, flailing, hand pulling, grazing, use of selective herbicides even burning and disuading the gulls from settling in specific areas. In the event the gull population was showing so large a natural decline by then that culling was not resorted to.

Herring gulls had a certain advantage over the others, which moved in first, because they were resident throughout the year and hence in possession of territories when the black backs returned from their winter further south. Ten thousand lesser black backs nested in the Bristol channel area but only one thousand wintered there. In fact the number of the darker birds which migrated was decreasing, but they behaved less aggressively than the silver backs and so often lost out.

Rae Vernon, an active participant in the Cardiff Naturalists' Society gull counts during the late 1950s and early 1960s, was also involved in ringing. Migratory lesser black-backs ringed in 1962 had flown to St. Nazaire in France and Salerno in Italy. Others ringed in 1965 were recovered in Portugal and Spain during January and France in August – with an October recovery at Caerphilly (on the way south?) and an April one at Chippenham (on the way back?) Recoveries of the non migratory herring gulls ranged only from Brean Down to Newport.

Ringing was only profitable with the migratory species and has continued until the present time, when the ringers are quite used to reports of their birds turning up on the Iberian Peninsula. A novel 2001 record not so far away but in another direction, came from a Flatholm-ringed bird breeding on Great Saltee Island in Ireland. Six hundred sightings, some of colour-ringed birds, logged on the data base are showing that chicks surviving their first three months have a good chance of a long life ahead. At least three of the documented birds have lived for fifteen years.

Rabbits were patently not the reason for the fundamental vegetation change They had been present all along and were estimated by Professor Bellamy's team in the mid eighties as being at a mere one fifth of maximum capacity, or eight rabbits per acre. Gulls by then had reduced suitable rabbit grazing terrain to just ten per cent of the plateau area.

The only parts of the plateau retaining the essentials of the former vegetation were a small area of clifftop above Coal Bay and parts which had been regularly mown over the years by the lighthouse installations. The narrow coastal strips of fescue, thrift and stonecrop were in better equilibrium with the prevalent salty winds than the taller rank outsiders and remained fairly intact.

Disintegrating thrift cushions and old anthills through the island centre were reminders of the past regime and salad burnet was one of the last of the lime-lovers to succumb. The densest nettle patches came to be avoided by nesting gulls, a case of self-exclusion by over population, but some available space remained uncolonised and nests could have been closer within the existing colonies.

Vegetation analyses in six different gull colonies during the early years provided the following data.

The black back colony in the east centre of the island was little different from those of the West Pembrokeshire Islands, with bluebells and meadow grass in spring, bracken and tall oat grass with an under-storey of ground ivy in summer.

The central colony was started in the odd mix of bracken and thrift, in an exposure regime more suited to the first, which may have suffered from former rabbit activity. Among these two were bramble, ragwort and ground ivy.

South-western gulls of both species inhabited an area of residual thrift and sea campion, with the intermediary of common sorrel and brash newcomers of nettle and spear thistle: herring gulls of the west likewise with the addition of white clover and those around buildings with curled dock. An open grassy preening area used by both species was dominated by Yorkshire fog with ground ivy, sorrel, spear thistle, thyme-leaved sandwort and mouse-ear chickweed.

It is interesting that the two common thistles became superceded almost throughout the island by the paler slender or seaside thistle (*Carduus tenuiflorus*) in subsequent years, this vying with ragwort as the late season dominant. There was but a single great black backed gull's nest on Flatholm during the early years, this on the southern cliffs among thrift and rock sea lavender with red fescue and buck's horn plantain. By 1974 there were two pairs and by 1980 three pairs.

The management plan finally adopted in the mid eighties was to mow and strim specified areas for two to three years to get a sward suitable for sheep or goats. Gulls were to be precluded from the Coal Beach and lighthouse plots by nest destruction early in the season, with the aim of establishing two main colonies elsewhere. The regularly mown walled lighthouse garden was rather precious as the only zone free of both rabbits and gulls. By excluding both from other small areas the rate of increasing plant diversity during the recovery period could be found. – although there was still the residual phosphate to be eliminated.

Peter Ferns and Jeoff Mudge estimated gulls' food preferences by examining the remains regurgitated from the crops of frightened chicks. Tip material won hands down. Only in the 1976 heatwave when large numbers of moribund eels were present in the channel due to low river levels, did eels approach comparable quantities. Other food items recognised were sprats, sand eels, elvers, a few crabs, earthworms and other invertebrates.

*   *   *

Shelduck, the other important shore birds, have been found by workers in various areas to feed principally on little laver spire shell snails scooped from the mud surface. These formed 89.5% of the food eaten by the birds examined, three thousand of the tiny shells being found in the gizzard of one. Other food items were a closely related spire shell (*Potamopyrgus jenkinsi*) and sand hoppers (*Corrophium volutator*). Green algae, Enteromorpha and Vaucheria, were taken, along with the seeds of sea sedge and annual sea blite. Cardiff Bay shelduck, prevented from gathering spire shells on the mud by erection of the barrage, were seen upending in deep water, like mallard, in pursuit of something very different from any of the above.

Nesting shelduck were not monitored during the early years, but there were usually up to about eight or ten birds on the surrounding water during 1961 visits, at a time when two of the former three to four pairs of lapwing and a pair of oyster-catchers were breeding on the island.

Eight to fifteen creamy white eggs are laid in May or June in an old rabbit burrow or spacious crevice, lined with grass and down. Incubation lasts thirty days and ducklings hatch in June or July to toddle in convoy to and over the cliff edge to the sea. Then begins the perilous passage to the mainland mudflats, which provide the only suitable feeding areas. Few of them make it, the mother duck quite unable to protect the entire brood on the open water from the horde of ravenous gulls screaming overhead. Ducklings can dive, like baby mallard, but they have to come up for air.

Island wardens have monitored the birds since 1997, doing counts in April and May when most are on the surface seeking nest sites. Average peak counts were eighty-nine birds in 1997, a hundred and twenty-two in 1998, eighty in 1999, sixty-two in 2000, fifty-two in 2001 and twenty-one in 2002, suggesting half these numbers of nests. Similar counts for 1992 and 1993 respectively were three hundred and sixty-two and two hundred and eighty, with the first duckling on 22nd May, so it is evident that there is a serious decline in numbers.

Care is taken to avoid shelduck territory during mowing operations, but the serious decline over the years is likely to be due to the large number of people encouraged onto the island during the summer to increase revenue. In 2001, despite cancellations in April and May because of foot and mouth disease, two thousand and twenty-eight passengers were added to the staff and workers, eighty per cent of them paying customers. Publicity for 2002 includes sixty-three day trips, sixteen residential weekends and four or more school parties staying for varying periods. The 2002 target of five thousand aims to have no more than fifty people on the island at any one time.

Flatholm is not one of those delectable islands where one goes to 'get away from it all' and enjoy a pristine land and seascape!

Passerines have been ringed with the aid of mist nets since Rae Vernon's era in the late fifties. *The Flatholm Society's News Letter*, Spring, 2002, records the ringing project's grand total of five thousand two hundred and ten birds ringed (excluding gulls), two hundred and ten of these during 2001. Fifty-three different species were caught, some in large numbers on spring or autumn passage.

Winning hands down were blackbird and swallow. One of those totalling only one was the house sparrow, an indication of how different these outlying sites can be from town gardens. Summarising those where more than a hundred individuals have been captured over the years, we have blackbird: five hundred and seventy-four; swallow: five hundred and fifty-two; robin: five hundred and fourteen; wren: four hundred and seventeen; song thrush: three hundred and ninety-one; goldcrest: three hundred and twenty-four; willow warbler: three hundred and twenty-three; dunnock: two hundred and seventy-two; greenfinch: two hundred and twenty-eight; meadow pipit: one hundred and nineteen; blackcap: one hundred and ten, and chaffinch: one hundred and two.

Pigeons come in for today's elderberries and peregrine falcons come in for the pigeons, while sparrow hawk and kestrel figured in the list of ringed birds. Unexpected rarities were wryneck, nightingale, black redstart, red-breasted flycatcher, firecrest and icterine warbler.

Of more land bound creatures mention must be made of the healthy population of slow worms, many of the males with pale blue spotting, and common or viviparous lizards. There are no snakes or amphibians, just four pet tortoises left over from the days of the lighthouse keepers.

FLATHOLM I

Tiled Water Catchment below 'Driftwood', 1986.

West Beach Mini Anticline showing eroding clay shales below limestone rock, 1983.

Two boats leave around Arch Rock, 1971.

Small Wrinkle Folds on limestone of West Beach, 1971.

FLATHOLM II

Peony flowers, June.

Peony fruits,
supporting three snails, October.

Small Tortoiseshells on Ragwort, October 2001.

Wild Leek flower head, August 1986.

Henbane seeds plundered by Goldfinches and Linnets,
October 1979.

Wild Leeks in June drought, 1989.

FLATHOLM III

Massed Scurvy Grass on East cliffs, April 1980.

Wallflowers and Great Mullein plants on East cliffs, April 1980.

Castle Battery in October 2001.

First Mohair Kids born on Flatholm, March 1992.

Crow's Nest in moribund Hawthorn, east side, 1963.

FLATHOLM IV

Marconi Memorial, erected 1974, photo 1983.

David Worrell, project manager, burning a heap of botulised Gulls, 1983.

Lime Kiln above West Beach, 1983.

Hounds-tongue from fruit burs preened off at Nissen Hut door, 1983.

20.

FLATHOLM:
THE EARLY YEARS OF CHANGE

The flora and fauna of Flatholm over the last three decades has been documented in detail by successive wardens, vice wardens, bird ringers and researchers and the archives are swelling with lists, tables and graphs of this and that. Details of methods and results of management programmes are all on record, to guide future conservationists.

This is not the place to try and summarise all the good work. Rather shall I use my final chapters, like my first, in a nostalgic looking back at individual visits scattered over the years.

Although Flatholm is in a quite different category from the true seabird 'dream islands' of West Wales, there is still interest and pleasure to be had in exploring at different times of year. No matter that others have seen these things before. That cannot take away the something special about just being on an island – shedding the trappings of the frenetic world that we have created, if only by default, and being at one with earth and sea and sky.

The earth here is scarred by rabbits and gulls, the sea discoloured by tons of swirling silt in perpetual motion, but the skies can be wonderful. Billowing black clouds may pile up over Lundy down channel, playing hide and seek with the setting sun. There can be brilliant sunshine over Somerset and a deluge over Wales – yes, and even the other way round – while Flatholm lies serenely on the divide.

Godfrey Nall, whom I met briefly on Skokholm in the 1950s, has recently been in touch again and has drawn my attention to a poem which sums it all up. It was written by an American, Rachael Field, who lived from 1894 to 1942, but is as relevant to contemporary life in Britain as it was to the early part of the twentieth century in the New World. I include it here, with acknowledgements to the memory of a like spirit.

> If once you have slept on an island
> You'll never be quite the same:

You may look as you looked the day before
And go by the same old name.

You may bustle about in a street and shop,
You may sit at home and sew,
But you'll see blue water and wheeling gulls
Wherever your feet may go.

You may chat with the neighbours of this and that
And close to your fire keep,
But you'll hear ship's whistle and lighthouse bell
And tides beat through your sleep.

Oh, you won't know why and you can't say how
Such change upon you came,
But – once you have slept on an island
You'll never be quite the same!

In the early years we were mostly on Flatholm to count gulls in the height of the breeding season, so it became associated in our minds with a bedlam of shrieking, swooping forms – a new batch of jealous territory holders rising in protest as each last lot resettled. Even now it seems strangely deserted in the 'off' season.

Gulls were less dependent on garbage at that time and cursory examination of pellets cast up around the nests on June visits in 1963 revealed traces of natural food, varying seasonally, depending on what was available. We were finding fish bones, possibly of sprats, during midsummer when these swim nearer the surface than in winter, and the crushed shells of molluscs.

Limpets are a tough proposition to detach from the rocks, as any child who has dabbled in rock pools knows. The most skilful gulls could achieve this with a surprise blow – something the general population was able to do only when the limpets lost their powers of adhesion during frosts. Most removed the flesh and discarded the shell, but those in a great hurry gulped down the whole, the limey wigwams appearing later, undamaged, in the crop pellets. Perhaps they had learned about limpets during those frozen winters of the early 1960s – which were still recent enough for us to be finding the emaciated corpses of woodcock, common tern and others less recognisable.

A herring gull might flap past with a slow worm wriggling in its beak – no wonder most of these legless lizards remain snugly ensconced under friendly sheets of sun-warmed corrugated iron left lying around for their benefit. Some had shed their tails, these the ones that got away, but they can only grow a new one a limited number of times. The gull would gulp its prize down in the air to avoid being robbed by piratical contemporaries. Lifting sheets we found more slow worms than lizards but both benefited from the warmth and protection. There are certain sorts of 'litter' that are allowed.

Common Lizard.

On 22nd June, 1963, the eggs in the great black-backed gulls' nest were a pretty sight with sea lavender flowering on one side and thrift on the other. By 30th June the young had hatched and were at the gawky stage, strutting about long-legged among boulders held together by flowering sea campion.

Shelducks.

Shelduck chicks and Silvery Hair Grass.

The later date yielded a brood of eight shelduck chicks. There were still rats on the island at that time, so eggs were in as much danger in the burrows as were the ducklings making their erratic way round obstacles to the cliff edge and launching into the murky waters for the four to five mile marathon to Cardiff Bay.

In recent years the mother ducks have learned to lead their broods out by night when the gulls are asleep – those predators forcing them to become nocturnal in this as they had forced the shearwaters of other islands way back in evolution. We counted a hundred and thirty adults loafing offshore and the number of breeders was to rise substantially before it finally fell to current levels.

At least one pair of oyster-catchers had a nest. The curlew which drew our attention by its mournful piping, was just passing. Three pairs of blackbirds shared the minimal cover, favouring trees in the eastern defensive dyke. Other passerines were foraging meadow pipit, trilling skylark and a chattering flock of fifty or so young starlings.

Lackey moth caterpillars had outgrown their gregarious phase and donned blue, orange and white striped livery to sally forth individually over sprawling bramble and scrappy hawthorn on the cliffs. Burnet moths were already on the wing, along with small coppers, meadow browns and whites, while field grasshoppers flipped among the drying herbage and bumble bees busied themselves among the flowers.

*   *   *

1975 was a busy year when the county council took over the lease of the island with its derelict buildings and invading army of gulls. 13th October that year saw the presentation of the South Glamorgan County Colours to SS *Margherita*, the training ship of the Reardon Smith Nautical College in Cardiff. After the 9.30 a.m. ceremony in Barry Docks, we set sail, complete with VIPs, press, radio and TV journalists for Flatholm – in this much larger boat than usual, manned by young students. With her need for deep water, we had to lie off under Castle rock and transfer ashore by dinghy.

After all the hoo-haa about vicious mobs of gulls worthy of the attention of Alfred Hitchcock, it was something of a let down for the press to find nary a one. The breeding season was over and the population had moved ashore en masse for a jolly day on the tips, sorting out Cardiffians' leftovers and laughing over their shoulders at the Cardiffians who had gone all that way to visit them.

With the only evidence of animal life the corpses of diseased gull chicks and predated rabbits scattered among the air-lifted carcases of non-resident super market chickens, wildlife came off poorly in the opinion of the media. The lowly specimen tempting the press photographer was half a dead tortoise, definitely not native and not one of the lighthouse men's four pets, which were still at large on the island, safely hidden, each shell marked with blue inscriptions. Plastic bottle tops and ring pulls from beer cans had been coughed up with the gulls' crop pellets, to mingle with the general chaos expectorated before swallowing or after passage through the interior.

Summer flowers were but a memory on this bleak October day and the shaggy parasol toadstool (*Lepiota rhacodes*) sprouting among flopped bracken fronds failed to impress. The rare lesser broomrape exploiting the hemlock, one a parasite, the other poisonous, evoked only grimaces of distaste among the journalists as they turned their attention to nobler matters such as rusted gun barrels and tumbledown buildings. It was high time that the Flatholm Project was launched to tidy things up!

Aggravated by the droughts of that summer and the following one matters got worse before they got better. Vegetation changes by August 1977 were so dramatic as to be hard to believe, with much of the soil scorched bare, leaving an open playing field for the rampant, gull-induced weeds. Where now was the level greensward on which the sea pilot's son had played cricket every summer and where the flowery turf on which the local lady had gathered mushrooms for the pot?

It is, however, an ill wind . . . This was an era of slender thistle, a lure for seed-eating birds, with finches cashing in on them in a big way. Ragwort, for some unaccountable reason not infested by the tiger-striped cinnabar caterpillars that completely defoliate so many plants on the mainland, threw a canopy of golden flowers that was an irresistible lure for nectar seeking butterflies. Hemlock and hogweed thrust up among the seeding docks but there was still no sign of alexanders, the scourge of Steepholm.

The whole island was rattling with the snap, crackle, pop of dead thistle stems rubbing against each other in the wind. Shed gull feathers wafted back and forth to pile in dark corners or impale on thorns.

I came across several gulls' nests built entirely of the prickly burs of burdock – no grass, no twigs, no stonecrop shoots. How the young had fared with all those hooked bristles clawing at their down I dread to think, knowing how those burs used to cling to the clothes of my school friends when launched from a little distance. There was so much burdock on the island by then that few nests were completely free of it, if only by default.

Much of the bared ground had a dried black scum of dung peeling up in flakes under the desiccating sun, more like bat guano than that of birds. Soil had shrunk and cracked under a sparse coating of straw coloured grass and dehydrated algae, the crevices an alternative haven for the sheeny blue ground beetles, which crept in under the many corpses to join the overworked carrion beetles labouring at the business of decent burial.

On St. Valentine's day, 14th February, 1978, the island seemed dead for other reasons, with scarcely time to recover from severe frost before being subjected to a gentle snow fall. It was, indeed, more barren than many a Welsh hillside, because the crisply bronzed bracken fronds and other trash got picked up by sea winds and rolled away instead of forming a covering blanket.

Most of the gulls were sitting the waters offshore, but blackbirds were flocking and wrens were popping up everywhere. Here, too, were robin, dunnock, linnet and house sparrow, but no starlings or shorebirds.

The lighthouse men had identified two distinct rabbit populations, a healthy one around the lighthouse, where all the most prized plants survived, and a slummy one in the gull blasted vegetation around the old hospital. Those animals were dying of Myxomatosis and other diseases, while the lighthouse bunnies were lively as crickets.

The men themselves were long term sufferers from ticks or harvest mites, which burrow under the skin and stay put for weeks, but have the decency to move out before laying the next batch of eggs. They were anxious to clear a thirty foot strip of plants back along each side of the tracks and wardens were trying to persuade them to make it fifteen.

Another winter visit, on 25th November, 1978, with Ray Price, Flatholm stalwart, in the Barry Yacht Club launch, was with a party to assess the feasibility of putting young folk on probation onto the island to accomplish specific tasks. It was a clear cold, finger-chilling day with bright sunshine and dramatic piles of silver-lined black clouds over the mainland as the wind built up to force five.

Two weeks of rain had boosted the autumn crops of seedlings and the island was greener than in October, with still a little colour from the scarlet Arum spikes, orange Iris seeds and crimson rose hips. Fumitory, pimpernel, field daisies, autumnal hawkbit, herb Robert and annual mercury were still in flower and pillbugs rolled up comfortably in declivities of gull carcases or old snail shells.

Trails of black bryony bearing red and orange berries twined around the teasel heads, but it was the myriad seeds of those that the twenty goldfinches were after, the air full of their sibilant chatter. The seven chaffinches and lone greenfinch favoured the scrub. Robin, wren, dunnock and blackbird scarcely lifted more than a few feet from the ground, skulking out of the wind and leaving the westerly slopes to rock and meadow pipits and skylarks. The two kestrels and two crows quartered the whole, unconcerned by the rising wind.

Shaggy parasols sprouted in their usual site among nettles and there were two kinds of blewits (*Lepista saeva* and *Lepista irinum*). Others were *Hebeloma crustuliniforme* with an inrolled downy edge to the umbrella, delicate conical-capped *Conocybe tenera* and even more delicate conical-capped *Panaeolus rickenii*. This last favours herbivore dung on the mainland but seemed happy with the avian sort here.

*   *   *

On 11th October, 1979, we were able to watch a peregrine falcon quartering back and forth along the east coast where there was a constant traffic of feral and wood pigeons to and from the rich harvest of blackberries and elderberries. A few dewberries were taken, but the rosehips remained untouched.

Kestrels had nested on the rafters of one of the old buildings near 'Driftwood', stock doves above the old stove in the hospital laundry. Late migrants lingering before setting off on the next lap of their journey were a small flock of swallows and a lone wheatear.

More linnets than goldfinches were making free with the teasels this time, these also pecking holes in the back of the henbane's flask shaped calyces to get at the myriad beige seeds within. This is a plant that they are only likely to have seen on the two Holms, but they knew exactly how best to get at the goodies.

Passage flocks of over four hundred finches sometimes pass through the island in October. Today a huge mob of starlings was lined up along the radiating guyline cables of the lighthouse radio mast, with little groups making sorties to the eastern elderberries but none venturing west. An unusual sighting was of two mute swans flying low and alighting on the sea towards the Penarth cliffs.

This had been a rather squawly crossing with *Margherita*, but the sun shone and there were plenty of late butterflies about – red admirals, small tortoiseshells and small whites, with silver Y moths, long narrow parasitic wasps and a veritable plague of craneflies, some coming to grief in the orb webs of patiently waiting spiders. Among the grasshoppers and earwigs were devil's coach horse beetles, bronze Chafers and Carabid beetles.

Fungi were doing well this year, the parasols emerging from the litter like scaly tennis balls and expanding to the size of dinner plates. Horse mushrooms, too, were spherical on breaking free, more like cream-tinged ping-pong balls above their bulging bases. True puffballs not aspiring to parasol shape, were the usual Bovista and *Lycoperdon ericetorum* pushing up through seedling swards of scurvy grass and storksbill lapping around the base of noble woolly thistle, a speciality of the Glamorgan Heritage Coast cliffs.

Insects taking advantage of plant hosts were gall wasps producing the pretty crimson tufts of robin's pincushions on the wild roses (*Diplolepis rosae*) and the gall gnats responsible for nettle galls (*Dasyneura urticae*).

An April visit in 1980 was by small open motor boat with Reardon Smith personnel. Thirteen shelduck took off as we hit the beach and jumped onto the rolling pebbles, handsome as ever in their breeding finery, and there were another thirty-four on the south side, with more, no doubt, underground, thinking broody thoughts about eggs. Then came a flock of thirty-one 'comic' terns flying up channel by Castle Rock, with the odd few less graceful cormorants beating their way past below.

Most gulls were still nest building, but a fair proportion had produced their full complement of three eggs, the first of which had appeared on April fool's day – the manifestation of an outsize joke on

Alfred Hitchcock lines, to perplex the powers that be and the hard-worked wardens. A chiff-chaff, my first of the season, dropped quietly into cover, trying to pretend it wasn't there and no more conspicuous than the bumble bees sipping from dandelion and wild turnip flowers.

The yellow mullein near the winch had been replaced by yellow cowslips and the scurvy grass and wallflowers beyond were as all embracing and as heart warming as ever. Lesser celandines were doing well, heralds of the bulbous buttercups to come. Daffodils and crocusses seemed immune to rabbits and burgeoned by the lighthouse garden, both now past flowering but the johnquills at prime.

All this spring freshness was long past when we visited in Arthur Hooker's little sailing yacht in July 1980, but the bird slum seemed less slummy than usual. This may have been because 1980 registered as the wettest summer since 1907 or perhaps all the hard work was paying off. Then again it could be because the indomitable nettles had closed over the top of the sodden nests, now that most of the chicks had left. Come autumn die-back and the tattiness would reappear. The few little 'trees' in the east had rotted and disappeared long since, but there would soon be a great exuberance of elders across the island centre to replace them.

Pink centaury flowers emulated the pimpernels in their sensitivity to light, closing up when the sun slunk behind clouds in the afternoon and the butterflies settled for a spell in their apparent purposeless butterfly-minded flights.

Among the usual Vanessid, brown and white butterflies were hairy robber flies (*Thereva nobilitata*), striped in yellow, brown and white, copulating tail to tail on ragwort leaves. Busy on the wing were hover flies, green and blue bottles (*Syrphus ribesii, Lucilia caesar* and *Calliphora vomitaria*).

Seven spot ladybirds were present in plague proportions, grouped particularly on ragwort and houndstongue, although this was not a plague year on the mainland. We saw few aphids, perhaps they had all been eaten, and there was no cuckoo spit left, the frog hoppers all having hopped. Eight species of aphids had been identified back in 1965, and more by Graham Rotheray, the Flatholm fly expert.

Some of the bright brown *Lagria hirta* beetles, abundant on flowers, had become impaled on burdock heads and one had fallen to a robber fly. Glossy black and yellow flea beetles, *Phyllotreta nemorum*, with fat thighs to power their flea-like jumps, leapt as much as eight inches vertically with no spreading of wings when we teased them. A Theridion spider, yellow with red stripes and a zig-zag between, was busy wrapping up her packed lunch of bluebottle, while little money spiders scuttled everywhere in the race to stay alive.

* * *

I was one of ten island addicts who escaped the human turmoil for four days over the late bank holiday weekend of August 1983, by joining a botanical safari to Flatholm. Six Glamorgan Wildlife Trust members, with Trevor Evans and Colin Titcombe from the Gwent Wildlife Trust joined David Worrell and Paul Surtees of the South Glamorgan County Council with sleeping bags, iron rations, binoculars and hand lenses at Barry Docks on the Friday, to sail on the *Naomi*.

All water had to be carried from the mainland, so we swelled the ranks of the great unwashed and stubble sprouted unchecked on masculine chins. One enamel mug of water apiece served for both teeth cleaning and face washing.

The cuisine was interesting, with sausages winning hands down. Two of the three Lloyds (Prof. Harry, Dr. Joy and physicist Kate) had returned only the week before from China and were dab hands with rice. Endless tins of baked beans materialised from Gwent and packets of crisps galore with Peter Jones of the Heritage Coast. Jeff Curtis always seemed to be stacking his dirty plates when the rest of us appeared, but looked well satisfied.

Flatholm had been marked out in fifty metre squares with flags on poles and our primary task was to list the plants in each. In spite of almost complete desiccation, Trevor, true to form as plant recorder for Gwent, discovered two new species, the stemless thistle and grey sedge (*Carex muricata ssp. leersii*). The Lloyds mapped the main vegetation, plotting the rapidly advancing elder and retreating grass in the overall matrix of 'nasties'.

The original 'nasty', bracken, appeared to have been knocked for six when the gull population peaked at eight thousand pairs in 1974, to be followed by the dry summers of 1975 and 1976, and it was having a thin time again in the drought of 1983. At its best in the acid, rainy hills, the concentration of bases in the shallow, porous, guano-impregnated soils of the limestone seemed to be proving a bit much.

There were no goats at present. Keepers said the last survivor, a billy, had 'met the axe'. As ragwort is poisonous in varying degrees to all herbivores and unpalatable to all but goats, they might have been tempted when there was little else and met their nemesis. Rabbits were currently attacking it with caution, nibbling off the outer layers of the lower stems, but not, apparently, those of the fasciated or flattened culms. We wondered what else they could be finding to eat with all the grass tinder dry. David Worrell told us that Myxomatosis struck most years in autumn, helping to keep their numbers in check.

The blaze of golden ragwort flowers had dwindled and the ground was covered with a layer of silvery down. As we pushed through, seeking stray survivors of better days, the fluff rose in choking clouds, making breathing a burden. Every so often we stopped to preen, pulling bristly hound's tongue and burdock heads from socks and trews. Thistle down was everywhere, and not a goldfinch in sight. With the almost constant mid-channel winds and increasing human traffic it was easy to see how these invaders had achieved such a rapid conquest.

Gulls had decreased to as little as two and a half thousand pairs in the last nine years. The pity was that the vegetation they had spoiled was not recovering proportionately. Active and arduous help would be needed to quell the exuberance of the newcomers, but Mother Nature was lending a hand, her weapon bacteria.

Botany was not our only concern; we all joined in combing the island for gull corpses, advancing on a broad front through the shroud of flying fluff, armed with plastic sacks and rubber gloves. It was as well that none of us suffered from hay fever, the ragwort parachutes shorter than those of thistles and more easily inhaled as we pushed through the blocks between paths.

Botulism type C was the killer (*Clostridium botulinum*), simmering gently in the anaerobic environment of black polythene bags on the rubbish tips of Cardiff and Penarth, to be air-lifted by the scavengers to their island stronghold.

Already two hundred and forty-five adult lesser black-backed gulls, a hundred and thirty-one herring gulls and two hundred and thirty-two fledged young had been gathered up and disposed of this year. The last collection had been three weeks earlier and the hot, dry summer was aggravating matters throughout Wales, as shown by post

Lesser Black-backed Gull.

Herring Gull chicks and Biting Stonecrop.

mortems of waders and wildfowl elsewhere, so there were plenty more to go.

Botulism C is a type of food poisoning which does not affect humans, this just as well, considering the gulls' access to water draining off roofs and the bricked catchment. Sick and dying birds sprawled in the undergrowth had to be left for the next collecting party.

Symptoms ranged from difficulty in flying to paralysis of the limbs and neck, staggering and gasping. The germs need prolonged temperatures of around twenty degrees Celsius and low oxygen concentrations to proliferate. Small doses are not necessarily fatal and those of us with wheelie bins, compost heaps and bonfires for our leftovers were not contributing to the fatalities. It was those airtight plastic sacks, which are still in fashion, that were causing the trouble. Eight out of ten of the dead gulls examined in the Public Health Laboratories showed traces of Salmonella poisoning, but botulism was thought to be more often the cause of death.

The heap of corpses soaked in diesel oil and dumped on West point Beach for burning, mostly fully grown juveniles, measured two metres across and one metre high. We collected driftwood and it was a beautiful blaze, but the 'Camp fire's burning' type songs which accompanied it got a little warped.

> "Gulls are burning, gulls are burning,
> Bone and feather, bone and feather.
> Bring the corpses, bring the corpses,
> Come wail and be sorry."

Lesser Black-backed Gull's eggs among the stonecrop.

It was still daylight when some of us peeled off with flashlights to explore the permanent darkness of the underground ammunition stores, which were veritable bone beds, both avian and mammalian. Annuals spilling from their entrances included dwarf nettle, black nightshade and red goosefoot. Most insects had already retired for the night and we found a common hawker dragonfly (*Aeschna juncea*), one of those that had been flitting round the farmhouse by day.

It clung to the stone ceiling, unmoved by the disturbance until a cheeky fly had the temerity, or inexperience, to settle on the long blue abdomen; a mere aperitif in the monster predator's normal diet. The dragonhead, seemingly all eyes, turned sideways and the intruder was sent packing with an irritated twitch of the torso. To be fixed by the stare of that great compound eyeball should have been enough. Another of its ilk got shorter shrift when it blundered into the orb web net of a giant house spider strung across an alcove. There were pale stripy pill bugs in the shadows and a green earthworm (*Allolobophora chlorotica*), tying itself in a knot on a peaty deposit by an old gull's nest.

Further on the walls were speckled with undersized peacock and small tortoiseshell butterflies which, like so many those days, had taken early retirement. Their muscles were so clamped that it was impossible to lever their wings open with the blade of a knife, this succeeding only in bending the wingtip, which sprang immediately back into position.

Red Admiral, Peacock and Small Tortoiseshell.

A dugout inspected in the afternoon had yielded fifty-one peacocks and thirty-two small tortoiseshells, with mallow moths and herald moths, these last two probably just waiting for night to go about their normal business. Another contained thirty of each butterfly species. There were orange herald moths there too, but not beaded with moisture, as we usually find them in cave and mine entrances.

The butterflies' small size was probably due to food failure in the July part of their larval growth phase. By now the nettles were quite dead, a palisade of dry stalks rising from a carpet of crisp, blackened leaves, although mainland plants were still green. Their early recourse to such suspended animation when day temperatures were still well up in the seventies, was probably due to the same drought that had killed the caterpillars' food plant. There were still flowers about but, in the absence of rain, this did not automatically imply a good flow of nectar.

Ten observers saw no peacocks on the wing during our four day stay and few tortoiseshells, although there were quite a lot of red admirals and the ubiquitous meadow browns were everywhere – these not such dab hands at hibernation. Eleven species were seen in all, including some of 1983's invasion of clouded yellows. Others were wall brown, small heath, small copper, common blue, large white and green-veined white, but only the last two were at all numerous.

While the tortoiseshells may merely have retired early to bed, the peacocks appeared to have gone prematurely into hibernation. It seemed unlikely that they would awake for an autumn feed if the rains came to boost the nectar supply, assuming there was anything left to flower by then. They had a long fast ahead before emerging to lay eggs in spring.

All the lusher ragwort stands were sheltered by the elder thicket around the western buildings, on the deeper red soil of the old farm fields, and this is where most of the less common butterflies were feeding. Few thistle or teasel flowers remained and the burdock, hemlock, Brassicas and hound's tongue had long since gone to seed.

The earlier plethora of spring flowers (scurvy grass, wallflower, sea campion, rock-rose, bird's-foot trefoil, lady's bedstraw, bluebell and the like) would have served only the early broods, if, indeed, their nectar had not been diluted or washed away by the 1983 spring rains, which were as ferocious and lasting as the summer drought.

Moths around by day included silver Ys and yellow shells, among those coming indoors by night were angleshades, dark-spectacled pugs and lime-speck pugs. With all those acres of ragwort at their disposal, we saw not a single black and red cinnabar moth.

Strangely, there was a broom moth caterpillar, its green and yellow stripes longitudinal, feeding in a silken web on a ragwort head. It was puzzling that it had not chosen a more conventional food plant such as bracken or bramble, and interesting that it was able to deal with the ragwort's toxic alkaloids, with which the cinnabars were adapted to prime themselves against predators.

The old farmhouse, so pristine in later years, was currently occupied by rabbits, the downstairs rooms thick with their pellets, the joists and floorboards in a bad way. where they burrowed beneath, but it was hoped to make the building watertight before winter. We were allocated accommodation in 'Driftwood', where a dark bush cricket (*Pholidoptera griseoaptera*) with long whiffling antennae strolled in to join us each evening at supper before we climbed into our double bunks.

Outside there was little grass but plenty of grasshoppers vaulting over aggregations of snail shells. Thrushes were still finding the old tombstones more useful as snail anvils than discarded asbestos, plastic and other bric-a-brac, but snails were everywhere, and any handy rock outcrop was made use of.

We saw minotaur beetles, carrion beetles and flea beetles, hover flies, drone flies, craneflies and the inevitable flesh flies, blow flies and green bottles on the carcases. Bumble bees of various sorts exploited the wood sage flowers, woodlice awaited darkness under stones and slates which

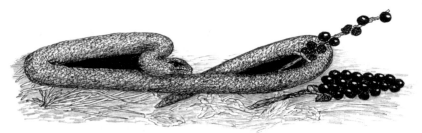

Slow Worm and late season Arum fruits.

they shared with blue-bellied slow worms and their coppery young, those having deserted their favourite corrugated iron sheets where they could have been baked.

Flatholm's blue-spotted form of slow worms is rare in Britain, occurring in Eastern Europe with fewer in the west. It has also been established that Flatholm slow worms are larger on average than mainland ones – not only the males – and so are some of the snail species. This is an island phenomenon, as seen in Skomer voles and St. Kilda wrens. Baby slow worms are only the size of earthworms and can be gobbled up in lieu by thrushes and blackbirds, as well as by little owls and the patrolling kestrels and buzzards.

Elderberries were ripening, but the blackberries were stonily hard, starved of plumpening rain. Some three thousand starlings had been counted by Dave Worrell a month earlier, roosting on the island, and these rose in reluctant hordes when their elder bushes were approached at dusk. They moved only a metre or so before dropping back into the twittering concourse.

About five hundred stayed to feed on the island by day, mostly on the ground, but the elderberries were nipped off almost before they were ripe. Pips were discarded by the birds from both ends, which was why little elder bushes were sprouting all over – hand pulling of saplings just another job to add to the wardens' daily tasks.

Oyster-catchers had had a poor year, but fifty came in to roost on the west coast by night, with a few turnstones. Scattered eggshells showed where shelduck had nested. and more eggshells lay under the stock dove's nest in the dilapidated roof of the isolation hospital. Robins were abroad with young. Chortling blackbirds erupted from the Napoleonic gun emplacements where they roosted and ten swallows hunted over the eastern buildings.

Chief of the passing migrants, as on Sully Island a few days before, were juvenile willow warblers, based in the elders but also feeding out across the ragwort, where two lesser whitethroats were identified. Wheatear, rock pipit, spotted flycatcher, greenfinch, chaffinch, carrion crow, wood pigeons and thirty-one feral pigeons completed the land bird tally.

The western shore at low tide was disappointing, a film of Bristol Channel mud deposited over the broadest stretch where seaward running reefs border the eroded anticline of West Point, settling out in bays and gullies. Some wracks and sea lettuce survived, even a little Chondrus carragheen, where brisker currents deposited sand instead of mud. Winkles and whelks were few and beadlet anemones were clamped upside down under overhangs, among Alcyonidium sea firs to avoid the settling film.

Filter feeding acorn barnacles were all small, no doubt silting up before attaining full size, and limpets seemed hard put to it to find enough algae to graze under the light-excluding 'pea soup' that covered them for half the day.

The shore crabs carried so much silt on their backs that they were difficult to see, but the *Sphaeroma rugosa* Isopods of an upshore pool were a little cleaner. Hermit crabs (*Pagurus bernhardus*) were here, and chiton shells. Small sea snails (*Cingula semicostata*) resembling spire shells might have provided a snack for shelduck chicks before they set off on their long voyage, if they left when the tide was right. It was rewarding to climb to the top of the lighthouse tower at low water to appreciate the layout of the seaweed beds below.

Less rewarding was our viewing of the Marconi Memorial, erected in 1974, where we posed for a group photograph. The lobed cement base was supposed to represent the island, the mobile cement and metal top

Blackbirds.

a revolving battleship bridge, swung to point in the direction of the famous radio messages. How much more dignified would a block of local limestone have been, inscribed appropriately!

Already, after only nine years, the cement was coated with orange lichen, individual colonies no more than an inch across but almost contiguous. Their growth had probably been boosted by guano from the overhanging elders. A gull's nest was tucked neatly into a declivity in the base, so it was not completely useless.

*   *   *

The personality of the island changes with the seasons and is at its most exuberant in May. It was on the third of this month in 1986 that I was again headed there with sleeping bag and iron rations. The old farmhouse had been rendered waterproof by then. Not a lot had been done inside, but it was habitable and we divided our forces between there and 'Driftwood'.

Weather was perking up after a cold grey April and the gulls were at their most belligerent, or should I be charitable and say 'were at their most dutiful in protecting their young? It behoved us to wear hats and carry a stick to deflect their aim. Their numbers were diminishing, however, and nests were closer together due to deterrents, so it was usually possible to steer clear of the danger zone.

John Zehetmeyer, ex-Forestry Commission chief, had only one real tree to look at, the horse chestnut in the fault gully by the lighthouse. Its size suggested a twenty-year-old, but it was probably a lot more, having filled the same amount of space in the gully fifteen years before. Living in a land of bushes it had adopted the same form, branching into several trunks at ground level in the gully and cutting out at ground level to either side. Blackthorn and dog rose were thickening around it, providing useful cover for small birds. He applied his expertise instead to the elder problem.

Alan Orange of the National Museum of Wales was sorting out mosses and lichens, while Derek Packer of the Merthyr Naturalists' Society was busy with his cameras. My job was to report on vegetation changes induced by mowers working back from the margins of 'good' areas into the weed dominated areas, rather than by starting in the middle of the scrum and working outwards. Hopefully pasture plants and grazers would follow the land management teams in.

Unfortunately rabbits (even goats) prefer the good things of life to the high fibre diet that is always being recommended for us humans. How wise they are! High fibre thistles were changing back at this time from slender to spear thistles, but neither appealed to them. As a plant's mission in life is to flower, fruit and perennate its kind, the cutting of ragwort and thistles at ground level merely changed them from biennials to perennials. Cut every year, they kept on trying, just like the humble groundsel if flower buds are consistently nipped off before achieving their ends.

A startling spread of houndstongue had occurred, due to the affinity of their bristly, four-partite fruits for woolly socks. Once this had been a plant of Nissen Hut doorsteps and sandbags, now it was everywhere. Ground ivy, spurned by rabbits but relished by bumble bees, was another unusual dominant. Most was a dwarf, red-leaved form, which created blue carpets of close set flowers through much of the summer.

It was useful ground cover around the helipad, which had been marked out in 1981 on the old railway track by the fog horn garden. The ragwort had been cut well back, so that flying fluff no longer filled the air at late summer landings and take-offs of the helicopter that had replaced the sturdy old supply ship.

Hemlock and Arum, wood sage and carline thistle were spreading and hairy violet was proving itself the most tenacious of the old limestone plants. Wild leeks continued to increase, helped by transplants to new areas. A fine stand grew alongside the fog horn cottage and the keepers nurtured the plants, which they used as garlic to liven up their rations. As it was disliked by livestock, they did not have to give it space in the walled fog horn garden – not that that was particularly livestock proof.

At one period the goats habitually trotted up and over the wooden steps by which the keepers surmounted the wall. A barrier placed across the top caused them to make running jumps at the wall, which they cleared without difficulty. Thrift, wallflower and, sadly, the fine spreads of scurvy grass, were retreating down the cliffs, but rock sea lavender was on the increase.

The water catchment was cleared in 1984, when folk were murmuring about the possibility of repointing, to seal the quarter inch cracks between the tiles and curtail the inevitable loss of water. In 1985 most of those in the lower, moister part were filled with feathery hemlock seedlings and the tiddliwink sized leaves of young scurvy grass. Other tinies finding room were early hair-grass, spring forget-me-not, dove's-foot cranesbill and sea storksbill, most soon pushed out by the first perennial coloniser, yellow stonecrop, or the two common sow thistles. Hemlock held its ground through to 1986 by the north-eastern underground tank, hopefully not letting go any of its toxins into the drainage waters.

An elder growing in the yellow brick crematorium of the hospital, was wind shorn at the level of the now absent roof alongside the square chimney. With it inside was a gull's nest, just below the side ledges where the coffins slid in. Nests in dugouts were increasing, and not only those of gulls.

I came across a blackbird's nest with four scribbled blue eggs on the dark window sill of a 1940s dugout, to which the only entrances were through a low level door and window. An elder bush against the outer wall may have deluded the birds into thinking this was a more rural site than it turned out to be. Another blackbird was sitting in semi darkness against a corner bracket in an earthed-over ammunition store in the north-west.

Yet another in an eastern dugout flew away from me along a dark corridor, chattering its alarm, and out through a partly opened skylight. Cock birds reserved their proper songs, however, for the open air, country dwellers in essence, although forced by circumstance to inhabit a world of brick and concrete, like so many of us. A wood pigeon had joined the stock doves in the old laundry, but chiff-chaffs, true to their birthright, found cover on the cliffs sufficient for their purposes.

Some splendid gatherings of shelducks stood around on the cliff edges, the biggest in the south-east, some in the north-west and two on the concrete stand outside the farmhouse. Fifty flew over our heads on one occasion, with a winnowing whistle of wings that would have done justice to a squadron of swans. Sixty pairs were said to be nesting in 1985.

The landing beach was a fine place to lie sunbathing when waiting for the boat's return, but Coal Beach, just around the corner, held so much of interest that it was difficult to sit for long.

There was less siltation here and the storm beach was of two distinct types of pebbles. Larger ones were of pale Carboniferous Limestone, some containing fossil Goniatites and scattered across a layer of smaller, darker stones, some worn down to shingle size, These came in various shades of yellow, orange and brown, but no Triassic red, and some contained translucent white or cream quartz veins. Seemingly they were derived from glacial gravels, pushed south from the coalfield, rather

Goniatites in Coal Bay.

than the Trias cap, thought to have once been present here, as it still is on Sully Island.

The parent limestone came in three forms. A continuous downshore platform surfacing haphazardly through the pebbles was criss-crossed with tension gashes and lightly filmed with silt. This provided holdfasts for saw wrack plants, which had to tolerate the brown pebbles building up around their base.

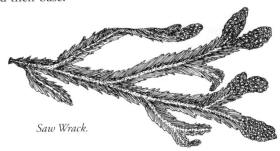

Saw Wrack.

Sharp-edged, yellow-tinged rocks of the middle zone were surfaced with a honeycomb of little solution pits, providing the only refuge available for winkles. They were speckled with black chert nodules standing proud of the uneven surface and hosted wrack sporelings.

Thirdly there was the smooth grey cliff face reaching down to the upper intertidal zone as a blocky, sandy limestone with none of the shaly bands and rotted clay beds of the west. Green algae, narrow-stranded Enteromorpha and woolly, branched Cladophora, penetrated up into freshwater seepages. One of the few red algae to survive was the crusty pink coralline weed.

Common limpets (*Patella vulgata*) occurred as two separate populations, one above the pebble storm beach and one below. Downshore limpets of the flat rock platform had low spreading pyramidal shells, whereas those on the upshore rocks had narrower, steeper-sided wigwams, reaching higher. The difference is said to relate to the muscular contraction necessary to seal the joint during the longer exposure to the air.

Upshore limpets were often clamped to rocks moistened by fresh water seeping from aquifers. This implies that the freshwater input was discernible by the animals when they were moving freely in salty water at high tide. There were more algae to be rasped off there, food, drink and an insurance against desiccation providing a triple attraction.

The few flat periwinkles browsing over the downshore saw wrack had bright orange shells. Edible periwinkles were clustered in solution pits of midshore rocks, sometimes with small limpets which would have to find new quarters as they grew, or they would get wedged. The four-plated *Elminius modestus* barnacles which had arrived from Australia in the 1940s, are tolerant of low salinities and were outdoing the six-plated natives.

A gull's egg, or was it a duck's? had been laid on the concrete of the old Coal Bay jetty without a shell, the yolk seeping from the stout membranes. There were two mysteries here. What had gone wrong with the mother bird and why had no hungry gull swooped down and eaten it? Offshore two mallard were breasting the gentle swell, a not too common sight, finally taking to the air and heading off for Cardiff Docks.

21.

FLATHOLM'S
EVER CHANGING LANDSCAPE

Ecological changes on the ground and renovations to the buildings proceeded apace in pursuit of aspirations for the future, but there were always links with the past. Workers lopping the big old elders north of the farmhouse happened upon a medieval settlement, and switched from labourers to archaeologists.

An ancient system of grass-banked enclosures came to light, with a smaller plot in the centre and a kitchen midden. They excavated a commendable array of pottery, along with the foundations of old farm buildings and a cottage with sturdy fireplace. More sample digs were planned.

By August 1986 and the visit of a deputation from the County Council and Flatholm Society, basic building work had been completed in the farmhouse except for the plumbing and the interior was cleared ready for painting and decorating. An underground tank had been sunk to collect rain water from the roof, so gulls were being discouraged from alighting and adding that little unwanted extra to the brew.

The lighthouse was being painted in the time-honoured fashion, with two men easing themselves down from the balcony around the lantern on a plank platform suspended by ropes on pulleys. At each descent they covered a strip rather more than four metres wide by reaching out sideways.

Balls of mauve flowers topped the colony of wild leeks below and beyond them scurvy grass flourished along the window sills of the Victorian Barracks. Foliage of the flowering wild turnip must have hosted veritable hordes of green caterpillars to account for the clouds of large white butterflies flitting everywhere – unless there had been a mass migration.

Seventeenth September 1987 again saw members of the County Council and Consultative Committee in discussion with the lighthouse keepers under their still pristine tower. One was reporting a recent skirmish when clearing rubble from a deep Victorian ammunition store with a long narrow passage leading to arched stone windows, where the soldiers' lamps had to be left before entering to avoid an explosion.

"Two mummified 'hooded' black rats down there with the fur still on – and preserved mummy rabbits. Everything tinder dry – no decay."

I had recently heard another keeper's tale of a rat invasion twenty-five years before.

"They ate the garden crops, sat on the window sills peering in at us, and sneaked inside, eating all the food that wasn't in tins."

Pest controllers were summoned from the mainland and the rats exterminated. That was about the time when Rae Vernon had been watching four black rats making free with the lighthouse blackberries.

A new helipad was planned on the concrete base of the World War II hospital near the farmhouse, where the danger of bird strike was less than by the foghorn, although this was likely to be little used. A helicopter visit cost Trinity House about £100 and could not be justified very often with a boat running almost every day from Barry. There was also a new radio aerial, with arms radiating from the top instead of guylines from half way down.

"A unique new system. Four big modules. Experimental. Too expensive for anywhere else. The RAF have bought more for the Falklands. They're the only ones who can afford them." It was hoped that the old traditional lighthouse equipment would be assembled in a museum to be set up in the foghorn buildings, but it hasn't happened yet.

We peered seaward to where a drilling rig or the like rose gauntly from the turbid flood. It was testing the sea bed for the building of the mooted Severn Barrage. After three day's working off Flatholm the team was moving for three weeks off Steepholm. At that stage it was thought the barrage might pass well to seaward, linking Steepholm with the land and leaving Flatholm on the upstream side in calmer, fresher water, but the years of planning and surveying came to nought.

In the meantime the lightships and some of the navigational aids warning seamen of sandbanks and rocks were being withdrawn for lack of finance. Big ships now navigated by satellite and it was the big ship owners who had paid for their upkeep. Small boats could not afford to keep them in business, so sailed now at their peril.

The rare sight of a merlin flying overhead brought our thoughts back to the island. Peregrines had nested on Steepholm this year and one of the youngsters was a not infrequent visitor to Flatholm. Another rare treat was a view of three guillemots alighting on the water offshore – further up channel than these essentially oceanic birds usually venture. A grey Atlantic seal, too, had been seen recently, but none had been known to haul ashore. Pursuing fish through the prevailing suspension of Bristol Channel mud must seem quite a problem for the likes of those, although there were old records of common seals off Denny Island much further up channel.

We were surprised at the multiplicity of small holes in the short turf of the grassy tracks. These were made by the myriad starlings – like green woodpecker holes in anthills. Watching the birds at work, we could see their beaks plunging in slightly open and guess when they had had a lucky haul by the bulging of the cheeks.

Starlings.

David Worrell had studied them at length, finding that seven out of ten probes were rewarded. He suggested that less would not be cost effective in terms of energy because the quality of the food obtained was too low. One bird arrived first and, if successful, others followed. With their short beaks they preferred the short turf of the mown pastures for reaching down to soil grubs. Councillor Longdon, one of our number, told of starlings following his lawn mower, feeding on the mown but not the unmown grass, like gulls behind a plough.

They and other small birds were welcome on the island and elder clearance was planned to leave sufficient bushes for nesting, roosting and passage birds. Felling of the big old elders around the farmhouse had shown that even branches three to four inches across were hollow where the persistent central pith had finally rotted. Few uses can be found for the inevitably brittle wood and these bore crops of Jew's ear fungus.

Edible mushrooms had returned this year, as had the star of Bethlehem after an absence of nearly a quarter of a century, in the same site as before near the lighthouse and in two further ones. Another newcomer had brought the number of island mints up to three, but the most spectacular incomer was the Himalayan balsam or policeman's helmet, springing up where the men who must have brought it had been working. This would please the bumble bees, which had room to turn round inside the capacious pink hood instead of having to back out into possible danger.

The next year Ceri Williams, apiarist, ornithologist and photographer, was keeping experimental honey bees on Flatholm in one of a dozen isolated hives. They had filled their combs with ragwort honey, which is not poisonous to humans as Rhododendron honey is. Wood sage, garlic and sea lavender were also useful nectar sources. Queen bees transported to the mainland were found to contain sperm from as many as half a dozen drones.

The comma butterfly in 1987 was an unusual sighting and common blues had been busy over the water catchment from where water was being pumped to the farmhouse via the tank on the roof of 'Driftwood', which now boasted flush toilets with settling tank in the brambles behind. Drinking water was still brought in from the mainland, as the filtration plant was not yet in full working order. A diesel-powered generator kept the lights burning.

Staff had been at work in the farmhouse garden raising a crop of potatoes and some rhubarb. The pink of wild Fuchsia and red valerian still romped along the wall outside the kitchen, but the more muted tones of the Duke of Argyll's tea tree were yet to come. Rabbits were a constant scourge, but a team of boys was busy rebuilding the bottom garden wall to keep them at bay.

*   *   *

1989 was another dry summer, with all the drinking water having to be brought in cannisters and the washing water situation so acute that only a sprinkling of overnight visitors could be accepted, despite the fine new sleeping accommodation now available. Re-grouting of the catchment in 1985 was still good, but the north slope was white with guano. With botulism still rife among the gulls and four cases in humans recently reported, the first washings when the rain came would have to be prevented from entering the recently re-lined settling tank, as the sand filters still left much to be desired.

In the distant future there might be another solution to the problem if the freshwater spring surfacing on the sea bed just off the lighthouse could be tapped and piped to the island. It emerged from the south, in the deepest part of the channel where the old River Severn used to flow through its wooded valley, so the water-bearing rock strata may not be replicated on the Flatholm side.

That water source was well known to the dredger captains because the water welling up through the sea bed cleaned the sand of much of its silt, eliminating some of the subsequent washings. Dredgings from elsewhere would be washed here and there was said to be a race in the mornings to see which boat could claim the prime position.

A student putting the scarlet dye, eosine, into springs disappearing underground into the limestone caves of the Mendips, had had no luck in discovering where this emerged until he was sipping beer in a pub and chanced to overhear a dredger captain commenting on "odd, orange-stained sand." A pleasurable way of solving a complex problem! With water so close, there might be more under Flatholm that could be tapped, divining its position more straightforward than that discovered accidentally at sea.

As early as 29th June in 1989 the turf was worn to crisped brown shreds, the few green patches being sea campion, burdock and slender thistle. With no rain to speak of in two months to wash it away, guano covered more ground than the diminished number of gulls seemed to merit. Was it just coincidence that most of the Cepaea hedge snails surviving had plain yellow shells to match their drought-blighted background?

The density of rabbit dung, too, was greater than might be expected from the number of occupied warrens. Numbers had been severely reduced by Myxomatosis in 1988, releasing more burrows for shelducks to nest in, but there was still competition for sites. Rabbits had scratched out two shelduck nests, the displaced creamy-buff eggs, the size of hens' eggs, all intact, except one languishing in its vitelline membranes. A remarkable quantity of down had been pulled from the nests, with soft white contour feathers, some tipped with black, in amounts of which an eider duck might have been proud.

Not all shelducks were nesting in burrows now, some were exploiting the dense nettle patches induced by the gulls – a backhanded way of paying for their exploitation of the ducklings. By the time the nettles died down the families had dispersed. It was September of that year when I saw a flock resting on the tiled catchment – a wide open space resembling the broad stretches of sand which they frequent in their feeding areas on the estuary margins. A hundred and sixty-four ducks had been counted earlier.

Three hundred gull victims of botulism, mostly juveniles, had been disposed of by September that year. Some nests had been fenced around during experiments, with cardboard and bracken piled to give shelter during the heat of the day, but a number of young succumbed, some with their heads wedged between rocks as though seeking shade in their last moments.

On the twelfth of that month we were able to watch the graceful soaring of three young buzzards, dropping from the sky onto myxoma-tosed rabbits, which were easy prey for inexperienced hunters. So too, were the botulised gulls, but these would look unfamiliar from their prospecting elevation and I have no knowledge of these ever being taken. This had been a good year for peregrines and sparrow hawks had been visiting, to assess the increase of song birds accompanying the increase of elders. An osprey had been sighted earlier in the year.

The free range hens and cockerel did not need to be locked up at night in the absence of nocturnal predators, but they took themselves to bed at dusk in a roost of their own choice – an old gun battery. This was a safe haven which they had refused to leave in their first few days in this strange, intimidating, gull-dominated environment. Numbers were down to one of each sex by September but another five hens were to be imported as soon as suitable nineteen week olds on the point of lay could be located. There was no shortage of seed around, but they were supplied with extra victuals, with new laid eggs in mind.

Only now, soon after the landing of a ten pound conger eel, did I learn that the national boundary between Wales and England brushes the south-eastern reef of Flatholm, so I was able to take a walk into England at low tide.

*　　　*　　　*

1990 saw the first storm petrel ever caught by the Flatholm bird ringers – an exciting catch, because it had been ringed in August 1971 as an adult on Skomer. This made it at least nineteen years old, an incredible age for a bird no bigger than a swallow and only one year less than the oldest stormie ringed in Britain at the time.

One of the lesser black-backs ringed in June 1989 turned up a year and a half later in Morocco, the destination of a dunlin ringed up channel. These distances were surpassed, however, by the Taff Estuary turnstone, picked up in the Gambia in West Africa.

The visit of County Councillors on 17th July, 1990, was more satisfying than their ill fated one of fifteen years before in October 1975 – with plenty to show for the hard work and nesting gulls now hovering at around fifteen hundred pairs. We were not harried. Breeding was over and most of the adolescents were idling on a limpid sea, awaiting their elders' return with provender.

Mowing and grazing were paying off and Destrox, described as an inhibitor rather than a weed killer, had been sprayed in April and May. This was effective against ragwort, docks, thistles and nettles, leaving grasses and bedstraws intact. It had had an intriguing effect on the burdock, producing attractive leaves with deeply undulant margins around flat centres, which could be a real hit in horticultural circles if introduced as an ornamental – as pretty as any of those frilly pink and purple cabbages.

Frilly Burdock leaves.

The grasses growing 'in lieu' were mostly tall oat, as in previous years, but patches were still bare where ragwort had been dragged out by tractor. The six sheep moved onto the island in October 1989 for winter grazing were shipped back to their farmer owner for dipping on 24th April, 1990, fit and well. He was so happy with them that he sent a second batch of eleven ewes with lambs at foot. These were small and white, probably North Wales mountain breed, and doing well on the lime-rich grazing here.

They were dosed for worms and liver fluke at the start and were not required by law to be dipped in spring while on the island, although due for another worming. It was too dry here for liver fluke infection, but the vector snail had just turned up in the new pond. There was talk of buying store lambs in autumn and selling them fat in spring, entailing little work and a possible profit.

The mohair-producing Kashmir goats which had arrived in such poor condition in the winter of 1989-90 from the overstocked Great Orme, had also waxed fat. They were lying down when we spotted them – a good sign that their bellies were full. Judging by the fine sweeps of spreading horns – another example of which is worn by the pampered mascot of the Welsh Regiment – we could well believe the fun and games experienced in transporting them here on the *Lewis Alexander*!

The nucleus of this famous Kashmir herd was presented to Queen Victoria by the Shah of Persia on the occasion of her marriage and was divided between Windsor Great Park, Whipsnade and the Great Orme. The initial input to Flatholm was nine billies, the nannies retained on the Orme to rear their kids, then some of those, or others from Whipsnade, were to join the billies as a breeding unit on Flatholm.

The goats were feral, avoiding people where possible, but the wardens would soon have to round them up for ear tagging and selective castrating so that they knew who was who and could plan a mating programme. Commercially those billies were said to be worth £2,000 each – and a mohair pullover £100!

Goats usually pose problems on islands worldwide for eating trees. Here that is exactly what they were supposed to do and they made a good job of stripping flowers and leaves from the elders which they obviously enjoyed, so that the roots of the rampant young trees could be dragged out by tractor. As ozone-friendly recyclers of trashy vegetation, they were first class, doing a wonderful job – even on bracken, which seemed not to harm them.

Their ministrations were needed only on the northern half of the island, so a rash of electric fences had appeared, and wires along the top of walls to prevent them hopping over. As nimble on rocks as other goats, it was a problem keeping them from straying into forbidden territory along the low western shore. Some barriers will be permanent, others seasonal, to allow for rotational grazing in the gull colonies when the birds have left. British Telecom came up with some telegraph poles for gateposts for hanging the new iron gates.

Goats in the home paddock, and this included the nannies and young kids in later years, had to share more meagre grazing with rabbits, so were supplied with hay. Managing a Nature Reserve is never as simple as it looks.

There had been an onslaught on the rabbits, with a hundred and sixty of them, thought to be around fifty per cent, killed in February 1990 with ferrets. The poor wee beasties, bred for generations on the island, had no experience of stoat, weasel, marten or mink, and were seen popping into their burrows by one entrance while a ferret was being put into another, to meet in the labyrinth below. All were emaciated and half of the remainder were said to have died during the following winter.

Human youngsters have a similar trampling effect to livestock and a paddock at the bottom of the garden had been walled off for them to play football and like shinnanikins, as they couldn't be let loose on the island in their free time. It was hoped to work off some of their energy rounding up the sheep for drenching and shearing.

Water for drinking was still coming from the mainland, but use was made of the water catchment yield for washing up and flushing loos and the staff, who were used to excess minerals, drank it. Water in the holder tank was good now that weeds were regularly cleared, and was piped up to a header tank for transport by pipe to the farmhouse. The tank capacity was sixty thousand gallons, its present content twenty thousand

The new YFC pond was lined with butyl, as rabbits would have burrowed through the polythene that was used under the encircling embankment to form a mini-catchment. The margins were producing mud for swallows to build their nests and the Gwent young farmers must have brought some useful disseminules on their gumboots, as the first plants to colonise had a distinct flavour of the Gwent reens, with frogbit, Canadian pondweed, ivy-leaved duckweed and two species of Potamogeton pondweed. There were no dragonflies yet, those 1983 hawkers must have blown across from the mainland. There were, however, stonefly larvae, water beetles, pond skaters, water snails and a seasonal soup of Daphnia water fleas. Also more tall vegetation, making it an ideal site for the bird ringers to erect their mist nets.

The faunal find of the day was an all black, melanistic, slow worm. A botanical phenomenon was the survival of the thrift where all else had died when storm waves bit into the western cliffs and swept across the sward near the old stone lime kiln. The gap had been walled across and infilled behind with rubble.

On an August visit in 1991 I was impressed by the rock sea lavender flowering profusely on both faces of Castle Rock as we pulled round to the landing. The original great black-backed gulls had abandoned the sea lavender site on the south cliffs and had been joined by another. New nesters this year at the other end of the size range were a perky pair of blackcaps.

Herb Robert and pellitory-of-the-wall were colonising a new spoil tip above the landing, but the old lead/zinc mine residue remained bare. It seems that the strains of fescue, bent grass and sea campion of similar areas that are genetically resistant to these metals are not present on Flatholm. Sea storksbill and doves-foot cranesbill, with white flowers as well as pink, were the principal pioneers of ground bared for other reasons. Most colourful were the tree mallow in the farmhouse garden, the massed teasels of the cliffs and the ragwort of just about every-

Wall Pellitory.

where else, particularly where trampling Soay sheep were excluded by electric fencing. Those were quartered on the island from May to October this year.

The Angora goats had settled in well but were very wild, with sufficient bush growth by now for them to lie low whenever they so chose. Five of the seven billies had been castrated, but the wardens had had a high old time catching them. Fortunately they don't have to be shorn, the mohair just drops out or rubs off, like the tousled dark brown wool of the Soays.

Sadly the bottom had just dropped out of the mohair market. It was planned, nevertheless, to gather up the shed fleeces and pass them to a local spinner to be used for craft work or pin money rather than as a commercial proposition. Line fishermen use goat hair for tying their 'flies', so this might provide another outlet.

This August 1991 visit was an 'official' one by the Flatholm Consultative Committee. We had 'inspected' the new porch on 'Driftwood', the new entrance opposite the water catchment and the interior brick walls which had replaced the old plasterboard ones and were admiring the white-painted walls and ceiling, when a radio telephone message came through calling us back to the boat.

It transpired that the rudder had come adrift and the Barry lifeboats, both the old one and the 1991 replacement, were coming to get us – quite soon, to get the incapacitated vessel up on the slip for repair in time for the morrow's duties.

The old lifeboat nosed into the shingle with a grinding crunch, as the tide was too low to use the jetty and there was insufficient water depth for the other, although both were fifty-two footers. We scrambled aboard and donned life jackets for the transfer at sea. The pensioned off vessel then returned to take the original transit boat in tow and all three ploughed their furrow through the coffee-coloured water to Barry Harbour down channel.

I was allowed to sit on the inside pilot's seat at the wheel, instructions as to how to interpret the radar screen at my elbow passing rather far over my head. The real pilot, the skipper, was way above me, up front, in the 'pulpit'. Most of the rest were sent down the ladder to the forward cabin – safe from rough seas when the boat was pursuing her normal rescue duties.

*　　*　　*

March 1992 was living up to its reputation as a month of mad March north-westerlies, with a penetrating nip sufficient to delay embarkation of the partakers in the 'Flatholm Society's Working Week' designed to get the island ship shape for summer visitors. It was touch and go today for the dozen or so hopefuls while the nautical faction assessed the pros and cons.

After an hour's indecision, the *Lewis Alexander*, commissioned in 1989, pulled into the wharf steps and we followed the stores aboard. As always, gazing up at the height of the solid stone wall above the bobbing boat, I was amazed at how far up the limpets managed to live – exposed to the air and unable to feed for most of the tidal cycle. Some above HWM of spring tides, would be unable to unclamp and browse except when wetted by wave splash or rain.

They were not alone, a generous sprinkling of small acorn barnacles was clinging on almost as high. The spat must have been borne thither on a high spring. They could not 'get up and go', even as ponderously as the limpets, and, as filter feeders, needed to be submerged before they could waft floating particles into their waiting maws. It was no surprise that none managed to grow to full size,

The gales of 1990 had destroyed the *Western Lady*, the only boat licenced to ply from Weston-super-Mare to Flatholm, so the *Lewis Alexander*, licenced to go anywhere east of Nash Point, was more in demand than ever, ferrying parties from the English side.

Today the sun shone without warmth from a sky the colour of a starling's egg, lightly flecked with clouds – a real 'island day', gusty and fresh. Half way across we retired to the cabin, deciding that we had got quite wet enough. It was low tide again and our craft ground her way in among the pebbles as we made fast and stepped easily onto the movable horizontal platform and gingerly over the section where the boards had broken away leaving only the covering wire mesh.

Stores and packs of those going into residence went ashore along a human chain as we set off up the steps – a train of pack mules, with enough baked beans and nescafé to keep the community going for quite a while.

Scurvy grass bloomed bravely from the cliff face, precursor of the sea campion, and there was more among the yellow and brown of wallflowers colonising roofs of the old buildings. Time forbade exploration of the north-east corner, where the entire terrain should be white with blossom at this time of year. Or should it? Perhaps Soays and Kashmirs would have found these plants as palatable as did the scurvy-ridden sailors of old who were responsible for the unsavoury name. But there had been sheep and goats here in the past and the plants had survived. No need to worry on that score.

A pair of Persil-white billies sporting admirable 'handlebars' stared at us insolently before making off. With that sort of armoury, it was as well that they should not be encouraged to become too matey.

Going was much easier on the goats' side of the electric fence where

Arum fruits and Rabbit pellets.

the underbrush had been cleared. The gulls milling around on the other would be invisible in a few weeks when the plants grew up around the nests and they obviously preferred this to sharing with the grazers. They rose in a noisy cloud as we passed, but it was too early for nests yet. The territorial urge was building up, but there was no dive bombing.

A striking feature of the gull vegetation was the abundance of wild Arum, the lush carpet of arrowhead leaves presaging good autumn colour as the spikes of scarlet berries ripened among the rotting spathes. Many clustered round mutilated elders, which lagged behind those of the mainland in bursting into leaf.

Starry golden celandines pushed up from tousled mats of grass and bracken fronds, while bluebell plants loomed large around the foghorn, without the elegance of woodland ones but as chunky rosettes like those of the Gower cliffs. The flower heads too, would be shorter and fleshier than the often loppy ones of woodland, but offering no meaningful competition to the magnificent displays of Skokholm and Skomer.

Ground ivy flowered throughout and greater periwinkles of similar hue peeped from beneath the newly roofed Victorian barracks. Star of Bethlehem leaves pierced the sward by the lighthouse.

Teasel heads stood proud, having defied the winds of winter and were hosting a flock of goldfinches tweaking residual seeds from among the

Goldfinches and Teasel heads.

spines. A blackbird shot away, squawking its alarm and there were flocks of starlings and jackdaws. Looking east we were rewarded by the colourful spectacle of massed shelducks on the low limestone ledge under the water catchment. Their breeding prospects were brighter than those of the mallard pair loitering by the new pond.

An early peacock butterfly ricocheted, wind-tossed, from flower to flower, although staying close to the ground, and seven-spot ladybirds had emerged from hibernation ahead of the aphids which would sustain them. An eruption of out-of-season fungi by the hospital laundry, with its raised roof section for ventilation, was of weeping widow (*Lacrymaria velutina*) and there were crusty orange remains of witch's butter or brain fungus on moribund elder boughs.

A delightful touch of spring around the farm buildings was supplied by two Angora nannies, each with twin kids. These were the first to be

Seven Spot Ladybird.

Weeping Widow Toadstools.

born here and were flirting with the free range hens enjoying their dust baths. The two billies spared their dignity in the former round-up had evidently been doing their stuff.

We picked up an apparent geode with angular crystals facing into the central cavity of a five inch diameter cobble resembling the alabaster 'potato stones' released from the cliffs at Barry.

*   *   *

A couple of months later, in May 1992, we were back for the 'official opening' of the renovated 'Driftwood' by the chairman of the county council.

Nettles, thistles, docks and the gulls which had spawned them, were now cleared from between landing and farmhouse, leaving a pleasant greensward, the mowings dumped in a western hollow to remove the excess nutrients. A large experimental enclosure on the west cliff nearby had the mesh fence heightened to exclude goats and wires strung across the top to exclude gulls. Changes inside were much the same as in my 1940s exclosures on Skokholm of nearly fifty years before.

There was a splendid spread of ground-hugging flowering thrift outside, sprinkled with tufts of sea campion, and a tall sward of bent-fescue grassland with a little Yorkshire fog and common sorrel inside. A difference in this less oceanic habitat was a taller thicket of nettle and curled dock occupying the more sheltered north and east margins of the fenced area. Other enclosed plots inland of the house were quite different, the changes complicated by mowing. One remained as pure nettles, another had fewer nettles with tall grass and celandines.

An ungrazed patch of wild turnip flowers in the island centre was almost as eye-catching as a fragmented rape field, but the real beauties on a smaller scale were birds'-foot trefoil, biting stonecrop and germander speedwell, blue as a butterfly's wing.

The bobble heads of wild leek were still neatly ensconced within peaked, straw-coloured bracts, later to be worn rakishly askew, like elfin caps. They had suffered no harm from being dug up to bury a water pipe and replanted on top – and the keepers were no longer sampling the bulbs in lieu of onions. In a few weeks the globose lavender flower balls would be towering a metre and a half above the surrounding plants over splaying leaves seared yellow by the sun.

A disorientated racing pigeon had taken up station on the bench outside the farmhouse door, cajoling donations from visitors' lunch packs, that might otherwise have fallen to the light Sussex and Rhode Island red hens.

More Angora nannies had been brought in to kid, the latest arrival very small and quite delightful as it gambolled over the woodpile and other impedimenta with a larger companion. Some Soay ewes looked on with interest, sharing the bond of motherhood, their own lambs about the size of the littlest goat. They were less timid now than in previous years.

On a late June visit that year we became acquainted with a junior partnership of kid and lamb. Inseparable friends, I wondered if they had noticed the difference. If so, it was of no moment and less momentous than the vagaries of the surrogate Mum who had reared them both on the bottle. Imprinted on humankind, their ties with their own kind were completely severed – until the sex hormones took control!

They mingled with each new party of visitors gathered to listen to the warden's welcoming spiel at the picnic benches outside the farm-house and joined the birds in clearing the proffered victuals. It was the kid who led the lamb across the rolling beach pebbles to meet our boat and came on our walkabout, until persuaded to join up with the electricians headed to 'Driftwood', where they were installing a new generator.

The lamb was likely to be the last of her blood group. Her father had been used to sire the line for as long as was conducive to the prevention of inbreeding. He would need to be sent ashore to a new harem and replaced before the next generation was conceived.

Around three hundred shelduck were counted in May and a hundred nests were forecast, but by June the number had been re-assessed at a hundred and fifty. This is much the best breeding site for shelducks in the Bristol Channel, although the biggest flocks converge in Bridgewater Bay on the other side for the annual moult, these a mingling of birds from Great Britain and North-western Europe.

Fifteen eggs in one brood is a big drain on energy resources and a shelduck cannot lay again if a rabbit kicks her eggs out of a shared burrow, as can gulls, whose clutch is of only three. If interrupted part way through laying, she might move elsewhere to deposit the rest of the clutch. She must leave sometimes to feed and this is when rabbits can become obstreperous but, thankfully, not rats any more.

On 22nd June, 1992, we happened upon a young oyster-catcher three quarters grown in the Castle Rock Gun Battery, hatched from a nest outside on the mini scree. The parent perched on a concrete block throughout our short visit, piping her displeasure. She had brought her one surviving youngster inside, to spare it from the gulls, which tend not to alight in confined spaces unless nesting there. Her kind are easily thrown into a panic, but she stuck to her post of vantage, hoping to divert attention from the chick, which had obeyed her instruction to freeze.

Oyster-catcher numbers were showing a slight increase from six pairs in 1990 to seven pairs in 1991 and eight pairs in 1992. Several of these were nesting among thrift on the cliff edge between farm and lighthouse and had been placed out of bounds to people, to give them their privacy. Snipe, dunlin and curlew were mere visitors, marathon migrants just passing through.

Our adolescent oyster-catcher was spotted when we entered the gun pit to examine a great mullein plant completely defoliated by caterpillars of mullein shark moths (*Cucullia verbasci*). The handsome black, yellow and greeny-white larvae were fully grown now, which was just as well, as they had exhausted their obligatory food supply. Warning colouration had kept them safe from predators. All they had to do now was to pupate preparatory to flying free. There was a considerable colony of mullein on the cliffs above Coal Bay to which the moths should be headed when the time came to lay their eggs.

An orb web spider sat patiently on her beautifully executed web, which was so far intact above the oyster-catcher's head. The usual colourful lackey moth caterpillars were exploring sloe twigs in the lighthouse defence trench among attractive dog roses. Discarded skins of their early instars clung to the outside of the once protective silken mesh where they had huddled together as bristly brown infants. They, too, would

Small Tortoiseshell.

soon be pupating. Small tortoiseshells of the midsummer brood were spooking the numerous white Crambe grass moths.

Stock doves were nesting in the cliffs among yelping jackdaws and another carrier pigeon had joined the one at the farmhouse. Gleaming navy blue swallows swooped in and out of the woodshed to tend their young and there were blackbirds, song thrushes and wheatears about. Robins stirred secretively in the undergrowth, like drying leaves about to fall.

Rabbits, usually everywhere, were sparse. When the wardens left in December 1991 the island was swarming with them. When they got back in early spring most had died of Myxomatosis. This killer disease lies low for long periods, then rears its ugly head and strikes.

A double pink opium poppy was sprouting in the peony enclosure, trying to outdo the legitimate residents, along with another handsome interloper, the purple toadflax. The peonies were currently bearing splaying green seed pods, so were not competing visually on equal terms. Henbane was doing well, the long stems uncoiling to as much as twelve inches already, to display their rows of goblet shaped seed vessels. Other striking plants were hound's tongue, common mallow, weld and dewberry.

Hound's Tongue.

Towards the end of July in 1992 a great skua or bonxie, a species rarely seen this far south, descended on the island to harry the local gulls, not just pirating their food but with intent to kill. It was first spotted on the sea off Castle Rock dismembering an adolescent, which was not yet used to the ways of this fearsome stranger – nor would be. The interloper expressed its dominance by ignoring the mobbing of the residents. Next day it was devouring an adult lesser black-backed gull off the landing beach, again unperturbed by the gullabaloo of the shrieking mob all around.

A Cardiff Naturalists' Society group visiting on 2nd July, 1994, saw another great skua. Was it, perhaps, the same one which had sussed out a good eating place in passing? Ted Jones and other dedicated ornithological sea-watchers at Lavernock Point, had recently established that both great and arctic skuas took the shorter overland migration route across Britain from the Norfolk Wash to the Severn Estuary – flying high across the Midlands, where no self respecting ornithologist would be expecting such exotica from the Scottish islands.

During the 1980-1990 decade there had been thirty-six sightings of great skuas involving forty-five birds, and ninety-six of arctic skuas encompassing a hundred and forty-nine birds. September is the optimum month, but there were also records for April and midsummer, suggesting that some non-breeders may stay in the Bristol Channel over the summer months.

The frequency of kestrel visits had given birth to a plan to erect kestrel nesting boxes on high points such as the anemometer tower. A first pair of house sparrow stayed to breed in 1992, possibly the start of a new colony, now that there were so many more people around for longer periods. Blackcaps were also nesting, along with wrens, dunnocks and the usual garden birds. Councillor Sharpe, visiting in March 1993, said he had never seen so may wrens on the island, so they must have had a good breeding year.

The shelduck population was still rising, with a maximum count of three hundred and sixty-two on the 21st April. It seemed more ducklings must be getting safely across to the mainland under cover of darkness to make this possible.

The mallard pair pioneering the new pond seemed not to have resorted to the nocturnal feeding pattern practised by many mainland mallard, and had lost their six ducklings by the 6th of May. The duck took refuge under the pond-dipping platform and was found dead the

Blackcap and Blackberries.

following evening. No injury could be found. Had she died of stress trying to protect her family from the unaccustomed menace swooping out of the sky?

The drake remained faithful for a while, returning regularly and calling for her in vain. On 17th May another pair came to set up home. Had he found another partner? Mallard tried every year at least until 1998 but fared no better. Gulls always took the ducklings and in later years we wondered what they could have been eating. The pond water by then was a foetid solution of gull guano with little or no small animal life. This was evolution in the making – establishing the incompatibility of gulls and mallard living in close association. Even shelduck and eiders, which are not dependant on fresh water for their ducklings, have a hard time of it.

A young gull trapped in the enclosure by the pond on 28th July made several unsuccessful tries to launch itself over the fence before coughing up a slabby white mass measuring 5 x 2 x 2 inches. It had evidently dined too lavishly. We opened the gate to help it out but, the load now lightened, it lifted easily over the barrier with a triumphant chortle. Another landmark in the learning curve of growing up had been achieved.

The farmhouse meadow was alive with meadow brown butterflies and the usual peacocks, admirals and tortoiseshells sipped from the weed patches, prime specimens from the late summer 'hatching'. A hedge brown was identified in the island centre – a butterfly of woodland and hedgerow, exploring the possibility of life among the elders.

Soon there might be speckled woods. 1992 was another good year for clouded yellows.

Bumble dor beetles were busy burying faeces, their dependence on mammalian dung for raising their young now satisfied by Soays and Kashmirs.

A surprising new arrival near the end of 1992 was a roe deer, which must have swum here, helped by the currents. It was fortunate to have made a safe landing after such an experience. The Steepholm deer are Muntjacs, so this one must have come from the mainland – of either England or Wales.

This was the year of the rebirth of the farmhouse garden, planned on Victorian lines, with a herb bed for the kitchen and vegetables to be grown in the lighthouse garden. Potted imports were being acclimatised to salty winds before being planted out and a central path of ballast was laid, to be topped by sand and paving stones, with cracks for rock plants.

*　　　*　　　*

Financial crisis loomed in 1993 when the County Education Department pulled out of all its environmental projects. In the general shuffling of too meagre funding, ecological training was regarded as an unnecessary luxury instead of the vital part of the curriculum that it has become since.

It was unthinkable that the whole project, with so much capital sunk in all the renovations, should be abandoned to mis-use by sea-borne pirates A reprieve was achieved by transferring the financial responsibility to the Planning Department, whose budget had not been so severely cut by the Welsh Office. The Countryside Council for Wales came up with grant aid and the Flatholm Society was among others contributing to this so worthy cause.

The permanent staff was cut from six to five – two on the island, two manning the boat and one in the mainland headquarters, which moved from the Barry Old Police Station to cheaper accommodation on the wharf. There were to be more visitors on the island, up to fifty at a time, and higher landing fees. Even the romance of island hopping has to bow to the stringencies of economic viability. Hopefully the dedicated staff would manage to keep some of the magic and sense of adventure alive for the many youngsters who benefited.

There were plenty of unforeseen ways in which the precious finance disappeared. Easterly gales early in 1994 had scoured beach pebbles away to expose the foundations of the jetty and ripped off some of the planks and their non-slip wire netting. Trinity House made smaller use of the landing facilities now than did the Flatholm Project, and contributed only ten per cent of the cost of repairs. Opportunity was taken to level the upper beach at the same time, to facilitate the humping around of stores.

Goats were prospering. There were now forty-one and a another kid due at the end of April. Nine nannies had produced seventeen kids between them, these penned by the farmhouse. Sickly though the Flatholm sward appears at times, the herd that had arrived in such poor health four years before was now in excellent fettle. Inbreeding had not yet been solved. One old billy had had sole responsibility since a vet came to castrate all the male kids. One of these, Gladstone, had been adopted by the Gladstone Primary School, but the idea of selling kids as a source of revenue had not yet borne fruit.

The Soay sheep were on loan from the Countryside Council for Wales' Newborough Warren flock on Anglesey, which took back most of the lambs produced to augment their breeding stock. Ewes and lambs had found out how to enter the no-go areas via the beach, so fencing was having to be extended. It was the goats that were making free of the old keepers' house through an inadvertently opened door, leaving their calling cards at different levels.

By 1994 the island was being manned throughout the year and I joined a party taking Christmas fare out to the wardens on 12th December. The lifeboat accompanied the *Lewis Alexander* on her errand of mercy, whether to protect the Christmas cheer or the passengers was not quite clear.

Land across the channel loomed iron grey, like a persistent fog bank and a long swell was rolling up the estuary from the south-west. I travelled out on the *Lewis* and there was an exciting moment when a single mighty comber hit us broadside on. I returned on the lifeboat, after a transfer at sea, because she took too much water to come into the slipway. We headed into the weather on our return, cutting straight through the waves, our speed such that her lively wake was meeting the swell crosswise in foaming crests eight to nine feet high.

A bottle-fed kid came to meet us off the boat, trotting along the footway and cleverly keeping its delicate hooves from catching in the netting. He solemnly joined the party of civic dignitaries on their island walk, like a pet pup, his fleece soft, grey and fluffy, not yet sleek, white and silky, like a baby bird still in down.

A Heligoland trap was being constructed for the bird ringers among the much lopped elders beyond the now completely roofless isolation hospital. The circumference of one of the double-trunked 'trees' was three full hand spans. Beyond were fresh parasol mushrooms and late flowers of dovesfoot cranesbill and germander speedwell.

The new garden had taken shape, with trellis, arched arbour, garden seats and beds of rounded pebbles. Rosemary, mint and rue had settled into the herb garden but the wild flower meadow was a tousled mass of grass. In between were late Chrysanthemum flowers, Fuchsia bells and fennel buds. We left the intrepid islanders with their goodies and returned to a hot lunch with the mayor of the Vale in the Barry Civic Offices.

During the summers of 1994 and 1995 Andrew Stanworth had been working on a PhD thesis studying the food of gulls. He found that adults and juveniles over four weeks old ate mainly garbage, as anticipated, but younger chicks received a more concentrated protein diet. Parents brought large items such as hunks of chicken skin at first, but the chicks couldn't cope. They soon changed to more suitable sized Annelids, mostly earthworms from the land but also ragworms from the mud flats. Material coughed up when the chicks were being handled included soil if they were being fed earthworms and with it the odd few seeds of new plant colonists and possibly small invertebrates.

One of his lesser black-backs had pink legs instead of yellow. Could this be a hybrid with the closely related herring gull? Fifteen thousand years ago the birds had been identical, the population centred around the Bering Strait. Herring gulls spread eastwards across North America, lesser black-backs westwards across Euro-Asia, darkening as they went. Great Britain is at the meeting point of the two and they are still compatible, but cross breeding is uncommon. Black-backs mate two weeks earlier than herring gulls and have slightly different calls – the language of love not quite so enticing perhaps?

Following the sudden crash in population levels caused by botulism after the 1975 peak and the two summer droughts, numbers had settled at around two thousand five hundred and three hundred pairs respectively. Unfortunately, although the malevolent botulism bacteria died when the plastic sacks burst to let the air in, the toxin which they had produced during the anaerobic phase persisted.

Solar panels and a wind pump had been installed for the Flatholm Project to help with energy production and children had concealed a 1995 time capsule under the new floorboards of the Victorian Barracks for the edification of future generations when those had rotted. Electric cables had been secreted above the plasterboard ceiling and sash type Victorian windows installed, the building already used by climbers and a first aid conference. Other children had planted hawthorns near the pond to accommodate passerines.

The lighthouse had become solar powered by 1998, the three light-emitting bulbs described as a mere two inches by half an inch each! The keepers' garden had degenerated to a stony waste, occupied by scant stonecrop and dovesfoot cranesbill. No use had yet been found for the foghorn building but the mechanism was still in order. A lottery grant for restoration was being applied for, but restoration of the old hospital was beyond the expectation of any forthcoming finance and there was no foreseeable use for the restored building, with numbers on the island limited on ecological grounds.

The farmhouse garden, in contrast to the other, was in fine shape. An army of foxgloves shared space with matching stands of common mallow and a long-trunked standard tree mallow. The old Fuchsia had been lopped, to be replaced by seedlings or suckering shoots. Mounded Santolina and spreading Campanula framed an arch over the central path, with ox-eye daisies peeping from eighteen inch high grass. A gazebo, a trellis and a garden seat completed the picture of the finally rabbit-free enclosure on soil enriched by decades of cultivation.

The northern reinstated grassland was not the limestone grassland of old, being a much too lush green and nettle-ridden. Like the pond, it was still affected by air-borne guano, although not a nesting area. Eggs had been repeatedly confiscated from gulls attempting to breed there, but these were sadly not regarded as edible for fear of botulism. The incidence of this had decreased by the end of the century, however, as the trash-burying bulldozers swung into their stride less tardily. Deprived gull parents continued to hang around during the initial year, but set up home elsewhere the next.

On a visit of sixth June in 1998 it was very apparent that gull chicks among the bracken were larger than those among tufted Arum and nettle. This pointed to bracken as top choice by first comers – the habitat favoured by lesser black-backs on the Pembrokeshire Islands, and the first to be colonised here back in the 1950s.

The goats had been exported. They had cleared the half of the island they were supposed to clear and had started on the other that they weren't. Fences failed to stop them, they sailed over the top like 'Foxhunter' in his prime, so they had to go. Two had got away and were still at large, while a blind billy was retained on humanitarian grounds. He knew his way around here, but was easily frightened and hence inclined to be aggressive, so had to be confined. Soays and poultry continued as before.

We left to the happy sound of children playing rounders after collecting boxes of firewood for a cooking and camp fire spree. There seemed to be armies of them and all very busy.

There were only two goats left by the year 2000, one of the billies having washed up dead, and only one by 2003. Soays were proving more intelligent than was desirable and were becoming difficult to manage compared with the domestic sheep, which were now being hand sheared. These were later replaced by old ewes, their years of producing lambs behind them. With no rams there was no chance of more. They functioned only as longer-lived grazing tools.

During the two winters to the year 2000 merlins were visiting. Smallest and streakiest of the falcons, they were like mini peregrines that had shaved off their moustaches. They did not stoop from the heights, but chased their prey low over the ground, pipits constituting favourite dietary items.

Ravens also called and were thought to be responsible for disembowelling the rabbits. Gulls seemed to take only young ones frisking in the sun and not the sluggish

Peregrine Falcon and Merlin.

and presumably more easily caught victims of Myxomatosis. The several pairs of oyster-catchers nesting among the gulls seemed not to be molested. The eggs were similar to gulls' eggs and the chicks scuttled off into hiding soon after hatching. The year 2000 saw some fifteen hundred pairs of lesser black-backs and six hundred of herring gulls but only sixty-two of shelduck.

Slow worms were increasing, lizards harder to find and so impossible to assess their numbers. Kevin Hogan, project officer that year, had not seen gulls taking slow worms, but a number had lost their tails in some sort of tussle.

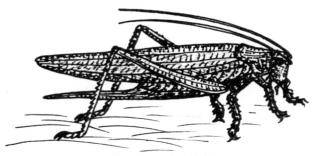

Great Green Bush Cricket.

George, the last of the lighthouse tortoises, still plodded stolidly around the island, seemingly oblivious of other inhabitants. Newcomers, or new discoveries, were the great green bush crickets (*Tettigonia viridissima*) come to join the dark bush crickets.

*   *   *

After following the fortunes of the feathered, furred and fleecy flocks for nearly forty years, it was fitting that I should return after the turn of the century to update my impressions. I should have chosen that most enchanting time of year when the western cliffs are bright with thrift, sea campion and stonecrop and the eastern ones with scurvy grass, bluebells and wallflowers, as when I first visited, but the greenswards were still crowded with rabbits, though there was scarcely a gull to be seen. The Soays were down to thirty and the mountain x lowland sheep, the 'white ladies', to ten, but numbers were to be increased in 2002.

It was the calmest, sunniest day of summer 2001, but it was not summer: it was 12th October, a high pressure interlude between two rumbustious lows. The rock samphire sprawled across Castle Rock by the landing was thicker than I ever remember and a lush greeny-blue instead of massed with purple fruitlets, as often at this season.

We stepped from the *Lewis Alexander* onto a three inch deep carpet of spiral wrack clinging to the surface of the slipway, the densely packed fronds pushing through the wire netting cover. No seaweeds grew on the beach below, which could be overturned by every tide. Any solid substrate would have held bladder or egg wrack from lower zones, as the structure was well above beach level.

After paddling through the footbath of anti foot and mouth disinfectant, I paused by the pellitory-of-the-wall at the top of the steps to watch three of the schoolgirls in residence struggling out from land to the waiting skipper with a long hose. This kept falling off, but was successfully fielded by the beach patrol. I thought it must be for a delivery of diesel, but it was for drinking water. The island had not suffered the weeks of deluging but local summer storms that had been emptied onto selected parts of the mainland.

Unable to identify the elegantly striped sawfly sunning on the wall, I mooched round to Castle Battery, leaving the rest headed to the farmhouse for their introductory talk. Yellow stonecrop was past its prime but a little pink and white storksbill peeped from the closely razed turf, where a pink-gilled mushroom had escaped collection.

There were rabbits everywhere, as there proved to be all over the island, but particularly on the shallow soil of these knolls where most of the rank weed species were non-starters. So little edible was left that they had to feed by day as well as night to get by. A high proportion was still half sized. It seemed they had been breeding like rabbits all summer, the spasmodic occurrence of Myxomatosis having made insignificant inroads on numbers.

It was strangely quiet, with no clamorous gulls riding the air currents. A few passed, far out to sea, but there were only corpses on the island, mostly of juveniles along the driftline, and a feeding midden on a cliff spur near the lighthouse.

This was the dining area of a gull which specialised in eating crabs and was able to deal effectively with the body and eight appendages but not the prey-crushing pincers, which were liberally spread over the whitened rock. It was Phil Bristow, ornithologist, who pointed out the Mediterranean gull on our return voyage, whiter than white above the coffee coloured sea, that lay as smooth as one of its bordering mudbanks.

Making my way to the West Beach for lunch, I was surprised to see a wheatear hopping among the thrift tussocks so late in the year. This is one of our first migrants to arrive – from the third week of March – and most of our summer residents begin to move back in July to pass out over the south coast in early August. Evidently this was of the larger Greenland sub-species, which arrive in the Scottish Islands around mid September to work their way down the country up to the third week in October, with stragglers lingering into mid November. One had been seen the day before.

I found the perfect lunch spot, where a cube of limestone a little larger than my posterior had split away, to leave me with a flat seat and back rest, elbow rest and side table for lemonade bottle and camera. Skeins of cormorants flapped past, straight as a die, low over the silt-charged water, and a rock pipit pottered where wavelets that were no more than ripples lapped the shore.

Spiders scurried everywhere, and a few ants, but more remarkable in the complete absence of flowers was the abundance of butterflies. Most were small tortoiseshells or red admirals, skimming over the sun-warmed rock slabs or basking with wings spread to the still powerful rays. The one large white favoured the ground-hugging sward of buck's-horn plantain on the low backing cliff.

Past the roofless isolation hospital I was among the elders where the unfarmed acres were advancing or degenerating, according to ones outlook, towards the climax vegetation of Steepholm. An astonishing number of hedge snails and garden snails clung to the uppermost bracken fronds in hundreds, sometimes six to the square foot. The hedge snails' livery encompassed most of the possible colourings and stripings to match the variegated backdrop of crisping fronds. Were they, too, warming themselves in the sun? It was certainly no place to hibernate, even when the fronds collapsed to ground level.

A kestrel soared overhead, one of the pair, probably, that had nested near the lighthouse, despite the absence of its normal small mammal prey. Mobs of linnets and greenfinches came and went in chirruping droves over the thicket. The ornithological group, which had spent much of the previous night here with their moth trap, had seen a couple of bramblings earlier in the day – and a little egret! Autumn was a time of surprises as the migrants came through. A chiff-chaff and a garden warbler were feeding among the elderberries left them by the whirring flocks of ravenous starlings, these, again, possibly incomers from colder climes.

Once more, however, it was the butterflies which caught the eye, as

I plodded over an eiderdown of discarded thistle heads lifting around my muffled footfalls. Those gull-nurtured nettles had brought forth a bumper crop of caterpillars and almost the only flowers left to feed the adult hordes were those of ragwort. Who said thistles, nettles and ragwort were noxious pests? Annual mercury, wild turnip, field daisy and sea beet, the only other flowers seen, were largely ignored by the fluttering clouds. Cameras were working overtime with plenty of close-ups featuring three pairs of wings completely obscuring the nectar source.

There was a fine display of fruits in the peony enclosure. The gaudily beautiful flowers last for little more than a week, but these were almost equally eye-catching. Capsules split into radiating boat-shaped segments to reveal shiny black seeds bursting from a crimson matrix. They had attracted more snails, one to three cosily ensconced among the seeds in almost every head.

Peony.

A honey bee flew alongside our returning boat in mid channel. Had she left with us or had we caught her up? Had she hitched a lift or was she lost at sea? Just one of those mysteries posed by the natural world to which we seldom find answers.

*   *   *

Destruction of gulls' nests and periodic mowing of the tall weed species in the north of the island was favouring the grasses but little else. Visits in late May and late June 2003 were disappointing from the plant point of view. Gone were the limestone specialities which compete poorly among coarse grass. Gone were the snowy sward of scurvy grass, many of the chunky bluebells and most of the cliff-hanger wallflowers.

Small nettle (*Urtica urens*), an uncommon species in the UK although an abundant British invader of sea-bird colonies in Australia and South Africa, had increased hugely along the southern cliffs. So, too, had the elegantly coiled spathes of wild Arum across the island centre. These gave rise to spires of scarlet berries, brightening the tired autumn landscape, but the wardens were waging war against it, in the belief that sheep eating it 'get the runs'. On the plus side were some fine stands of wild leek, a few attractive plants of star of Bethlehem and a new species – white horehound.

The extent of change could be assessed only in a few marked or

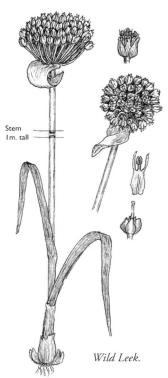

Stem
1 m. tall

Wild Leek.

photographed spots such as one on the west coast. Outside the animal exclosure here in 1992 was a colourful sward of flowering thrift sprinkled with sea campion. Eleven years later this had converted to a low, trodden carpet of sea storksbill and Danish scurvy grass,

Star of Bethlehem.

Inside in 1992 was a thick bent-fescue sward with tall sorrel, nettle and dock. In 2003 when rabbits but not sheep had access (as in the Stevenson screen enclosure) there was sea campion, a favourite of hungry sheep, short sorrel and persistent nettles.

Sheep numbers were around forty-six 'commercial' animals and twenty-eight Soays, with all the rams neutered, the sea campion now almost confined to areas which they could not reach. The one goat made little difference and rabbits were so scarce at present that only two were seen in a four hour walkabout. The most eye-catching flowers were of distasteful or poisonous plants such as foetid Iris and hemlock. Goats can graze out noxious plants but do not choose to do so until they have demolished most of the palatable ones.

Precocious gull chicks were pecking their way from the eggshells on the late May visit, with young of all ages and chipping eggs in late June. There were thought to be around four thousand pairs of lesser blackbacks now, in 2003, and perhaps five hundred pairs of herring gulls, totalling around half of the 1974 peak of some four thousand and fifty pairs of each. Many, deprived of their nests by the wardens, were standing idly around on the reclaimed sward – at least for the rest of the current breeding season. Wheatears were now in residence.

Members of the Flatholm Society had planned to welcome in the new millennium with a celebratory blast on the long defunct foghorn. They had repaired one set of the necessary machinery and were ready for off when the powers that be forbade them to sojourn on the island at midnight in midwinter. This had to do with the expectation that the 'millennium bug' would scupper the smooth running of all computers if, indeed, our world was not to come to an untimely end.

Having survived unscathed, they blasted off successfully once a month during the first quarter of 2000 until the Department of Health and Safety, one of the more interfering sections of our Nanny State, put a stop to it. Since then, this link with the days of live lighthouse men instead of land-based computers, has been heard no more.

Flatholm Island's ecology is turning full circle or, more accurately, pursuing a spiral which started well before my first visit and has a long way to go yet, with equilibrium a very distant goal so long as gull and rabbit numbers keep fluctuating.

All natural habitats are in a state of flux and bird islands, as clearly defined entities with no marginal mergings, moreso than most. Changes in animal life have deep-seated repercussions on plant life and both are at the mercy of wind and salt spray.

Dynamic in their short term fluctuations, they jealously guard their long term integrity – natural ecosystems for us to enjoy but with which we meddle at our peril if we wish to preserve their magic individuality as a refuge from the madness of the modern world.

I leave the rest of the story for others to tell but, having slept on so many islands across the world, I and many another, will never be quite the same!